Russell "Know. of Ex...

THE PHILOSOPHICAL IMPACT
OF CONTEMPORARY PHYSICS

The Philosophical Impact
of Contemporary Physics

by

MILIČ ČAPEK
Professor of Philosophy
Carleton College, Minnesota

D. VAN NOSTRAND COMPANY, INC.
PRINCETON, NEW JERSEY
TORONTO   LONDON
NEW YORK

D. VAN NOSTRAND COMPANY, INC.

120 Alexander St., Princeton, New Jersey (*Principal office*)
24 West 40 Street, New York 18, New York

D. VAN NOSTRAND COMPANY, LTD.
358, Kensington High Street, London, W.14, England

D. VAN NOSTRAND COMPANY (Canada), LTD.
25 Hollinger Road, Toronto 16, Canada

PRINTED IN THE UNITED STATES OF AMERICA

PREFACE

The purpose of this book is stated in the Introduction. Its main ideas had been slowly maturing in my mind since my graduate years, and the systematic writing began in the academic year 1954-1955 when I was at New Haven as a recipient of The Fund for the Advancement of Education. Its main bulk was finished by the fall of 1955. Two concluding chapters and a summary were added later.

My intellectual debts are many; most of them, though not all, can be found in the references in the text as well as in the notes. If there is any scarcity of references to the most recent writings relevant to the problems discussed in the book, it is because they appeared after the manuscript was finished and submitted for publication. I express my gratitude to The Fund for the Advancement of Education, whose generosity provided me with the whole year of free time for gathering the material and preparing the manuscript. Also I gratefully recall the stimulating discussions which I had at that time with various members of Department of Philosophy of Yale University as well as those which I had with my colleagues at Carleton College. In particular I gratefully acknowledge the kind help of my colleagues in reading the proofs: Professor Eugen Mayers, who read all the proofs, and Professors David Sipfle and James Doyle, who each read a part of them. I appreciate the help of Miss Elaine Pimsler and Mrs. Robert Scott, who retyped the manuscript during my absence in Europe.

Milič Čapek

Carleton College
April 11, 1961

CONTENTS

vii

Contents

INTRODUCTION

THE PRESENT BOOK has grown out of the conviction that no true understanding of contemporary physics and its philosophical implications is possible without first fully realizing in what sense and to what extent modern physical concepts differ from the concepts of classical physics. The classical concepts of space, time, matter, motion, energy, and causality have been radically transformed recently; although the words used by contemporary physicists are the same, their connotations are altogether different from those of their classical counterparts. There is hardly any similarity between the "matter" of modern physics and the traditional material substance of the classical period, and this is true in varying degrees of other concepts as well. The revolutionary character of modern concepts cannot be fully grasped as long as the contrasting background of classical physics is not kept constantly in sight. To bring into full focus an awareness of the contrast between the classical and the modern conceptual frameworks is one of the purposes of this book.

At first such a task may appear superfluous. Nearly everybody now claims to be aware of the contrast between Newtonian physics and the physics of the twentieth century. But the situation is not as simple as it superficially appears to be. The main part of the revolution in modern physics took part in the first three decades of this century. It was then that the theory of relativity, the theory of quanta, and, finally, wave mechanics came into being. It is true that the effect of these theories on the imagination of physicists, philosophers, and even laymen was truly shattering; the contrast between the new theories and the appealing clarity of classical concepts was sharp and shocking. But as the years went by, awareness of this contrast grew dimmer. The intensity of every astonishment gradually wears off; the human mind, by the sheer effect of repetition and habit, gradually becomes accustomed to even the strangest and least familiar ideas.

Thus even in this case a feeling of familiarity eventually replaced the original feeling of strangeness. As early as 1929 Sir Ernest Rutherford wrote on the occasion of the fiftieth anniversary of Max Planck's doctorate: "It is difficult to realize today, when the quantum theory is successfully applied in so many fields of science, how strange and almost fantastic this new conception of radiation appeared to many scientific men twenty-five years ago." [1] If the baffling effect of the new theories began to recede as early as 1929, it is not surprising that it is almost completely absent now. Since then a whole generation of physicists have come into being, who, after their elementary undergraduate courses, have been exposed to new theories almost exclusively, and who, if they have not lost all contact with classical physics, certainly are hardly aware of its former prestige and appeal. This phenomenon is probably even more conspicuous in the United States, where historical awareness is generally weaker than elsewhere. As Freeman J. Dyson wrote in 1954 in reviewing the second volume of E. T. Whittaker's *History of the Theories of Aether and Electricity:* "For us who have grown up after 1940 and have accepted quantum mechanics as a *fait accompli*, it is extremely difficult to imagine the state of mind of the men who were creating the theory before 1926." [2]

The awareness of the contrast between two conflicting theories usually disappears when the inadequacy of one is established beyond any doubt while the other is, provisionally at least, empirically verified; then the inadequate theory is quickly forgotten and only historians of science remember it. Such was the case with the theory of epicycles in astronomy and of the phlogiston theory in chemistry, to mention only two examples. But in contemporary physics the situation is far from being so simple. Classical physics simply cannot be forgotten, even though its prestige no longer survives. It cannot be forgotten not only because it still remains valid at the macrophysical level, that is, for our daily experience; not only because it is being taught for that reason in high schools and in the basic undergraduate courses; but also because its principles are embodied in the present structure of the average human intellect or in what is usually called "common sense."

Euclidean geometry and Newtonian mechanics are both based on deeply ingrained habits of imagination and thought whose strength is far greater than we are generally willing to concede.

Kant was so much impressed by this strength that he regarded it as a manifestation of the unchangeable a priori structure of the human mind; Herbert Spencer, in spite of his radically different epistemology, eventually agreed with Kant, at least as far as the immutability of the Newtonian-Euclidean form of intellect was concerned. This form of intellect is, according to Spencer, the final and definitive outcome of the long process of adjustment; in this process the external world created, so to speak, its accurate replica in the human mind in the form of the Newtonian-Euclidean picture of nature. No change in this picture was to be expected, according to Spencer and the positivists and naturalists of the last century. In this respect they shared the general belief of their time in the irrevocably final character of classical science. This belief was justified not only by what then seemed overwhelming evidence in favor of the classical view of nature, but also by the evolutionary argument referred to above: classical physical science was regarded as the *final* and *complete* adjustment of human cognitive faculties to the objective order of things. Thus the idea of *the absence of evolution* in Kant led to the same conclusion as the idea of *already completed evolution* in Spencer's evolutionary empiricism.

The examples of Kant and Spencer are fairly typical; they show how two outstanding philosophers of the classical period, though representing rival trends in epistemology—rationalism and empiricism—nevertheless agreed in their claim that no future experience will seriously challenge the classical modes of thought embodied in Euclidean geometry and Newtonian mechanics. The classical picture of the physical world was regarded as definitive in its essential features; the future, it was believed, would bring a better understanding of some of its details, but would never modify its main outlines. "The world is now without mysteries," exclaimed Marcellin Berthelot in 1885, and Whitehead recalled the same belief of his young days: "We supposed that nearly everything of importance about physics was known. Yes, there were a few obscure spots, strange anomalies having to do with radiation which physicists expected to be cleared up by 1900."[3] Examples of such an attitude could be multiplied indefinitely. It is true that positivists and Neo-Kantians were epistemologically more careful as they —in contrast to scientists themselves and materialistically oriented thinkers—insisted on the phenomenal character of the world-view of physics; but as far as the world-view itself was concerned there was hardly any disagreement between a sophisticated philosopher and an epistemologically innocent rank-and-file scientist—physics remained Euclidean and Newtonian for both of them. It is certainly instructive to see the philosopher-physicist Ernst Mach at the end of his life resisting the emerging theory of relativity—the very theory for which he himself prepared the way by his bold criticism of the Newtonian concepts as early as 1883.[4]

Today we are less inclined to regard Euclidean geometry and Newtonian mechanics as either unchangeable necessities of thought or faithful replicas of objective reality. There is an increasing tendency today to realize that the classical modes of thought are applicable only to what Reichenbach called "the zone of the middle dimensions," situated between the world of galaxies and the microcosm, while they fail utterly outside of its limits. If there was any evolutionary process of adjustment in the sense indicated by Spencer, it took place on a limited scale because it is clear that our Newtonian-Euclidean form of understanding is adjusted only to the zone of the middle dimensions, i.e., to the only zone which originally was of practical importance. Yet even now when we explicitly reject the authority of Euclid and Newton, our intellect remains far more conservative than we are ready to admit. This is especially true of the areas which lie outside of physics and which the echo of contemporary revolution in physics reaches faintly and indirectly: in biology, psychology, and the social sciences the classical form of determinism, modeled consciously or unconsciously on the Laplacian pattern, remains practically intact. But even within physics, notwithstanding our declarations to the contrary, the classical habits of thought persist and the fact that they are driven into subconsciousness by being consciously rejected makes their influence only less easily detectible and far more insidious. We shall see numerous instances in which physicists or, even more frequently, philosophical interpreters of modern physics failed to draw all the consequences from some new revolutionary discovery mainly because their thinking remained tinged by the influence of some hidden classical habit. It frequently happens that within one and the same mind the true grasp of the mathematical side of the theory coexists with serious misapprehensions of its physical and especially its philosophical meaning. This is psychologically understandable; the mental habits which constitute what may be called our "Newtonian-Euclidean subconscious," and whose roots lie deep in the phylogenetic heritage of man are too obstinate to be modified by a bare mastery of mathematical formalism, which merely suppresses them without eliminating them. It is, in my opinion, this incongruous association, this conflict of the subconscious classical imaginative background with the abstract formalism which is the main source of paradoxes and confusions occurring in various interpretations, or rather misinterpretations, of contemporary physics.

The task of an epistemologist in contemporary physics is therefore a little like that of the psychoanalyst: to detect the remnants of classical thought beneath the verbal denials and conscious rejections. This can be done only if we bring classical concepts into as sharp a focus as possible. This is the task of Part I, where the basic classical concepts are analyzed and their links, logical as well as historical, with the general philosophical climate of the same period are traced. Nothing strengthens our conviction about the close connection, so often overlooked or

underestimated, of the problems of science with general ontological questions like the spectacle of the continual contacts
and interactions between physics and philosophy in that period.

In Part II, keeping fresh in mind the meaning of classical
concepts, and being aware of the influence which they retain
on our thinking, we shall be in a better position to avoid unconsciously smuggling them into the interpretation of modern
discoveries. What will eventually emerge will certainly not be a
"picture" or "model" in the old classical and pictorial sense, but
this does not mean that the resulting view must necessarily be
divorced from every aspect of our immediate experience, provided that the term "experience" is understood more broadly
than in its usually narrow sensualistic, and more specifically,
visual-tactile sense. For, contrary to widespread prejudice, "concrete" and "pictorial" are not synonymous. Unless we become
unwitting Pythagoreans, it is difficult to adhere to a panmathematism according to which nature is *constituted* by mathematical relations. Yet, this claim is, implicitly at least, made by all
those who insist that nature is devoid of *any* quality and that
any search for a concrete interpretation of modern physics is
futile or even devoid of sense. Such a concrete interpretation
will frequently be hinted at in Part II; and although its detailed
elaboration is beyond the scope of this book, its outline will
be found in the concluding chapter.

Thus the emphasis on the contrast between classical and contemporary physics, which pervades Part II, is eventually coun-
terbalanced by the equally strong emphasis on the basic identity
of one problem which the physicist faces today as much as in
the days of Newton and Laplace: What is the nature of physical
reality and to what extent can it be understood? All specific
problems of physics are merely concrete and partial aspects
of the same basic question; in truth, if we disregard its naive
phrasing, the question which the pre-Socratics tried to answer:
"What is the world made of?" was not essentially different.
When Greek atomists, in defiance of their sensualistic epistemology, postulated the existence of invisible atoms; when Aris-

totle constructed his model of the spherical and geocentric universe; when the prophetic imagination of Giordano Bruno moved "from the closed world to the infinite universe," they all were inspired by the same intense feeling of the objectivity —of "the edge of objectivity" as it was recently called [5]—of the physical reality whose structure exists independently of our preferences and idiosyncrasies and which our conceptual models try to represent with varying degrees of adequacy and completeness. It was the same motive which in our century led Einstein and Whitehead in spite of their profound philosophical differences to be equally dissatisfied with the misleading note of epistemological idealism and positivism which crept into discussions of both the principle of indeterminacy and Michelson's experiment.[6] The same motive inspires the hope expressed in this book that the philosophy of physics will move beyond its present phenomenalistic stage and its present concentration on methodology toward a search for new ways of understanding, toward a new more comprehensive view of reality while understanding that the word "view" in this case will certainly not retain its original pictorial sense.

NOTES FOR THE INTRODUCTION

1. Rutherford in *Naturwissenschaften*, Vol. 17 (1929), p. 483.
2. F. J. Dyson, in *Scientific American*, Vol. 120 (March 1954), p. 92.
3. M. Berthelot, *Les origines de l'alchimie* (Paris, 1885), p. 151; *Dialogues of Alfred North Whitehead as Recorded by Lucien Price* (New American Library, 1960), p. 12.
4. E. Mach, *Science of Mechanics*, preface to the 9th ed. (1933) by Ludwig Mach, p. xxvii.
5. C. C. Gillispie, *The Edge of Objectivity, an Essay in the History of Ideas* (Princeton University Press, 1960).
6. See p. 304 of this book and references 15 and 16 on p. 330.

PART I · THE CLASSICAL PICTURE OF THE PHYSICAL WORLD

I · THE GENERAL CHARACTER
OF CLASSICAL PHYSICS

When we speak of the classical *picture* of physical reality, we are indicating by the very choice of the word its most significant feature: its *pictorial* character. This character became conspicuous only in recent times. Before 1900 it appeared so natural and obvious that hardly anybody noticed it; what appears obvious is rarely conspicuous and rarely attracts attention. Nobody talked about *Euclidean* geometry before Lobachevski and Riemann, during the centuries that "geometry" and "Euclidean geometry" were entirely synonymous terms. But the emergence of new conceptions of matter provided a necessary contrasting backdrop against which the classical picture appeared in a new and unfamiliar light.

The words "picture" and "conceptions" well indicate a difference between classical and modern theories: in classical theories sensory features—especially visual and tactile—played a decisive role; modern theories, by virtue of their abstruse nature, defy all attempts at consistent visualization and pictorialization. Optical and tactile qualities, which seemed to classical physicists the inherent attributes of matter, are in the light of modern discoveries hardly more than superficial aspects of the reality whose intrinsic nature lies very probably beyond the reach of our imaginative faculties. To modern theories it is impossible to apply the precept which John Tyndall recommended in his Liverpool address to the physicists of the Victorian era as a reliable criterion of satisfactory scientific theories: "Ask your imagination if it will accept it,"[1] i.e., ask yourself if you are able to draw a mental picture of the phenomenon in question; reject it if no visual diagram, no mechanical model can be constructed. This demand hardly varied from the seventeenth to the nineteenth century; Tyndall's recommendation is basically the same as that of Descartes and Huygens. The Cartesian ideal of explanation by figures and motions [*par figures et mouvements*] remained the inspiring motive of Faraday, Maxwell, Hertz, and Kelvin and even, at the beginning of this century, of Lorentz and J. J. Thomson.[2] From the epistemological point of view this is probably the most significant and revealing trait of the classical theories.

In spite of its visual and, more generally, sensory character, the classical view was certainly not a simple duplication of naive sense perception. On the contrary, the whole development of classical physics led to a progressive sifting of the original sensory data. The so-called secondary qualities like color, sound, flavor, and scent were regarded as private reactions of the perceiving mind. Only the sensation of contact and that of resistance—the latter being considered as a mere intensification of the former—retained their privileged epistemological status in providing us with a direct insight into the intimate nature of matter. It was believed that the objective counterpart of the sensation of resistance was *impenetrability* or *solidity*, and this constituted the very essence of matter. All other physical properties of matter—softness, roughness, smoothness, resilience, flexibility, ductility, wetness, fluidity, and the like—were assigned, not to matter itself, but to the subjective sphere of human perception. In this view fluidity, for instance, is a mere psychical addition to matter; the physical reality itself, or at least its constitutive elements, are completely devoid of fluidity. Similarly, there is a sensation of warmth, but there is no objective occult quality of warmth residing in the nature of reality.

Thus only a small subclass of tactile sensations—the sensations of contact and resistance—possessed the special privilege of disclosing the true nature of physical reality. While the mechanical properties of matter were thus constructed of our tactile sensations, its geometrical and kinematic attributes were conceived in visual terms. The particles of matter were *imagined* to possess a certain bulk, shape, and position; their positions were *imagined* to vary in time, or, in more ordinary language, the particles were *imagined* to move through space.

This is what may be called the *corpuscular-kinetic view of matter*. Its first formulation, a surprisingly accurate one, appeared in early Greek atomism. Its basic premises have hardly changed through the ages. Although atomism suffered a temporary (by no means complete) eclipse in the Middle Ages, it reasserted itself with renewed vigor in the century of Gassendi and Newton and since then has exerted a persistent and fascinating influence on the imagination of physicists, at least until the end of the last century. Today, for reasons expounded in Part II, its attractiveness is weakened, but not altogether destroyed.

The very persistence of this influence shows that it was due not to a simple accident of history, but rather to some inherent tendency of human intellect, a tendency that will be more extensively analyzed later. Suffice it to say here that the classical view of matter, though itself a result of a profound modification of immediate sense perception, nevertheless did not challenge seriously our imaginative faculties. As it was built of the elements of two basic senses, sight and touch, it did not transcend the limits of our sensory imagination. The subordination of all other senses to sight and touch probably explains why elimination of the secondary qualities hardly required a great mental effort even at the very dawn of Western thought. On the contrary, this elimination resulted in a distinct advantage.

The world of atoms, in which all qualitative diversity is reduced to differences in configuration and motion of the homogeneous and permanent elements, stands in striking contrast to the "confused" realm of perishing and heterogeneous sensory qualities. There is no question but that the corpuscular-kinetic scheme of nature, in virtue of its greater simplicity, clarity, and manageableness, represented a true economy of thought in the sense of William of Occam and Ernst Mach; for while it eliminated what Professor Margenau calls "the haziness of the immediately given," [3] it retained its pictorial and, more generally, intuitive (*anschaulich*) character. It is true that Mach himself did not recognize in atomism an application of his own epistemological principle; in this respect his attitude remained dogmatically negative in spite of increasing empirical evidence for the existence of atoms. (Curiously enough, his attitude was much less critical toward atomism in psychology, on which his associationism was based.)

The question to what extent the principle of parsimony is a reliable epistemological criterion in modern physics will be discussed later. The fact is that the general constitution of the human mind, together with the steadily increasing amount of empirical evidence at the end of the last century, strengthened the conviction that the corpuscular-kinetic scheme was an adequate and final representation of physical reality. The universe was regarded as an enormous aggregate of bits of homogeneous material whose quantity remained constant while the spatial distribution was continuously changing according to the immutable laws of mechanics. Classical concepts of space, time, matter, motion, and causality were the main constitutive parts of this pictorial scheme, and in spite of their highly abstract nature, they all were based on the same visual and tactual elements as were characteristic of the whole imaginative background of classical physics.

NOTES FOR CHAPTER I

1. John Tyndall, "Scientific Use of Imagination" in *Fragments of Science for Unscientific People*, New York, D. Appleton Co., 1872, especially p. 131.
2. See Chapter VI below, The Corpuscular-Kinetic View of Nature.
3. Henry Margenau, *The Nature of Physical Reality*, McGraw-Hill Book Co., New York, 1950, p. 56.

II · THE CONCEPT OF SPACE

THE SUBSTANTIALITY AND IMMUTABILITY OF SPACE

IN CLASSICAL science space was regarded as a homogeneous medium existing objectively and independently of its physical content, whose rigid and timeless structure has been described by the axioms and theorems of Euclidean geometry. This self-sufficiency of space and its independence of the matter which it contains was clearly formulated by Newton in his *Principia:* "Absolute space, in its own nature, without regard to anything external, remains always similar and immovable." [1]

This was a basic assumption of classical science. Newton was not the first who formulated it, even though it is frequently associated with his name. To say nothing of Pierre Gassendi, Henry More, and several philosophers of the Renaissance—in particular Telesio, Pattrizzi, Bruno, and Campanella[2]—Newton's conception was virtually present in ancient atomism, as Einstein, shortly before his death, emphasized.[3] As soon as matter was defined as a *plenum*—that is, *occupied space*—in contrast to the *void* or *empty space*, the distinction was established between the immutable and independent container and its changing physical content.

We do not need to be confused by the fact that the Greek atomists of the fifth century B.C., Leucippus and Democritus,

7

called space "Non-Being" and contrasted it with eternal and indestructible "Full Being," παμπλῆρες ὄν. First, the term τὸ μὴ ὄν (Non-Being) is one they accepted from the earlier Eleatic philosophers Parmenides and Melissos, for whom Non-Being was a simple nothingness. Leucippus took over the Eleatic language but not the Eleatic thought. In his view there was no solution to the paradoxes which had been so much stressed by the Eleatics unless even the void was granted a certain degree of existence— the kind of existence that belongs to empty space, the necessary condition, as it was thought, for the reality of motion and diversity. Indeed, Democritus, taking advantage of the subtle distinction between two Greek negatives, coined his own term for space—"not Being" (τὸ οὐκ ὄν); he thus avoided the original misleading term, accepted by Leucippus, which was so strongly reminiscent of the sheer Eleatic nothingness.[4]

Second, matter itself, though in its essence immutable and quantitatively constant, was in a certain sense subject to change because its constitutive parts were endowed with *motion*. It is true that this change did not affect the particles themselves, but only their distances apart; nevertheless in contrast to the changing configurations of matter, space possessed unchangeability in a full and absolute sense.

Thus, in the last analysis, the notion of independent Newtonian space lurks behind any explicit distinction between material stuff and the place it occupies: the underlying positions remain eternally the same, their occupants vary from time to time. In more common language, *matter moves in space*. It is precisely this logical separability of the empty immovable container from its movable material content which makes *displacement* possible. Greek atomists, in stressing this separability of space and matter, undoubtedly prepared the way for the Newtonian concept of independent and absolute space.

True immutability thus belongs to space alone. With respect to space even the eternal atoms of Democritus and of later atomists appear as accessory, contingent, and even subject to change. They appear *accessory* because, being defined as "full volumes of space," they need space for their existence, while the converse is not true—space can exist without them. They appear *contingent* because their occupation of certain positions is only accidental in the sense that it does not possess a logical necessity comparable to the timeless geometrical relations holding between the positions themselves. Finally, they appear even *changing* in a certain sense—if not themselves, at least in their mutual relations in space.

This may be stated in another way. In classical atomistic science *space was logically prior to its material content*. It is true that classical physics and the mechanistic philosophy which grew out of it loudly proclaimed that material substance is the only true reality; it would be hardly compatible with this allegedly strict monism if the reality of any entities other than matter were equally emphasized. But whether the existence of empty space was silently assumed or whether it was explicitly asserted as, for instance, by the atomists, its logical priority to matter was not sufficiently realized. This was only natural. How could such a negative reality, called τὸ οὐκ ὄν (not Being) by Democritus, *inane* by Lucretius, *nihil* by William Gilbert and Otto von Guericke,[5] be regarded as logically antecedent to the solid reality of eternal and indestructible atoms? How could Non-Being be logically prior to Being? The reluctance to accept such apparently absurd conclusions was increased by an easy confusion of logical priority with ontological or temporal priority. Nothing would have seemed more absurd than to elevate Non-Being to the rank of the ontological first principle. Yet this is precisely what happened. In his *Enchiridion Metaphysicum* (1671) Henry More observed that the attributes of space are the same as those traditionally assigned to Supreme Being by scholastics:

> Unum, Simplex, Immobile, Aeternum, Completum, Independens, A se existens, Per se subsistens, Incorruptibile, Necessarium, Immensum, Increatum, Incircumscriptum, Incomprehensibile, Omnipresens, Incorpo-

reum, Omnia permeans et complectans, Ens per essentiam, Ens actu, Purus actus.* [6]

Thus, as Alexander Koyré observes, "by a strange irony of history, the κενόν [vacuum] of the godless atomists became for Henry More God's own extension, the very condition of His action in the world." [7] This irony is less strange when we remember that the roots of the apparent paradox lie in the very nature of atomism; as both John Burnet and Cyril Bailey pointed out, it was a strange achievement for the founder of the great materialistic school of antiquity to have claimed that "a *thing might be real without being a body*." [8] It was this incorporeality of space which yielded so easily to its divinization.

It is fairly well known how More's divinization of space influenced Newton's philosophy of nature, in which absolute space is regarded as an attribute of God—the *sensorium Dei*, by which the divine omnipresence as well as the divine knowledge of the totality of things is made possible. [9] But not infrequently this was dismissed as a mere private theological fancy, superadded in an artificial manner to Newton's scientific achievements. Not so. If we disregard Newton's theological language, we see clearly that he merely confused the logical priority of space to matter with an ontological priority. If we know today that this was a confusion, we have to remember that the confusion was shared by nearly all classical scientists and philosophers for two centuries after Newton. The logical, if not the temporal, priority of space to its physical content was a dogma which few dared to doubt. For Newton as for Gassendi and More, this priority was temporal as well; absolute space, being an attribute of God, naturally had to exist prior to the creation of the world. [10] There was nothing absurd in this belief, although the coeternity of space and matter was equally compatible with the conceptual framework of classical science. The option between these two views depended on personal religious

---

* One, simple, immovable, eternal, complete, independent, existing by itself, existing through itself, incorruptible, necessary, measureless, uncreated, unbounded, incomprehensible, omnipresent, incorporeal, all-pervading and all-embracing, Being in essence, Being in act, Pure act.

preferences. With the shift of the public mood from deism to pantheism or atheism, the second alternative, logically simpler, was adopted. But lack of logical simplicity and lack of consistency are two different things. The coeternity of space and matter appears to be a more economical and more elegant assumption than the arbitrary creation of matter at a definite date in the past; this is the reason why a complete return to the classical atomism seemed to the later materialists and monists incomparably more satisfactory than a hybrid combination of Lucretian metaphysics and Christian theism as found in Gassendi and Newton. But while Newton may be accused of making an artificial assumption, he cannot be blamed for an intrinsic contradiction; the temporal priority of space to its material content, though it does not follow from its logical priority, at least *does not* contradict it.

Whether space and matter were regarded as coeternal or not, the absoluteness of space, i.e., its independence of matter, had hardly been questioned. There were a few dissenters: Leibniz, Huygens, and Berkeley are the most famous.[11] On the other hand, the difference between the rival Cartesian philosophy and the philosophy of Newton was in this particular point more apparent than real. It is true that Descartes, in insisting on the inseparability of space from matter, apparently challenged the logical priority of space asserted by Newton. But Descartes made his philosophy of nature ambiguous by retaining only the geometrical properties of matter. If even impenetrability is relegated to the realm of subjective secondary qualities,[12] in what intelligible sense can space still be called *plenum?* This is not the only intrinsic difficulty of Cartesianism; another no less serious, concerning the possibility of motion, will be mentioned in a different context.

The Cartesian philosophy of nature was in a certain sense even more Newtonian than that of Newton; while for Newton space was the *primary* reality, for Descartes it was *the only true reality* of the physical world. It is hardly surprising then that Spinoza, and to a certain extent even Malebranche, who owed so much to Descartes, arrived at nearly the same divinization of space as Newton; for Spinoza, too, extension was one of the attributes of God.[13]

Spinoza has been much less criticized for his theological language than Newton. Yet if we are tolerant of the theological garment of Spinoza's thought, we should adopt the same attitude toward Newton's "mysticism." For both thinkers it was the absoluteness of space which led to its divinization, and not vice versa. Greater indulgence towards Spinoza's religious language is probably due to the fact that his pantheism is more congruous with the modern mood than the philosophy of Newton, with its deistic overtones. Certainly nobody would suspect Bertrand Russell of lurking theological—not even of pantheistic—tendencies; yet, religious terminology apart, Newton's insistence on the independence of space from its material content has hardly been restated with greater precision and clarity than by Russell in his *Principles of Mathematics:*

> There is no logical implication of other entities in space. It does not follow, merely because there is space, that therefore there are things in it. If we are to believe this, we must believe it on new grounds, or rather on what is called the evidence of senses. Thus we are taking an entirely new step.[14]

The book was published in 1903. Part VII, from which the quotation is taken, is probably one of the most accurate systematizations extant of the basic principles of classical science. The date is significant; it shows how Newton's philosophy of nature dominated even minds which were never prone to conservatism as recently as the beginning of this century.

A philosophical digression will perhaps not be out of place here. The relation between classical space and classical matter has an interesting counterpart at a more abstract level of philosophical speculation. It has been already pointed out that space for the ancient atomists was called Non-Being in contrast to the solidity of Being, which was synonymous with the impenetrable material stuff filling space. We have seen how the logical priority of space, at first only implicit, was eventually made explicit, and how Non-Being finally became an attribute of Supreme Being. The very same process took place at a more abstract level when the terms Being and Non-Being were freed of concomitant spatial imagery and began to be understood in their present more comprehensive sense. The relation between abstract Being and Non-Being remained basically the same as that between matter and the void. Just as the void seems to precede matter which fills it, Non-Being seems to be logically antecedent to Being. While nothingness seems to be self-sufficient and self-positing, Being appears to require a sufficient reason for its own presence.

All metaphysical questions concerning the origin and justification of existence in general stem from this assumed priority of Non-Being. As Bergson says:

> From the first awakening of reflection, it is this that pushes to the fore, right under the eyes of consciousness, the torturing problems, the questions that we cannot gaze at without feeling giddy and bewildered. I have no sooner commenced to philosophize than I ask myself why I exist; and when I take account of the intimate connection in which I stand to the rest of the universe, the difficulty is only pushed back, for I want to know why the universe exists; and if I refer the universe to a Principle immanent or transcendent, that supports or creates it, my thought rests on this principle only a few moments, for the same problem recurs, this time in its full breadth and generality: Whence comes it, and how can it be understood that anything exists? . . . Now, if I push these questions aside and go straight to what hides behind them, this is what I find:—Existence appears to me like a conquest over nought. I say to myself that there might be, that indeed there ought to be, nothing, and I then wonder that there is something. Or I represent all reality extended on nothing as on a carpet: at first was nothing, and being has come by superaddition to it. Or, yet again, if something has always existed, nothing must always have served as its substratum or receptacle, and is therefore eternally prior. A glass may

have always been full, but the liquid it contains never-theless fills a void. In the same way, being may have always been there, but the nought which is filled, and, as it were, stopped up by it, pre-exists for it nonetheless, if not in fact, at least in right. In short, I cannot get rid of the idea that the full is an embroidery on the canvas of the void, that being is superimposed on nothing, and that in the idea of "nothing" there is *less* than in that of "something." [15]

This was written in 1907, and its correctness has been since then amply substantiated. When Paul Valéry a few years later wrote

Que l'univers n'est qu'un défaut
Dans la pureté du Non-Être! [16]

he used merely a different metaphor for illustrating the same basic assumption about the logical and ontological priority of the nothingness on which Being is superimposed in an irrational and inexplicable way.

The same question of the basic irrationality of Being contrast-ing with the logical self-sufficiency of Non-Being was raised shortly afterwards by Martin Heidegger: "Warum ist überhaupt Seiendes und nicht vielmehr Nichts?" (Why does any being exist, and not just nothing?).[17] This, according to Heidegger, is the fundamental question of metaphysics around which con-temporary existentialism revolves.

It is beyond the scope of this chapter to reproduce Bergson's criticism of our almost irresistible psychological tendency to regard Non-Being as self-positing and logically self-sufficient while Being appears to need a special justification—Leibniz' "sufficient reason"—for itself. Here it suffices to recall Bergson's conclusion: The concept of absolute Non-Being is a pseudo-concept which cannot be self-consistently maintained in mind; the tendency to posit Non-Being as pre-existing to Being is nothing but an obstinacy of the mental habit whose deceptive cogency disappears, once psychologically analyzed. Conse-quently existence in general does not need any transcendent jus-tification; its irrationality disappears as soon as the rival Non-

Being is recognized as a verbal fiction. For only the supposed logical pre-existence of nothingness makes reality appear as a contingent and superadded entity which, in the words of Paul Valéry, only spoils the original purity of Non-Being. Bergson does not say explicitly that the relationship between Non-Being and Being is the same as that between the void and matter in classical science. But his whole analysis indicates it, and the expression about the full as "an embroidery on the canvas of the void" almost states it. Thus even the most abstruse metaphysical speculations are tinged by mental habits acquired in systematizing our sensory experience. Does this mean that certain metaphysical puzzles may disappear when our physical experience is widened and modified? We shall return to this question in due course.

THE HOMOGENEITY OF SPACE AND ITS CONSEQUENCES

Closely related to the independence and immutability of space is its *homogeneity;* indeed, as we shall see, its independence and immutability follow from its homogeneity. Logically a better way would have been to begin with the homogeneity of space and point out all that is implied in it. If the order of our exposition is reversed, it is so because we began with the historically important definition of Newton which stresses the immutability and independence of space while its homogeneity, though silently assumed, is not mentioned explicitly. The tacit assumption of the homogeneity of space was made as soon as space was separated from its physical content; and this, as we know, had been done by the Greek atomists. In their view all qualitative diversity in the world comes from the various positions, shapes, and motions of matter, not from some intrinsic differentiation of space itself, as Aristotle and his followers believed; the rejection of the idea of "natural place," that is the qualitative heterogeneity of space, is precisely one of the modern features of the Democritean atomism.

It is natural that in the century of Newton, which in so many respects made a conscious return to ancient Greek ideas, the homogeneity of space began to be explicitly stressed. Newton's contemporary and friend John Locke, while rejecting the possibility of defining space, tried nevertheless to make explicit its meaning: space according to him is the *principium individuationis* —which enables us to distinguish two qualitatively identical simultaneous sensations; two simultaneously perceived objects can be numerically distinct only if they are at two different places.[18] In other words, space is a principle of differentiation other than that of qualitative differentiation; as far as their quality is concerned, all positions in space are entirely *equivalent*, i.e., qualitatively identical; their only distinction is due exclusively to their *relations of juxtaposition* or *coexistence*. Otherwise two qualitatively identical objects would remain undistinguishable; only their juxtaposition makes them numerically distinct. Locke thus simply formulated what was tacitly assumed as soon as the idea of space was born.

How widely Locke's definition was accepted, even by two philosophers of our own century who in other respects were diametrically opposed, may be seen from the two following quotations:

> For it is scarcely possible to give any other definition of space: space is what enables us to distinguish a number of identical and simultaneous sensations from one another; it is thus a principle of differentiation other than that of qualitative differentiation, and consequently it is a reality with no quality. (H. Bergson, *Time and Free Will*, p. 95.)

> All points are qualitatively similar, and distinguished by the mere fact that they lie outside one another. (B. Russell, *Essay on the Foundations of Geometry*, p. 52.)

The independence of space from its physical content is an immediate consequence of its homogeneity: differences other than those of juxtaposition do not belong to the points themselves, but are due to the presence of the adventitious stuff *occupying* the points. The parts of space which are empty and those which are occupied by matter differ essentially in *one* respect only—that they lie outside one another; only in a secondary, accessory, and temporary way do they differ because of their content or lack of content. The adjective "temporary" is important; it indicates that change belongs only to the configuration of the material particles, not to space itself. What is changing is the occupation of a certain region of space, while the region itself remains, as Newton emphasized, eternally the same.

Two other features of classical space—infinity and mathematical continuity (infinite divisibility)—follow directly from its homogeneity. Every limit of space will appear to our imagination as arbitrary, due to the presence of some material barrier which, being located *in* space, cannot be a boundary *of* space. The crystalline vaults of Aristotle's and Ptolemy's cosmology were such material barriers, and all Aristotle's elaborate proofs that outside the sphere of the fixed stars there is no space at all are utterly unconvincing. They appeared so even to some of his contemporaries and predecessors. The question what lies *behind* the alleged uttermost limit of the world had already been asked by Archytas of Tarentum:

> If I am at the extremity of the heaven of the fixed stars, can I stretch outwards my hand or staff? It is absurd to suppose that I could not; and if I can, what is outside must be either body or space. We may then in the same way get to the outside of that again, and so on; and if there is always a new place to which the staff may be held out, this clearly involves extension without limit.[19]

Archytas' question was restated by Lucretius when he asked whether it is possible to shoot an arrow beyond the alleged limit of space. This passage of Lucretius is quoted by Giordano Bruno,[20] while Newton's contemporary John Locke repeated Archytas' argument nearly *verbatim*.[21]

Archytas' question expressed our irresistible tendency to regard every limit in space as provisional and to continue to imagine farther and farther regions of space beyond any alleged boundary. This tendency is embodied in the second postulate of

Euclid, according to which any straight-line segment can be extended beyond its extremities. The same tendency led Greek atomists to postulate the infinity of space and later inspired some philosophers of the Renaissance, in particular Bruno, to sweep away the celestial spheres of Aristotle.

With the advent of Newtonian physics the idea of infinity became so natural that when Kant discussed his First Antinomy, he was concerned with the dilemma whether the *material universe* is finite or infinite, not whether space, which contains it, has limits or not.[22] A hundred years after Kant, William Thomson said confidently: "I say finitude is incomprehensible, the infinitude in the universe is comprehensible. . . . Even if you were to go millions and millions of years the idea of coming to an end is incomprehensible."[23] The irresistibility of our belief in infinite space is, at bottom, a refusal of our mind to accept an obviously contradictory proposition that beyond certain regions of space there is no further region, no "beyond." The assumption that there is a privileged class of points constituting the boundary of space would destroy the homogeneity of space.

> How can a certain line, or a certain surface, form an impassable barrier to space, or have any mobility different in kind from that of all other lines or surfaces? The notion cannot, in philosophy, be permitted for a moment, since it destroys that most fundamental of all the axioms, the homogeneity of space.[24]

This was written by Bertrand Russell in 1897—that is, almost at the threshold of the contemporary revolution in physics which changed so profoundly the classical concept of space. It certainly does not require much imagination to recognize in this passage of Russell the old argument of Archytas, Lucretius, and Bruno: under the elegant name of Russell's "axiom of free mobility" we recognize the ancient claim that it is always possible to hold out a staff or to shoot an arrow no matter how far we go.

From the preceding follows what at first glance may appear paradoxical: the homogeneity of space implies *the relativity of position*. But this assertion has nothing to do with the relational theory of space nor with the modern relativity theory. All positions are equivalent in classical space because of its homogeneity. This stands in a sharp contrast to the absoluteness of position in Aristotelian physics. In Aristotle's universe the so-called "natural places" were differentiated not only by their mutual externality but also by their respective distances from the earth, which, together with the system of the celestial spheres, represented the absolute frame of reference. Positions within such a frame of reference were *absolute* positions and their different distances from the absolute motionless center of the universe determined the intrinsically different qualities of different "natural places." There is a clear connection between the absoluteness of position and the heterogeneity of space. Only by the removal of the boundaries and of the center of the universe could the relativity of position and the homogeneity of space be preserved. Thus when Giordano Bruno attacked the finite universe of Aristotle, he was at the same time destroying Aristotelian physics; in returning to the infinite space of the ancient atomists, he was reasserting the homogeneity of space, which was incompatible with the doctrine of four elements and their "natural places." In limitless and qualitatively undifferentiated space there are no privileged places and no privileged directions; consequently, there is no ground for the old dualism of earth and heaven nor for the qualitatively different elements residing in their proper regions. One century before Newton, Bruno clearly discerned the main features of the future cosmology.[25]

The homogeneity of space also implies its *infinite divisibility*. As the relation of juxtaposition is universal, it relates *any* pair of points, no matter how near they are. In other words, no matter how minute a spatial interval may be, it must always be an *interval* separating two points, each of which is *external* to the other. To claim that certain intervals of space are indivisible means that it is impossible to discern within them any juxtaposed parts; but as juxtaposition is the very essence of spatiality, this would mean that such intervals are themselves devoid of spatiality! The thesis of indivisible spatial intervals is thus self-destructive: while it denies the possibility of "zero lengths" (i.e., points), it at the same time surreptitiously reintroduces their existence when it speaks of the atomic intervals separating two very near *points.*

If we admit the existence of points at all, we have to admit their equally dense distribution over the whole of space without excluding them from certain forbidden zones, no matter how small they may be. The atomic structure of space would be incompatible with the homogeneity of space, for it would lead to the absurd conclusion that there are "holes" in space, i.e., regions devoid of spatiality. This is utterly unthinkable; when we try to imagine "holes" in space, then, as Lotze says, "the lacuna which we try to create is at once filled by space as good as that suppressed." [26] In classical space the attribute of indivisibility can belong only to the "zero lengths," i.e., to the points.

The concept of the infinite divisibility of space can also be traced to Greek thought. It underlies the arguments of Zeno the Eleatic against the possibility of motion; it is implicit in the first postulate of Euclid, according to which it is possible to draw a straight line between *any* pair of points, no matter how near or far apart they may be. This excludes the possibility of "holes" in space. It is more explicit in the tenth proposition of the first book of Euclid, which proves the possibility of bisecting *any* straight-line segment; this also excludes the possibility of any atomic length. In this respect the modern period added hardly anything except a greater explicitness of formulation. The following statement of Kant, whose philosophy was so thoroughly imbued by the spirit of classical physics and Euclidean geometry, is fairly typical:

> The properties of magnitude by which no part of them is the smallest possible, that is, by which no part is simple, is called their continuity. Space and time are *quanta continua,* because no part of them can be given save as enclosed between limits (points or instants), and therefore only in such fashion that this part is itself again a space or a time. Space therefore consists only of spaces, time solely of times. Points and instants are only

limits, that is, mere positions which limit space and time.[27]

In the Kantian view the emphasis is laid on the wholeness and unity of space which exists *prior* to the points; the latter are merely ideal limits which are never actually attained. According to Bertrand Russell, the opposite is true; the points are *constitutive parts of space*. In this view space is regarded as an infinite aggregate of all dimensionless points.[28] But, philosophically speaking, there is hardly any significant difference between these two views; the infinite divisibility of space is accepted by both. The only difference is that while for Kant space is *divisible without limit*, for Russell it is *actually divided* into an infinite number of parts. Besides, as Whitehead observed, Kant's view was not consistent in this respect and the view identical with that of Russell may be found only a few pages before the quoted passage.[29] But bearing in mind that the concept of unextended point and the infinite divisibility of space are correlative, it is fairer to regard the difference between the two passages as one rather of emphasis than of substance. Russell's view seemed to express more completely and more explicitly the trends of classical thought, for which the concept of the pointlike geometrical position was, as we shall see, of fundamental importance.

THE "THEME OF GULLIVER" AND THE RELATIVITY OF MAGNITUDE

Belief in the mathematical continuity of space was of tremendous importance for *the classical view of microphysical reality*. It led to the assumption that microphysical space is like the space surrounding our bodies and that the world of atoms differs only in size from the world of our sense perception. In other words, by reducing the dimensions of visible bodies in the same ratio we can obtain a satisfactory model of microphysical objects. As Pierre Maxime Schuhl recently observed, our imagination seems to be dominated by the "theme of Gulliver"—a picturesque term for the postulate of the homogeneity of space. Lilliput is exactly like our human world except for size; all proportions are exactly preserved. Similarly, Brobdingnag is basically nothing but our world constructed on a larger scale.[30] This idea of geometrical similarity between various layers of spatial magnitudes is one of the most characteristic themes of classical thought. As we shall see, it is being given up now by physicists (and especially by philosophers) only with considerable reluctance.

For nearly three centuries the "principle of Gulliver" seemed to be well substantiated, not only by our common sense but also by the increasing number of discoveries made by microscope and telescope. There was ever growing evidence that to our unlimited subjective capacity to imagine smaller and smaller or larger and larger volumes of space there corresponded objectively the infinite convergent series of real physical volumes, each contained in an immediately larger one, while the whole infinite series was, in Whitehead's words, "like the Chinese toy with a nest of boxes, one within the other." [31] This was what the microscope began to show in opening before our eyes an apparently unlimited vista in the direction of the infinitesimal, while the telescope was extending our visual field in the opposite direction. Here was the source of Pascal's anxiety when he was overwhelmed by the position of man floating between "two chasms of infinity" and when he professed his inability to grasp either the infinitely large or the infinitely small. His humility was doubtless sincere; but he did not realize how, contrary to his declarations, the world really appeared *transparent* to him. What he was doing was merely to draw the consequences from the Euclidean concept of the homogeneity of space and to accept even the one that appeared most baffling—that is, *the relativity of magnitude*. Man is an insignificant atom in comparison with the stellar universe, but he is a true universe in comparison with the tiny world of the flesh worm. And this worm in turn contains an infinite number of still smaller worlds:

> But to show him [i.e., man] another prodigy equally astonishing, let him examine the most delicate things he

knows. Let a mite be given him, with its minute body and parts incomparably more minute, limbs with their joints, veins in the limbs, blood in the veins, humors in the blood, drops in the humors, vapors in the drops. Dividing these last things again, let him exhaust his powers of conception, and let the last object at which he can arrive be now that of our discourse. Perhaps he will think that here is the smallest point in nature. I will let him see therein a new abyss. I will paint for him not only the visible universe, but all that he can conceive of nature's immensity in the womb of this abridged atom. Let him see therein the infinity of the universes, each of which has its firmament, its planets, its earth, in the same proportion as in the visible world; in each earth animals, and in the last mites, in which he will find again all that the first had, finding still in these others the same thing without end and without cessation. Let him lose himself in wonders as amazing in their littleness as the others in their vastness. For who will not be astounded at the fact that our body, which a little while ago was imperceptible in the universe, itself imperceptible in the bosom of the whole, is now a colossus, a world, or rather a whole, in respect of the nothingness which we cannot reach? [32]

I quote this famous literary passage at length, not only because it expresses the homogeneity and continuity of space much more graphically than Swift's fantasy, but also as witness that the idea of worlds within worlds was far from rare. The discovery of microorganisms showed that beyond the limits of our sensory perception the microcosm inaccessible to the senses has basically the same features as the world seen around us.

This thought explains the curious popularity of the preformation theory to which the most outstanding scientists of the seventeenth century subscribed, including Leibniz, Swammerdam, Malpighi, and Hartsoeker. According to this theory an adult animal pre-exists in a complete form, though on an exceedingly small scale, within an original embryo. The only disagreement concerned the question whether it is an ovum or a spermatozoon which contains the future animal.[33] The idea that the embryonic organism differed from its adult form only in size and not in form was certainly dead in the last century; but the similar belief that the atom of matter is a miniature of the solid body of our ordinary experience was one of the cornerstones of Victorian physics and is surreptitiously present even today in the imagination of a considerable number of physicists. Yet these ideas are on the same footing as natural outgrowths of the belief in the homogeneity of space or the *geometrical similitude* between the world of atoms and the world of our dimensions.

Two famous physicists of the Newtonian era, Christian Huygens and G. W. Leibniz, did not shrink from Pascal's idea of an infinite chain of the worlds differing in size but not in form, when they faced the problem of explaining the elasticity of atoms.[34] What is even more significant, this theory was seriously proposed as late as the beginning of this century by Fournier d'Albe, who claimed that the atoms of our universe are the suns of the next smaller universe while the electrons are its planets, and so on *in infinitum;* in the true spirit of Pascal he even spoke about the "chemistry and biology of the infraworld." It was only consistent to complete such speculations by similar ones concerning the "supraworld" of galaxies, which were regarded as giant superorganisms.[35] Such fantastic speculations sound weird, but their author was entirely correct when he stressed their logical compatibility with the principle of the relativity of magnitude, which is only one aspect of the homogeneity of space.

Pascal's theory of the infinite chain of worlds within worlds is probably more excusable than that of the twentieth-century physicist. In the seventeenth century the wave theory of light was not generally accepted. As the case of Huygens shows, even to those who defended the theory it was not clear that the undulatory nature of light imposes a definite limit on the magnification of the microscopic image. And when this limit was convincingly established in the nineteenth century, it was regarded as a purely technical obstacle which in no way affected the magnification of the "mental image." The imagination of physicists went freely and uninhibitedly beyond the limits of the microcosmic image in constructing models of what John Tyndall called "the sub-sensible world." [36] The same sensory elements of which our perceptual world is built were used as a construction material for the micromodels. Even Bohr's first planetary model of the atom seemed to confirm the belief that the microcosm is merely the macrocosm with all its dimensions enormously reduced in the same ratio. This probably accounts for the great popularity of this model even today, as is evidenced by the covers of numerous popular books and magazines bearing diagrams of the orbits on which the planets-electrons move around the sun-nucleus.

The belief in the similarity of microcosm and macrocosm also account for the sudden reappearance of Pascal's view not only in the thought of Fournier d'Albe, but also in that of the philosopher of whom it should be least expected. In the last dialogue with Lucien Price only a few weeks before his death Alfred North Whitehead expressed a view identical with that of Pascal and Fournier d'Albe:

> "From what science has discovered about the infinitely small and the infinitely vast, the size of our bodies is almost totally irrelevant. In this little mahogany stand" —he touched it with his hand—"may be civilizations as complex and diversified in scale as our own; and up there, the heavens, with all their vastness, may be only a minute strand of tissue in the body of a being in the scale of which all our universes are as a trifle." [37]

It is certainly astonishing to hear the thinker who so emphatically stressed that "reality is incurably atomic" [38] sink back into the Pascalian vision of the infinitely divisible universe. In this respect Jonathan Swift, the inventor of Gulliver and his fictitious adventures in Lilliput and Brobdingnag, took his own theme less seriously than the philosopher two centuries later:

> So, naturalists observe, a flea
> Hath smaller fleas that on him prey;

And these have smaller still to bite 'em,
And so proceed *ad infinitum.*[39]

The underlying note of amusement, which is not too remote from scepticism, is clearly discernible here.

But Leibniz, who was an older contemporary of Swift, found nothing queer or amusing in the continuous subdivision of space; on the contrary, he regarded any interruption of this process as a mere result of our mental fatigue.[40] His rejection of the finite divisibility of matter led him to his own concept of the monad: true indivisibility can belong only to extensionless pointlike entities. Hardly in any other system can the correlation between the infinite divisibility of space and matter and the affirmation of extensionless points be seen more clearly than in the system of Leibniz; here was the main source of inspiration for young Russell. In Chapter IV it will be shown that although physicists generally did not follow Leibniz in his rejection of physical atomism, none of them ever challenged the infinite divisibility of space nor the principle of relativity of magnitude. The view that the structure of the universe is, so to speak, repeated, per-haps an infinite number of times, at different levels of magnitude, is much closer to the subconscious preferences of our imagina-tion than we like to admit; the case of Whitehead, referred to above, shows how strong a temptation "the theme of Gulliver" is even for a thinker intensely aware of the difference between classical and modern physics.

THE EUCLIDEAN CHARACTER OF SPACE
AND ITS THREE-DIMENSIONALITY

The principle of the relativity of magnitude is, as we shall see, related to the Euclidean character of space. The Euclidean na-ture of space as well as its three-dimensionality were until re-cently tacitly assumed. The very term "Euclidean space" was hardly used at all before the first doubts about the fifth postulate of Euclid emerged in the minds of nineteenth-century mathe-maticians.

Non-Euclidean geometries, based on the denial of this postulate, demonstrated the logical possibility of other "spaces" in which some propositions of classical geometry were not valid. Thus it was shown, for instance, that the infinity and limitlessness of space are logically separable features: the surface of the sphere and of its three-dimensional counterpart is finite, though without limits. But it was generally assumed that non-Euclidean geometries, in spite of the lack of intrinsic contradiction, have no physical counterparts, being merely free creations of the mathematical imagination. The same attitude was generally adopted toward geometries of four or more dimensions; prior to the advent of modern physics their main pseudophilosophical use was in justification of occultist phenomena. Real physical space was believed to be without curvature and three-dimensional.

The question of how these last two features are related logically to the homogeneity of space was much debated. The continuity of space is implied in the first postulate of Euclid, which requires the possibility of drawing a straight line between *any* two points; the limitlessness of space is implied in the second postulate, according to which it is always possible to extend a finite straight segment. Thomas L. Heath observed in his commentary on Euclid that the third postulate, which removes any restriction on the size of the circle, requires both the continuity and infinitude of space, while the fourth postulate, asserting the equality of all right angles, is a consequence of the *principle of invariability of figures*, which again is equivalent to the homogeneity of space.[41] (The axiom of invariability of figures, called by Russell *the axiom of free mobility*, asserts that geometrical figures are unaffected by a change in their positions; this follows from the relativity of position which, as stated above, is only another aspect of the homogeneity of space.) The fifth and most famous postulate, as was already recognized by Wallis, can be replaced by its logical equivalent, which admits the possibility of constructing *similar figures on any scale of magnitude.*[42] This is the *principle of relativity of magnitude* which, as shown above, also follows from the homogeneity of space. The last postulate is valid *only* within Euclidean geometry; its great importance in physics, recognized even by Laplace, becomes evident if we realize that only in virtue of its validity may concrete models of the extragalactic universe or of the universe in its totality be constructed. It underlies Pascal's idea of the structural identity of the universe at different levels of magnitude. Thus it seems that all five classical postulates of Euclid express various aspects and consequences of one fundamental feature—the homogeneity of space.

Non-Euclidean spaces are generally not homogeneous, and even those which have constant curvature are not homogeneous in the sense stated above; for while they are characterized by the relativity of position, the principle of relativity of magnitude does not hold for them. The term *isogeneity* was proposed for such types of spatial structure, to distinguish them from the true homogeneity of Euclidean space.[43] The latter requires relativity both of position *and* of magnitude; it requires the structure of space to be qualitatively identical no matter where and how far we go *and* no matter what scale of magnitude we consider.

This unique feature was the main reason why Euclidean space was preferred by some philosophers and mathematicians as recently as the beginning of this century; for while it was true that the theoretical discoveries of Riemann and Lobachevski showed that space *in general* does not have to be Euclidean, on the other hand they brought into full focus the unique feature of Euclidean space—its homogeneity in the sense defined above.[44] Truly homogeneous space *has* to be of Euclid's type. It looked as if the unity of nature could hardly find a more complete and more consistent expression than in the unity of classical space.

The task of relating the three-dimensional character of space to its homogeneity proved to be much more arduous, and attempts were far from successful. These attempts were of different kinds and of very uneven value. Some of them—those of Schelling and Hegel—are as grotesque and unconvincing as the search of some medieval scholars to find a rational ground why the number of the divine persons should be exactly three; others, more intelligent and more interesting, possess a certain plausibility at first glance, but are usually criticized for concealing *petitio principii*.[45] It is beyond the scope of this chapter to dwell on these proofs and criticism of them; if we mention them at all it is in order to show how strong the urge was to trace *all* the various features of space to one single fundamental attribute. This unconscious Eleaticism among philosophers and scientists is far stronger than is generally admitted and was especially strong in the classical doctrine of space. The effort was surprisingly successful; with a single exception of the number of dimensions, *all* features of classical Euclidean space did follow from its homogeneity: its independence of physical content, its infinity and continuity, the relativity of position and magnitude, its causal inertness, and its immutability.

THE CAUSAL INERTNESS OF SPACE

"Causal inertness" and "immutability" require a few additional words, though their meaning is implicit in the foregoing pages. The causal inertness or *passivity* of space denies that place or change in place can have any causal effect; already in the seventeenth century Gilbert, in conscious opposition to Aristotle, had observed:

> Sed non locus in natura quicquam potest: locus nihil est, non existit, vim non habet; potestas omnis in corporibus ipsis. Non enim Luna movetur, nec Mercurii, aut Veneris stella, propter locum aliquem in mundo, nec stellae fixae quietae manent propter locum.* [46]

All physical effects on bodies should be traced to *bodies themselves* or, more generally, to the material present *in* space. Space is nothing but an inert receptor of things completely indifferent to all changes; unchangeable itself, it does not cause any change either. We shall return to this point in dealing with classical dynamics; then we shall see that a completely consistent uphold-

---

* But position can have no effect in nature. Position is nothing; it does not exist; all power resides in bodies themselves. Neither Venus nor Mercury nor the moon moves because of its position in the world, nor do the fixed stars remain at rest because of their position.

ing of the causal inertness of space was not possible, not even within the classical framework, for space appeared to be indifferent only to some but not to *all* kinds of motion.

As far as the immutability of space is concerned, it followed automatically from the assumption that all changes are to be looked for in the bodies in space and none in the spatial *receptaculum* itself. Does this also follow from the homogeneity of space? Today we know that it does *not;* if we assume, for instance, an empty spherical space expanding uniformly in all directions, we would have an instance of space which is at every instant perfectly homogeneous in all its parts while it changes. The immutability of space cannot then be derived from its homogeneity unless the latter is understood tacitly also as homogeneity *in time* and not merely as homogeneity of simultaneous parts of space; for change of space would imply *heterogeneity in time.* Yet, precisely this wider sense of the *identity through time* was tacitly or even explicitly assumed when the homogeneity of space was spoken of. The opposite idea seemed so absurd that it was only rarely rejected explicitly. When the French mathematician Calinon prophetically envisaged the possibility of the *space constant varying with time,* he was at once rebuked by young Bertrand Russell:

> This would involve a causal connection between space and other things, which seems hardly conceivable, and which, if regarded as possible, must surely destroy geometry, since geometry depends throughout on the irrelevance of causation. Moreover, in all operations of measurement, some time is spent; unless we knew that space is unchanging throughout the operation, it is hard to see how our results could be trustworthy, and how, consequently a change in the parameter could be discovered. The same difficulties would arise, in fact, as those resulting from supposing space not homogeneous.[47]

The passage shows how closely the inertness and immutability of space were connected in the mind of Russell, whose view in this respect was representative of classical science. A definite assumption was made about the relation of space to time; although this reference to time was rather negative—space being regarded as absolutely independent of time—it had an immense significance, whose importance did not clearly appear until recently. Independence of space with respect to time is only another term for the *rigidity of the spatial structure*. The full significance of this last feature of classical space will appear more clearly in connection with the concepts of classical time and motion.

NOTES FOR CHAPTER II

1. Newton, *Mathematical Principles of Natural Philosophy*, translated by A. Motte, revised by F. Cajori (University of California Press, 1950), Scholium II.
2. On the views of Telesio, Pattrizzi, Bruno, Campanella, and Gassendi, see Max Jammer, *Concepts of Space* (Harvard University Press, 1957), p. 83-88, 90-92.
3. In the Foreword to M. Jammer's book *Concepts of Space*, p. xv.
4. C. Bailey, *The Greek Atomists and Epicurus* (Oxford, 1928), p. 118.
5. W. Gilbert, *De mundo nostro sublunari philosophia nova* (Amsterdam, 1651), lib. II, cap. 8, p. 144; Otto von Guericke, *Experimenta nova (ut vocantur) Magdeburgica de vacuo spatio* (Amsterdam, 1672), p. 61; C. Bailey, *loc. cit.*
6. Henry More, *Enchiridion Metaphysicum* (London, 1671), VIII.
7. A. Koyré, *From the Closed World to the Infinite Universe* (John Hopkins University Press, 1957), p. 154.
8. John Burnet, *Early Greek Philosophy*, 2d ed. (London, 1920), p. 389; C. Bailey. *op. cit.*, p. 76.
9. On the influence of Henry More on Newton, see Jammer, *op. cit.*, p. 111; Koyré, *op. cit.*, Chaps. V, VI, VII, in particular p. 159.
10. Pierre Gassendi, *Opera omnia*, Florence, 1727, Vol. I, p. 163: "spatia immensa fuisse antequam Deus conderet mundum." H. More, *op. cit.*, cap. VIII, 10, p. 71; E. A. Burtt, *The Metaphysical Foundations of Modern Physical Science*, revised ed. (Humanities Press, 1951), p. 257.
11. *The Leibniz-Clarke Correspondence*, edited by H. G. Alexander (Philosophical Library, 1955); Max Jammer, *op. cit.*, p. 114-122; *Œuvres complètes de Christian Huyghens* (Hague, 1905), Vol. X, p. 609; H. Reichenbach, "Die Bewegungslehre bei Newton, Leibniz und Huygens," *Kant-Studien*, Bd. 29 (1924), p. 421; G. Berkeley, *De motu*, in particular §§ 52-65.

12. *Principia philosophiae,* pars II, 4, in Ch. Adam and Paul Tannery, Eds., *Œuvres de Descartes* (Paris, 1905), Vol. VIII, p. 42.
13. *Ethica,* II, prop. 2: "Extensio attributum Dei est, sive Deus est res extensa." Malebranche similarly identified the immensity of the Divine Being with the infinity of space, but he tried to avoid the eternity of space by differentiating between "intelligible" and "material" space. Such a verbal distinction, obviously drawn for theological purposes, did not save Malebranche from the accusation of Spinozism. (A. Koyré, *op. cit.,* p. 155-159.)
14. B. Russell, *Principles of Mathematics* (New York, Norton, 1903; 2d edition 1938), Chap. 53, p. 465.
15. *Creative Evolution,* translated by A. Mitchell (New York, Modern Library, 1944), pp. 299-300.
16. "That the universe is but a flaw in the purity of Non-Being!" Paul Valéry, *Les Charmes* (Paris, 1922), the poem "Le serpent."
17. Martin Heidegger, *Was ist Metaphysik?* 7th ed. (Frankfurt a.M., 1955), p. 42. (The first edition in 1924.)
18. John Locke, *An Essay Concerning Human Understanding,* Book II, Chap. XXVII, "Of Identity and Diversity."
19. F. M. Cornford, "The Invention of Space" in *Essays in Honor of Gilbert Murray* (London, Allen & Unwin, 1936), p. 233.
20. Lucretius, *De rerum natura,* I, vv. 968-983, about the possibility of shooting an arrow beyond any alleged limit of space; G. Bruno, *On the Infinite Universe and the Worlds,* translated by Dorothea Singer (New York, Schumann, 1950), the introductory epistle in which the preceding passage from Lucretius is quoted.
21. Locke, *op. cit.,* Book II, Chap. XIII, "Vacuum Beyond the Utmost Bounds of Body."
22. I. Kant, *Critique of Pure Reason,* translated by Norman Kemp Smith (Humanities Press, 1950); "Antinomies of Pure Reason," pp. 396 f. The infinity of space is explicitly asserted by Kant in the Transcendental Aesthetic, p. 69-70.
23. W. Thomson, *Popular Lectures and Addresses,* I, (New York, Macmillan, 1891), pp. 314-315.
24. B. Russell, *An Essay on the Foundations of Geometry* (Dover, 1956; the original edition 1897), p. 49.
25. H. Höffding, *A History of Modern Philosophy* (Dover, 1956), I, pp. 123-130.
26. H. Lotze, *Metaphysic,* edited by B. Bosanquet (Oxford, 1884), II, p. 189.
27. I. Kant, *op. cit.,* p. 204.
28. B. Russell, *Principles of Mathematics,* p. 443.
29. A. N. Whitehead, *Science and the Modern World* (New York, Macmillan, 1926), p. 184; *Critique of Pure Reason,* p. 198. Whitehead quotes this passage from Max Müller's translation: "I call an extensive quantity that in which the representation of the whole is rendered possible by the representation of its parts, *and therefore necessarily preceded by it.*" (Whitehead's italics.)

30. Pierre Maxime Schuhl, "Le thème de Gulliver et le postulat de Laplace," *Journal de psychologie*, 51e année (1947), pp. 169-184.
31. *The Concept of Nature* (Cambridge University Press, 1950), p. 61. Here Whitehead deals with the continuity of classical time, which was treated in the same way as that of classical space.
32. Pascal, *Pensées*, translated by W. F. Trotter (New York, Dutton, 1931), p. 17.
33. E. Meyerson, *De l'explication dans les sciences* (Paris, 1921), I, pp. 156-159; P. M. Schuhl, *loc. cit.*, pp. 176 f.
34. Ch. Huygens, *Treatise on Light*, translated by Silvanus P. Thomson, Chap. I: "And it must not be thought that in this there is anything absurd or impossible, it being on the contrary quite credible that it is this infinite series of different sizes of corpuscles, having different degrees of velocity, of which Nature makes use to produce so many marvellous effects." The same view was expressed by Leibniz: "And as this fluid must be itself composed of little solid bodies, elastic among themselves, we see that this replication of solids and liquids continues to infinity." *Leibnizens Mathematische Schriften*, edited by G. J. Gerhardt (Halle, 1850-1863), VI, p. 228.
35. Fournier d'Albe, *Two New Worlds* (London, 1907), p. 134.
36. John Tyndall, *Lectures on Light* (New York, Appleton, 1873), p. 34.
37. *Dialogues of Alfred North Whitehead as Recorded by Lucien Price* (Boston, Little Brown, 1954), pp. 367-368.
38. *Process and Reality* (New York, Macmillan, 1930), p. 95: "Continuity concerns what is potential; whereas actuality is incurably atomic."
39. Jonathan Swift, *On Poetry, a Rhapsody*. Quoted by Karl Pearson, *The Grammar of Science* (Everyman's Library, 1949), p. 212.
40. The *Leibniz-Clarke Correspondence*, the postscriptum to Leibniz's fourth letter.
41. T. L. Heath, *The Thirteen Books of Euclid's Elements* (New York, Dover, 1956), pp. 199-200.
42. Heath, *op. cit.*, pp. 210-211.
43. The term was proposed by the Belgian philosopher Joseph Delboeuf. (B. Russell, *An Essay on the Foundations of Geometry*, p. 110.)
44. For instance, in Louis Couturat's review of Russell's *Essay*, in *Revue de métaphysique et de morale*, Vol. VI (1898), pp. 334-380, especially its concluding part.
45. On Schelling and Hegel: E. Meyerson, *De l'explication dans les sciences* (Paris, 1921), Vol. II, p. 145, note. The attempt of Lotze in his *Metaphysic*, p. 135, was criticized by Russell (*Essay*, pp. 105-107) and that of Natorp in his *Logische Grundlagen der exakten Naturwissenschaften* (Leipzig, 1910), by Max Jammer (*Concepts of Space*, p. 178). On the other hand the attempts of Kant and Poincaré belong to a different category because they both tried to justify the three-dimensionality of space by some empirical feature of the physical world: Kant by the law of gravitation, Poincaré by our psycho-physiological organization, which he regarded as a result of the

evolutionary adaptation to the order of nature. Cf. Kant, "Thoughts on the True Constitution of Living Forces," in *Kant's Inaugural Dissertation and Early Writings*, translated by J. Handyside (Chicago, 1939); H. Poincaré, *Dernières pensées* (Paris, 1913), pp. 55-98.

46. W. Gilbert, *op. cit.*, p. 144.
47. B. Russell, *Essay*, pp. 112-113.

III · THE CONCEPT OF TIME

THE INDEPENDENCE OF TIME FROM ITS PHYSICAL CONTENT

TIME is the second fundamental concept of classical physics. While space was defined as the three-dimensional manifold of coexisting homogeneous terms, time was regarded as the one-dimensional manifold of successive terms. The basic relation in space is juxtaposition; the basic relation in time is *succession*. The points of space are *beside* one another; the instants of time *follow* one another. While we keep this fundamental difference in mind, we can apply a large part of what has just been said about space to time as well. Both space and time were regarded as species of manifold, and both were believed to share the property of being homogeneous. As in the case of space, the basic attributes of time followed from its homogeneity: its independence of its physical content, its infinity, continuity, and uniformity. The uniformity of time was a counterpart of the immutability of space; it might be more expressively designated *uniform fluidity*. Thus it is only natural that the principles of relativity of magnitude and of position have their counterparts in the doctrine of classical time.

The independence of time in regard to concrete changes which take place in it was again explicitly formulated by Newton:

35

Absolute true and mathematical time, of itself and by its own nature, flows uniformly, without regard to anything external. It is also called *duration*. Relative, apparent and vulgar time, is some sensible and external measure of absolute time (duration), estimated by the motions of bodies, whether accurate or unequable, and is commonly used instead of true time; such as an hour, a day, a month, a week.[1]

According to this view time flows no matter whether something changes or not; in its own nature time is *empty* and is only in an accessory and contingent way filled by changes. Changes are *in* time; they are not *time* itself. This distinction between time and concrete becoming is at the very foundations of classical physics. As space does not imply matter, time does not imply motion nor change in general. This had been clearly stated by Newton's tutor and predecessor Isaac Barrow, whose influence on the formation of Newton's concept of time was as important as the influence exerted by Henry More on Newton's view of space:

But does time imply motion? Not at all, I reply, as far as its absolute, intrinsic nature is concerned; no more than rest; the quantity of time depends on neither essentially; whether things run or stand still, whether we sleep or wake, time flows in its even tenor. Imagine all the stars to have remained fixed from their birth; nothing would have been lost to time; as long would that stillness have endured as has continued the flow of this motion. Before, after, at the same time (as far as concerns the rise and disappearance of things), even in that tranquil state would have had their proper existence, and might by a more perfect mind have been perceived.[2]

This could hardly be stated more explicitly.

Basically the same argument was still used at the beginning of this century. When Bertrand Russell in 1901 defended the absolute theory of time, he began by defending the fundamental distinction between the temporal series itself and its qualitative content:

> In the absolute theory, we have two classes of entities,
> 1) those which *are* positions, 2) those which *have* posi-
> tions. Any two terms of the first class have an asym-
> metrical transitive relation; in the present case either
> *before* or *after*. The terms which have positions are
> terms each of which has, to one or more of the terms
> which are positions, a certain specific relation, which
> may be expressed by saying that the new terms are *at*
> the positions, or that they occupy the positions. . . .
> We may call *qualities* the terms which have positions
> in time; thus quality may be at many moments, or even
> at all moments.[3]

The argument is more general and the language evidently more
abstruse than that of Barrow, but its substance is the same. Barrow tried to show that the absence of motion does not prevent
time from flowing; Russell gave the argument a more general
form by pointing out that no absence of *any* change (not only
of change of position) affects the flow of time; a certain quality
can endure through *many* moments or even through *all* moments. Barrow and Russell had an identical target at which they
were aiming: the relational theory of time. Russell's distinction
between "qualities" and "moments" is equivalent to the assertion that the physical content of time is underivable from time
itself just as matter is underivable from space. What Russell said
of space may be repeated word for word of time: "There is no
logical implication of other entities in [time]. It does not follow,
merely because there is [time], that therefore there are things in
it." Because the concept of matter as well as that of motion cannot be logically derived from the concepts of space and time
respectively, we must recognize that both are indefinable:

> What is meant by *occupying* a point or instant, analysis
> cannot explain; this is a fundamental relation, expressed
> by *in* or *at*, asymmetrical and intransitive, indefinable
> and simple.[4]

This means that time—if not *de facto*, at least *de iure*—is empty.
The use of the term *occupancy* for both space and time is

characteristic of the whole of classical thought. The term itself is distinctly spatial in its original meaning, and its use suggests the close analogy between space and time in which classical physics as well as classical philosophy so firmly believed. Just as matter *fills* or *occupies* portions of space, so motions or, more generally, changes *fill* or *occupy* portions of time. Just as space is a container of all matter, so time is a receptacle of all changes or, in Barrow's words, "Time is in some sort the Space of Motion." [5] This was the basic dogma of classical science.

The influence of the Newtonian view of time was far deeper than is generally believed, for it went beyond the limits of physical science. In the thought of Kant, for instance, time was regarded also as a sort of homogeneous frame or container which is filled out from outside by the changing material of sensations. It is true that time for Kant did not possess extramental reality, being only an a priori form of intuition; but this does not alter the fact that the sharp distinction between an immutable homogeneous container and its changing and heterogeneous content is essentially Newtonian in its nature. In this respect we can speak of a certain *isoformism* between the thought of Kant and Newton. Even today we are hardly aware that when we speak of our psychological states as occurring *in* time, we retain this distinction between the receptor and its content, the distinction which under the double impact of Newton and Kant still dominates to a great extent our mode of thinking.

THE HOMOGENEITY OF TIME AND ITS CONSEQUENCES

The independence of time with respect to its content is a direct consequence of its *homogeneity*. Concrete changes are or appear to be heterogeneous. Qualitative change is one of the most striking features of our private stream of consciousness and appears to be present even in the public world of physics. But even if we accept the reduction of all qualitative changes in the physical world to *changes in position* only, as proposed by the corpuscular-kinetic scheme of nature, the feature of heterogeneity does not altogether disappear; it is reduced to a minimum and apparently an innocuous degree, but it is nevertheless present. Successive configurations of particles still remain *different*, even though the particles themselves and underlying space remain the same. And we have to add that the stretch of time underlying these successive configurations is just as indifferent to change as is space and the quantity of matter involved.

In other words, while the successive moments of physical becoming are different, if not in quality, then at least in their geometrical and dynamical aspects, the successive instants of true mathematical time are lacking any other differentiation than that which results from their succession. As far as their quality is concerned, temporal instants are *perfectly equivalent;* their only differentiating features are due to their *different positions* in the temporal series. When Kant declared that the distinction between two consecutive moments is *basically different* from any other purely qualitative differentiation empirically known, he simply codified Newton's logical priority of time to change. Only the independence of time from change makes it possible to speak of different moments of duration when no actual change seems to occur; as when, for instance, a body retains its position unchanged through time, or when a certain psychological quality persists through a certain interval of time. When we speak of the possibility of the recurrence of an identical psychological quality in the stream of our private experience, we implicitly assume that, in spite of the qualitative identity of the content, the corresponding two moments, the moment of the original experience and that of its repetition, are precisely *two*, i.e., *different*, not because of the difference in quality, but because of their succession. As the relation of juxtaposition makes it possible to distinguish two qualitatively identical and simultaneously existing entities, so the relation of succession makes it possible to distinguish two qualitatively identical states of one and the same entity. In this sense, time is analogous to space in being a *principle of differentiation of a kind other than qualitative.*[6]

The infinity and continuity of time follow naturally from its homogeneity. The infinity of time implies the absence of any initial moment in the past or of any final moment in the future; for such moments would possess a privileged character which would be utterly incompatible with the homogeneity of time. If time is truly homogeneous, *every* instant must have its ancestors and successors; consequently, the concept of The First Moment which had no predecessor or that of The Ultimate End which will lack successors is utterly unthinkable.

The infinity of time imposed itself on the minds of classical physicists with as much cogency as the infinity of space. The assumption of the temporal beginning of the world was due mostly to extrascientific, especially theological, motives; and even so, it was sometimes regarded as the beginning *in* time, not *of* time. The logic inherent in the philosophy of Barrow, More, Gassendi, Newton, and Clarke required the existence of time even *before* the creation of the world, that is, the existence of the beginningless duration devoid of any physical content until the date of the creation.[7] For all these thinkers except Gassendi this beginningless, physically empty duration was regarded as an attribute of God, being an adequate manifestation of the eternally enduring divine nature, as absolute space was an expression of his all-pervading presence. But again it must be emphasized that it was the absoluteness of time which led to its divinization rather than vice versa; Newton and Clarke simply stated in religious language the scientific conviction of the whole classical period.

The mathematical continuity of time follows with equal logical force from its homogeneity. The passage from Kant's *Critique of Pure Reason* quoted in Chapter II, affirms the infinite divisibility of time as well as space. No matter how narrow a temporal interval may be, its limits remain always in the relation of succession, the first being earlier, the second later. Time flows even within its smallest intervals, because, strictly speaking, *there are no smallest intervals*. To claim the opposite would amount to the admission of "atoms of time," that is, intervals in which the temporal flux would be standing still, for there would be no possibility of distinguishing within such intervals further successive moments. The atomic structure of time is thus a contradiction in terms because it ends up with the obviously contradictory conclusion that there are intervals of time which are *not* temporal. The divisibility of time has no limits as long as we deal with finite temporal series; the only true indivisibility belongs to durationless instants.

Again it does not ultimately make a difference whether these durationless instants are regarded as mere ideal limits, never actually attained in a concrete process of division, or as *prior* to temporal intervals. The latter view was held by Russell; the former, stressing the priority of intervals to instants, was held (though not very consistently) by Kant; but the continuity of time is accepted by both. When classical physics from the times of Galilei up to Bertrand Russell kept insisting that each interval of time contains an actually infinite number of durationless instants,[8] its motive stemmed from the refusal of our imagination to conceive any limit to the divisibility of time. Any such limit is regarded as arbitrary and, in the last analysis, incompatible with the nature of time. Besides, this imaginative urge to continue indefinitely the process of ideally subdividing any stretch of time into its consecutive parts seemed to be substantiated by experience. This important fact should now be considered at greater length.

THE RELATIVITY OF TEMPORAL INTERVALS

The homogeneity of space implied the relativity of spatial magnitudes; the homogeneity of time similarly implies the relativity of temporal intervals. Let us again stress that this has nothing in common either with modern relativity theory or with the relational theory of time. Relativity of temporal intervals simply means that the structure of *microchronos* should be substantially the same as that of *macrochronos* in the same way as the spatial microcosm resembles our world of middle dimensions. We estimate temporal intervals by comparing them with our specious present in the same way as we gauge spatial magnitudes by the size of our bodies or measuring instruments.

Consequently, there is a counterpart of the Gulliver theme

in the realm of temporal relations. Our life is merely a glimpse in the life of mankind; on the other hand, our most fleeting moment is an enormously long history in comparison with the quasi-instantaneous events of the microphysical world. For this reason the term "psychological present" is a misnomer, and it was significantly replaced by the term "specious present." The latter term indicates that what we usually call "now" is only a spurious present, since the only true present is a mathematical durationless instant. The totality of instants anterior to this mathematical present is called "past" while the totality of all instants which follow it is called "future." From this point of view only one durationless present is truly real; both the past and the future are perfectly symmetrical in their property of being *unreal*. The relation of the present to the past as well as to the future is that of *absolute externality*.

This is another aspect of the infinite divisibility of time, which was conceived in the same way as the mathematical continuity of space. Successive instants were considered to be just as discontinuous as geometrical points located on a straight line. When there is a present moment, *all* the past moments are gone and *no* future moments are yet present. This absolute externality of successive moments seemed to be a simple application of the law of contradiction. How could the past, which *ex definitione* no longer is, still be present? What we call our present moment is, in the full sense of the word, only a *specious present*; in fact, it is a *stretch of time* which consists of two equally unreal parts, one of which is *no longer* and the other *not yet*. The whole of reality thus shrinks into a punctual present floating between the vanished past and the unborn future.[9]

It would be premature to consider here all the enormous logical and epistemological difficulties involved in the view of time stated above. Our present task is to draw all the consequences from the classical definitions. It has already been shown that the relativity of magnitudes holds for both space and time. Like the structure of space, that of time is the same no matter how small or how big the intervals considered. Von Baer has indulged in some interesting computations as to how much the aspect of nature would change if the rhythm of our consciousness were changed:

> Suppose we were able, within the length of a second, to note 10,000 events distinctly, instead of barely 10, as now; if our life were then destined to hold the same number of impressions, it might be 1000 times as short. We should live less than a month, and personally know nothing of the change of seasons. If born in winter, we should believe in summer as we now believe in the heats of the Carboniferous era. The motions of organic beings would be so slow to our senses as to be inferred, not seen. The sun would stand still in the sky, the moon be almost free from change, and so on. But now reverse the hypothesis and suppose a being to get only one 1000th part of the sensations that we get in a given time, and consequently to live 1000 times as long. Winters and summers will be to him like quarters of an hour. Mushrooms and the swifter-growing plants will shoot into being so rapidly as to appear instantaneous creations; annual shrubs will rise and fall from the earth like restlessly boiling-water springs; the motions of animals will be as invisible as are to us the movements of bullets and cannon-balls; the sun will scour through the sky like a meteor, leaving a fiery trail behind him, etc.[10]

Today by means of ultrarapid photography and by slowed or speeded-up motion pictures we are able to produce changes in our time perspective just as we modify our space perspective by means of telescope and microscope.[11] But no matter how striking the modifications thus obtained are, they affect only the *qualitative content* of our perceptions, not their temporal structure. As William James, who reproduced Von Baer's words, noted, "the specious present would be of the same subjective length as now, giving us the same time feeling." [12] In fact, if the rate of all changes in the world were increased or reduced in the same ratio we would not notice any change at all.

Slowed-down and speeded-up motion pictures look bizarre

only because we remember the *normal* rate of the changes in question and compare our recollections with the modified rate of changes just perceived. But when this standard measuring unit is psychologically absent, no feeling of strangeness, no awareness of difference in temporal rhythm arises. An incident which normally takes hours or even longer is lived subjectively within a few seconds of public time in certain dreams or in some situations when death seems to be imminent; but the amazement that this was possible comes only in retrospect, when the subjective length is compared to the corresponding objectively measured interval on a chronometer. In classical science it is as meaningless to speak of the absolute temporal interval as of the absolute spatial magnitude.

This famous "problem of similar worlds," raised first by Laplace, was much discussed at the turn of the twentieth century by French philosopher-scientists Delboeuf, Lechalas, and Poincaré: Would there be any discoverable difference if the dimensions of all objects were modified in the same proportion, or if all changes were modified in the same ratio? [13] Only one answer was possible: such a hypothetical change would remain unnoticed. But it would be a mistake to regard this relativity of spatial and temporal magnitudes as an anticipation of relativistic ideas. On the contrary, this principle, as we have seen, strengthened the belief in the privileged character of Euclidean space, and it might have been used as an argument for the homogeneity of time. Only Euclidean space admits the possibility of constructing geometrical figures on any scale; similarly, only homogeneous uniformly flowing time, symbolized by a Euclidean straight line, admits the possibility of contracting or expanding temporal segments without distortion. This means that while the length of interval is relative, the *order of succession* remains constant, no matter how small or how large the stretches of time considered.

Nature itself seemed to provide more and more illustrations of the relativity of temporal size. First, the specious present, as indicated above, may vary curiously even within a single human individual:

In hashish-intoxication there is a curious increase in the apparent time perspective. We utter a sentence, and ere the end is reached the beginning seems already to date from indefinitely long ago. We enter a short street, and it is as if we should never get to the end of it. This alteration might conceivably result from an approach to the condition of Von Baer's and Herbert Spencer's short-lived beings.[14]

James here refers to the passage from Von Baer quoted earlier and to a passage from Spencer's *Principles of Psychology* in which Spencer comes to the conclusion that, if there is any rudimentary consciousness in gnats, it must be of an enormously shorter temporal span than in man or higher mammals in general.[15] It thus seems that the length of the specious present, variable within the human species, varies incomparably more within the whole animal realm.

Even more convincing illustrations of the principle of relativity of intervals were supplied by physics, especially by microphysics. The discovery of the microcosm seemed to open an unlimited vista not only into smaller and smaller volumes of space but also into shorter and shorter intervals of time. When the measurement of the wave lengths of different colors made possible the computation of the corresponding luminous frequencies, a concrete idea of the extreme minuteness of certain temporal intervals was gained. Four hundred trillions of "ethereal vibrations"—if we use the language of classical physics—are required to fill a single second. And this is true only of the red end of the visible spectrum, that is, of its slowest vibrations; the frequency increases correspondingly for shorter waves. For the violet extremity of the spectra it reaches 750 trillions per second and it keeps increasing for the shorter wave lengths in the invisible ultraviolet portion. For gamma rays the duration of a single "ethereal vibration" is of the order of 10^{-20} seconds.

But no matter how unimaginable such minute intervals of time were, they were no surprise for classical scientists; on the contrary, physicists would have been astonished had any definite limit in the divisibility of time been found. Their minds, conditioned for two centuries by infinitesimal calculus, led them to expect *not* to find any ultimate indivisible interval; true indivisibility must belong to durationless instants only. As long as we deal with finite intervals, the process of ideally subdividing them into smaller and smaller subintervals may be continued *ad infinitum*, and consequently we should not be surprised to find empirical evidence for the existence of shorter and shorter subevents in nature. It really looked as if nature conformed itself to Kant's "anticipations of perception," as if the idea of the Chinese toy applied to both space and time, as if the theme of "worlds within worlds" in the realm of spatial magnitudes were matched by one of "histories within histories" in the realm of temporal intervals, with no end of infinite regress in sight. The computations of Fournier d'Albe are no more fantastic than Pascal's idea of two infinities; they are only logical applications of the principle of relativity of magnitude. According to Fournier d'Albe, hypothetical inframen, inhabiting the surface of the electrons, would experience a specious present equal to 10^{-22} second; to them the planet-electrons would appear to roll with as leisurely a motion through space as that of the planets in the eyes of the earthly observer; his microsolar system would seem as steady to inframan as the solar system seems to us; countless generations would succeed each other before an external disturbance, introduced by another microsun passing by, would occur.[16]

This will sound less weird if we remember Kelvin's idea of applying the statistical methods used in the kinetic theory of gases to the motion of stars in the Milky Way:

> Consider now the Milky Way; there also we see an innumerable dust; only the grains of this dust are not atoms, they are stars; these grains move also with high velocities; they act at a distance one upon another, but this action is so slight at great distance that their trajectories are straight; and yet, from time to time, two of them may approach near enough to be deviated from their path, like a comet which had passed too near Jupiter. In a word, *to the eyes of a giant for whom our*

*suns would be as for us our atoms, the Milky Way
would seem only a bubble of gas.*[17] [Italics added.]

The same theme is again present here, expressing the same
conviction about the basic identity of microcosm and macrocosm, of microchronos and macrochronos. For chapters to come
it is important to realize that this conviction stems from the
belief in the homogeneity of space and time.

THE UNIFORM FLUIDITY
AND THE CAUSAL INERTNESS OF TIME

Do not the foregoing considerations justify the relational
theory of time? For if no observable difference would result
if the rate of all changes or motions were modified, is it still
possible to assign a definite meaning to the uniformity of time
flow? Where is there any guarantee that such uniform acceleration or deceleration of motion does not actually take place?

It is true that the relational theory of time may be traced to
the very dawn of classical physics; long before Leibniz and
Berkeley, Giordano Bruno foreshadowed it and one of its first
anticipations may be found in the frequently quoted passage
of Lucretius, according to which "time is nothing by itself."
We shall soon see that there were some important philosophical
and apparently even scientific reasons for not assigning to time
the same ontological status as to space. It was certainly significant and not accidental that a philosophical contemporary of
Newton, Spinoza, listed space, *but not time,* among the attributes of the ultimate reality. But these doubts about the ontological status of time were expressed mainly by philosophers or
philosophically minded scientists, some of whom raised similar
questions concerning the ultimate status of space; the *phenomenal* reality of space and time has never been questioned.

Such doubts therefore are not to be confused with doubts
about the uniformity of the temporal flow, which certainly did
not appear before the last century. There were several reasons
why they appeared so late and why, once they appeared, they

were dismissed. First, why assume a perfectly useless hypothesis which is by its own nature unverifiable? All appearances remain identical no matter whether we assume a constant time rate or an arbitrarily changing one, and it always appeared logically and aesthetically simpler to assume constancy instead of variability. It is true that no empirical evidence can be found for the uniformity of the temporal flow either, but this inaccessibility of time to direct empirical observation was held as an additional proof of its absolute and quasi-divine character. (Later Neo-Kantians used the imperceptibility of space and time as an argument for their unique epistemological status: they are not objects of experience but "transcendental conditions" which make experience possible; but ultimately their arguments were intended to justify the absolutist claims of Newtonian physics.[18])

The decisive reason why the idea of the nonuniform flow of time was considered absurd was that it would contradict the alleged passivity or causal inertness of time which, like that of space, followed from the fundamental postulate of homogeneity. As Bertrand Russell formulated it only a few years before the coming of the relativity theory:

> Such an hypothesis [of the variability of the rate of all changes] is mathematically possible, but, like the similar one for space, it is excluded logically by the comparative nature of the judgment of quantity, and philosophically by the fact that it involves absolute time as a determining agent in change, whereas time can never, philosophically, be anything but a passive form abstracted from change.[19]

Kant probably had the same idea in mind when he insisted on the unchangeability of time, although his statement is much less definite.[20] If time is truly homogeneous, that is, if different instants of time differ *only* by their positions in the temporal series, then no physical changes, whether observable or not, can be produced by a mere flow of time.

The argument is in all respects analogous to that for space. As all physical effects on bodies must be traced to bodies themselves and not to space, which remains their inert and unchangeable receptor, so it must be with time. A mere displacement through space does not result in any physical change; if there is any, it is due not to the action of the place, but to some agent acting *in* space. To this relativity of position in space corresponds the relativity of position in time; a mere displacement in time, in virtue of the qualitative equivalence of successive instants, can have no physical effect whatever; consequently, the changes in physical bodies must result only from physical causes acting *in* time, not from time itself. The principle of the causal inefficacy of space and time was stated before Russell with great clarity and precision by James Clerk Maxwell:

> The difference between one event and another does not depend on the mere difference of the times or the places at which they occur, but only on the differences in the nature, configuration, or motion of the bodies concerned.[21]

The homogeneity of time was regarded as *the basis for the unity of nature in time*, that is, as the logical ground for induction; the belief in the timeless universality of the laws of nature was based on the same ground. The conservation laws and the law of inertia were explicitly or implicitly believed to rest on the assumed causal inefficacy, i.e., homogeneity, of time.[22] It now becomes clear why the structure of space had to be regarded as *rigid*, that is, independent of time; the opposite assertion would presuppose the causal action of time on space which, in Russell's words, cannot be assumed without falling into the "grossest absurdities." [23]

THE PROBLEM OF THE DURATION OF SPACE

There was, however, a certain ambiguity in this assertion of the timelessness of space. Apparently, in the relation of juxtaposition which is the essence of spatiality, there is no reference to time; conversely, in the relation of succession no trace of spatiality can be found. In Kant's words: "Time has only one dimension; different times are not simultaneous, but successive (just as different spaces are not successive, but simultaneous)." [24] By completing the assumption of the timelessness of space by the spacelessness of time, Kant drew between space and time a sharp line which no physicist dared to blur before the advent of the theory of relativity.

But even before the revolution in physics there were certain obtrusive questions concerning the relation of space and time which were difficult to ignore. Granting that diverse portions of space are *juxtaposed* or *coexisting* and never successive; is not there at least an indirect reference to time by silently assuming that the juxtaposed terms are thought of as being *simultaneous*, i.e., as being at *the same time?* It was possible to avoid this question by claiming that simultaneity is not a temporal relation at all. This is what Kant did, though he was not always consistent in this respect.[25]

But there was a far more serious question. Even if we grant with Newton, Locke, Maxwell, and nearly all other classical thinkers that the structure of space is completely devoid of any change and in this sense is "eternal," it cannot be denied that space, though immutable, *still endures through time.* Otherwise, how could we speak of motion occurring *in* space? Are not the successive positions of a moving body not only in different points of space but also *in different instants of time?* If so, then Kant's statement about the impossibility of different successive spaces is not valid. It is true that these successive spaces are not qualitatively different and this is the reason why we are inclined to fuse them into a single unchanging timeless space, but this timeless space is merely a convenient label applied to what is in truth an *infinite series of successive instantaneous spaces* which, though qualitatively identical, still differ by their positions in the universal flow of time.

Thus, although it is true to say that classical space was immutable, it is *not* true that it was timeless. As has been shown above, changelessness and duration were not incompatible according to the classical doctrine of time. True timelessness belonged only to individual successive spaces, each of which, in virtue of its instantaneous character, contained only purely spatial relations. Thus even classical science seemed to lead to the conclusion that time is a receptacle not only of the changing physical material but of *space itself*.[26] But this implicit subordination of space to time was rarely emphasized, and in most cases the opposite tendency prevailed: to subordinate time to space, and even to deny the objective status of time entirely. This opposite tendency was due to the habit of regarding the properties of time as analogous to those of space and was strengthened by some implications of the classical concept of causality which will be analyzed later.

NOTES FOR CHAPTER III

1. I. Newton, *Mathematical Principles of Natural Philosophy*, scholium I.
2. *Mathematical Works of Isaac Barrow D.D.*, Whewell edition (Cambridge, 1860), Vol. II, pp. 160 f. On the influence of Barrow on Newton: E. A. Burtt, *Metaphysical Foundations of Modern Physical Science*, pp. 144 ff.; G. Windred, "The History of Mathematical Time," *Isis*, Vol. XIX (1933), especially pp. 126-138.
3. B. Russell, "Is Position in Space Absolute or Relative?", *Mind*, Vol. X (1901), p. 294.
4. B. Russell, *The Principles of Mathematics*, p. 465.
5. Barrow, *loc. cit.*, Lecture X ("On Space and Impenetrability"); quoted by G. Windred, *op. cit.*, p. 130.
6. These are Bergson's words about space, but they apply to classical time as well; hence Bergson's claim that mathematical time is merely a disguised space.
7. Gassendi's belief in the existence of time prior to the creation of the world is implied in his belief in the eternity of space (cf. Chapter II, above, note 10). According to Voltaire's *Éléments de la philosophie de Newton* (*Œuvres complètes*, Paris, 1879, Vol. XIII, p. 410) Newton knew and admired the views of Gassendi, whose influence on him is thus very probable. Even more obvious is the influence of I. Barrow and H. More. St. Augustine's assertion, "Non in tempore, sed cum tempore finxit Deus mundum," was criticized by Barrow (Windred, *op. cit.*, p. 134) while More against Descartes claimed that time would persist even if the whole world were annihilated. A. Koyré points out that More's argument is a restatement of Plotinus' argument against Aristotle (Koyré, *op. cit.*, pp. 120-121; 290). It is thus evident that the roots of the conflict between the absolutist and relational theory of time are in Greek philosophy. The dispute

continued in the famous Leibniz-Clarke controversy, in which Clarke defended the absolutist theory and, consequently, the existence of time before the beginning of the universe.

8. *Le opere di Galileo Galilei, prima edizione completa*, Vol. XIII (Florence, 1855), p. 158: "in ogni tempo quanto, ancorche picolissimo, sono infiniti instanti"; p. 156: "essendo il tempo subdivisibile in infinito." B. Russell, *Principles of Mathematics*, p. 144: "To say, for example, that a certain length of time elapses between sunrise and sunset, is to admit an infinite whole, or at least a whole which is not finite."

9. About the classical division of time into three nonentities, i.e., "instantaneous present," vanished past, and nonexistent future, see W. James, *Principles of Psychology* (New York, Holt, 1890), Vol. I, p. 609; A. N. Whitehead, *The Concept of Nature*, p. 73. This view may be traced to Aristotle's *Physica*, IV, 10.

10. W. James, *op. cit.*, I, p. 639.

11. Cf. A. Magnan, *Cinématographie jusqu'à 12,000 vues par seconde*, Actualités scientifiques et industrielles, No. 46 (Paris, 1932).

12. W. James, *op. cit.*, I, p. 640.

13. Laplace, *The System of the World*, translated by H. H. Harte (Dublin, 1833), Vol. II, pp. 321-2; G. Lechalas, "Le problème des mondes semblables," *Critique philosophique*, IVème année, Vol. II (1888), pp. 373-379; the same author, "M. Delboeuf et le problème des mondes semblables," *Revue philosophique*, Vol. 37 (1894), pp. 73-78; H. Poincaré, *Science et méthode* (Paris, 1909), p. 96. Other references in the article already quoted of P. M. Schuhl (cf. note 30 of Chapter II, above).

14. James, *op. cit.*, Vol. I, pp. 639-640.

15. H. Spencer, *The Principles of Psychology* (New York, Appleton, 1897), Vol. I, §§. 90-91, pp. 211-219.

16. Fournier d'Albe, *Two New Worlds* (London, 1907), pp. 10-12 and 47.

17. H. Poincaré, *op. cit.*, English translation by G. B. Halsted in *The Foundations of Science* (Lancaster, Science Press, 1913), p. 524.

18. Cf. P. Natorp's defense of absolute time against Mach's criticism, *Logische Grundlagen der exakten Naturwissenschaften*, pp. 326 f., esp. pp. 333-334.

19. B. Russell, *An Essay on the Foundations of Geometry*, p. 157.

20. I. Kant, *Critique of Pure Reason*, p. 82: "Time itself does not alter, but only something which is in time."

21. James C. Maxwell, *Matter and Motion* (New York, Dover, 1953; the original edition 1877), p. 13. About the causal inertness of time see also E. Meyerson, *La déduction relativiste* (Paris, 1925), pp. 106-107.

22. Kant, *op. cit.*, p. 217, about the correlation of the unity of time with the principle of permanence of substance; E. Meyerson, *De l'explication dans les sciences* (Paris, 1921), Vol. I, Chap. V ("L'identité et l'identification"), especially pp. 150-153.

23. B. Russell, "Les axiomes propres à Euclide sont-ils empiriques?",

Revue de métaphysique et de morale, Vol. VI (1898), p. 773.

24. Kant, *op. cit.*, p. 75.

25. Kant's inconsistencies and hesitancies concerning this point were convincingly exposed by Norman Kemp Smith in his *Commentary on Kant's Critique of Pure Reason* (London, Macmillan, 1918), pp. 135-136 and 358-359.

26. That this was the silent assumption of classical science was pointed out by Whitehead, *The Concept of Nature*, p. 71.

IV · THE CONCEPT OF MATTER

THE CLASSICAL DEFINITION OF MATTER
AND ITS CONSEQUENCES

THE third basic entity of the world of classical physics was *matter*. This concept has hardly changed from the times of Leucippus to the beginning of the twentieth century: an impenetrable *something*, which fills completely certain regions of space and which persists through time even when it changes its location.

This is evident from the definition: matter = full space. Full of what? Occupied by what? To everybody imbued by the spirit of classical science such a question was utterly meaningless; it merely showed the failure to grasp the meaning of the definition stated above. The function of occupying space is not one of several properties of matter; it is its *only* property. As a result of the abstracting operation, performed for the first time by the school of Elea, of all observable attributes of matter, only the attribute of space occupancy or, as Windelband says, "abstract corporeality," [1] was retained; the others were relegated to the realm of "appearances." The source of the distinction between primary and secondary qualities is precisely in this abstracting operation. The primary qualities other than the fullness were the geometrical properties which matter shared with the space which it occupied.

54

Thus at the very dawn of Western thought matter became a concept of the highest generality, comparable to the concept of Being, and it was not accidental that matter and Being were originally identified. If the fullness of space is the essence of matter, it cannot be further specified or subsumed under some more general concept because it becomes, like Being itself, the concept of the highest generality. Bertrand Russell only stated it in different terms when he insisted on the basic indefinability of the relation of space-occupancy. The term "relation," however, may be misleading because it may convey the wrong impression that there are *three* terms involved: *terminus a quo*, that is, matter, the relation of occupancy itself, and the *terminus ad quem*, space. But the first two terms really coincide; their differentiation is purely verbal and is due entirely to the structure of the language or symbolism used. Subtract from classical matter its attribute of space-occupancy and nothing will be left but a bare word.

The empirical fact of motion led the early atomists to admit the existence of *empty space* or *void* as the only possibility of escaping the paradoxes of the Parmenidean changeless *plenum*. This conclusion was adopted not only by all later atomists but also, as we shall see, by all classical scientists, who clearly realized that the denial of empty space and the reality of motion can be only verbally reconciled. This will be more extensively covered in Chapter V, concerning motion. For our present purpose it is sufficient to state that in a consistent corpuscular-kinetic model of nature it was assumed that only certain volumes of space are filled, constituting thus what we call physical bodies. A number of important empirically verifiable physical attributes of matter, though by no means all of them, can be derived from its basic definition. If matter is full space, then its constitutive elements must be by their own nature impenetrable, indivisible, indestructible, rigid, and homogeneous. The deductive power of the classical mechanical conception of nature, and what before 1900 looked like its complete and undisputed triumph, can be illustrated only if we consider the above list in some detail.

The fact that we speak about matter in the plural, that is,

about its constitutive *elements*, instead of in the singular is justified by the admission of empty space: only the void can break the continuity of matter into individual bodies. Their impenetrability and indivisibility follow necessarily from the basic definition: matter = full space. The fullness does not admit of degrees; what is already *full* cannot be *fuller*, that is, it cannot be simultaneously filled by something else: material bodies are therefore *impenetrable*. This is apparently contradicted by our daily experience; the facts of mixtures, solutions, diffusions, chemical compounds, etc., seem to indicate that matter is penetrable. But this discrepancy disappears as soon as the pertinent facts are correctly interpreted. As Bergson says:

> Try to picture one body penetrating another: you will at once assume that there are empty spaces in the one which will be occupied by the particles of the other; these particles in their turn cannot penetrate one another unless one of them divides in order to fill the interstices of the other; and our thought will prolong this operation indefinitely in preference to picturing two bodies in the same place.[2]

Bergson concludes that it is not a physical but a *logical* necessity which leads us to the proposition that two bodies cannot occupy the same place at the same time.

In this respect he is only partly right. It is true that as long as atomism was in its speculative stage, the impenetrability of the ultimate elements was only a logical inference drawn from its basic postulates. But it had already been asserted that the so-called penetrability of matter is only a surface phenomenon due to the limitations of our senses and that if our perception were refined enough we would be able to *see* that within the apparently uniform mixtures, solutions, and chemical compounds the particles of different substances are strictly juxtaposed without any mutual penetration. Only the limited discriminating power of our senses prevents us from perceiving the indestructible individuality of the component particles within the deceptively homogeneous and continuous aggregates. And this was precisely confirmed by refined experience: today by means of X-ray spectrograms it is possible to compute even the width of the interstices separating the juxtaposed individual components, for instance, the distance between the atoms of sodium and chlorine in the crystalline lattice of common salt. Thus what was brilliantly anticipated centuries ago by a few daring individuals such as Nicolas d'Autrecourt and defended by them at great odds against the tyrannical authority of Aristotle is an experimentally established fact today.[3]

The indivisibility of the ultimate particles was another consequence of the basic definition of matter. This attribute of matter became one of the cornerstones of the atomic theory. The observed divisibility of matter does not contradict it. Matter is divided only when some foreign mechanical agency (usually regarded as corpuscular) penetrates into the fine gaps between the particles of a given substance and, by widening their distances, loosens its texture. Mechanical division can affect only aggregates, not their constitutive parts; it can only increase the distances between what is already *actually divided*.

Again we have to be on guard against the deceptive character of our sensory perception of apparently "compact" bodies. The only truly compact bodies are, as Lucretius stressed,[4] the elementary particles themselves; what is completely full excludes any foreign penetration and is in consequence absolutely indivisible. This indivisibility must not be compared to any empirically known hardness—for instance, that of iron or diamond. The hardness of all empirically known substances has a certain *degree* which, no matter how high, is not infinite, and can therefore be overcome, provided that the disintegrating external agency is powerful enough. For this reason the impenetrability of macroscopic substances is only *relative*, because of their composite nature. In contrast, the atoms have an absolute solidity which, as Huygens already observed, must be regarded as *infinite*.[5] The empirical fact of different degrees of hardness is due to different ways in which the ultimate particles, themselves absolutely compact and solid, are associated into various structural patterns. The indestructibility of atoms then follows as a mere consequence of their unlimited resistance to any dividing agency.

The claim of Leibniz, Kant, Fechner, etc., that matter must share with space its infinite divisibility has been dismissed by distinguishing *geometrical* divisibility from *mechanical* divisibility; the former is unlimited, but it belongs to the void only, that is, to the geometrical container of matter, not to matter itself; the very fullness of the constitutive elements of matter imposes a certain limit on its physical division.

THE CONSTANCY OF MATTER

A more adequate and less negative term than *indestructibility* is *constancy* or *permanence*. The ultimate elements of matter were believed to be constant in their *mass*, their *volume*, and their *shape*. The principle of constancy of mass implies what is known today as the *principle of the conservation of matter*; if the total cosmic mass is the sum total of the atomic masses, then the constancy of the atomic masses implies the constancy of the whole mass of the universe. This principle was distinctly anticipated not less than twenty-two centuries before its experimental verification by Lavoisier. It is not accidental that Lavoisier's philosophical contemporary, Immanuel Kant, in upholding this principle in his First Analogy of Experience, quoted the ancient Latin maxim: *Gigni de nihilo nihil, in nihilum nil posse reverti.* (Nothing can arise from nothing, nothing can turn into nothing.)[6] It is even more significant that this principle, which implies both the indestructibility and uncreatability of matter, has been regarded by different thinkers and in different periods as a basic axiom, incapable of further proof, without which the orderly world would be utterly unthinkable; the terminology changes, but the substance of the argument remained the same in Lucretius, Gassendi, Spinoza, Kant, and Spencer.[7]

This shows that the roots of this principle lie deeper than in any historically dated discovery; they are determined by the very structure of the human mind even if it is *not* necessary to believe that this structure is immutable and incapable of modification. The belief in the permanence of matter may be traced to the famous Eleatic tautology: *Being is* and cannot be thought of as nonexisting; nothing can be predicated of it except that it exists in an eternal and changeless fashion. It has been said correctly that the atom is nothing but the Eleatic Being on a microscopic scale which possesses all properties of the Parmenidean One: its undifferentiated *unity* and absolute *immutability*.[8] Not only material atoms but also *every substantial entity* was modeled after the Eleatic pattern; in this respect the impact of Parmenides on the whole of Western thought was far more profound than is generally realized. Indeed, even alleged spiritual entities—monads, the transcendental Ego, the Absolute, and others—were endowed with the same basic homogeneous unity and radical changelessness. Although the principle of the conservation of matter was a preconceived anticipatory idea which stimulated a search for its experimental verification, it would be unjust to forget the tremendous amount of experience from Jean Rey to Hans Landolt which substantiated it. The whole science of chemistry would be utterly impossible without this experimental work. This, however, does not change the fact that all empirical data confirming the law of conservation of matter obediently seemed to fill a preconceived intellectual frame, formed by men independently or almost independently of experience.[9] This is true, of course, of other features of the corpuscular-kinetic model of nature, but it is certainly not true of other empirical discoveries, especially in biology and related sciences; above all it is not true of recent discoveries in physics. Later we shall try to grasp the full epistemological significance of this fact.

The constancy of atomic volume is another consequence of the basic definition. For the variability of atomic volume would imply either an increase or decrease of the quantity of matter contained in atoms or it would mean a certain primary *elasticity* of atoms. The first possibility is obviously excluded by the postulated immutability of atomic mass stated above; on the other hand, the assumption of the basic elasticity of the primary particles would allow the same quantity of atomic mass to occupy volumes of different size. It is evident that this would be equivalent to a simple denial of the *proportionality of mass and volume* which is the very core of classical atomism. The belief in the compressibility and extensibility of the elementary particles was always a sure sign of a certain immaturity of thought and of a lack of insight into the true nature of atomism. Consistent atomists have always regarded the compressibility of macroscopic bodies as a result of the displacement of the elementary particles, which, in decreasing their distances, cause an apparent shrinking of volume registered by our senses; but the particles themselves remained constant and incompressible for Lucretius as well as for Gassendi, Newton, and Dalton. According to the basic premises of atomism, elasticity can belong only to the atomic aggregates, not to the atoms themselves. For this reason the first suspicion that the molecules of gases are not ultimate units, but complex aggregates, was aroused by their observed elasticity.[10]

Constancy of shape is, mathematically speaking, not equivalent to constancy of volume. In atomistic theories they were treated as equivalent, because they both follow from the assumed rigidity of atoms. Though it is logically conceivable that a particle varying in shape retains the same volume and the same mass, such a possibility was never seriously considered, at least not in the period when the kinetic-corpuscular explanation was accepted. The "extensible atoms" of Johannes Chrysostomus Magnenus belong to the period when atomistic thought still lacked the clarity and consistency of its mature age,[11] while the famous Lorentz-FitzGerald hypothesis of the electrons as deformed by their motions was imposed by experience which eventually proved to be inassimilable by classical physics, dominated as this was by the concept of the rigid atom. Thus Lorentz deformable particles really meant the beginning of the end of what may be called the "Democritean era." The classical concept of the atom is by its own nature incompatible with any idea of variability in the atom, whether of mass or volume or shape; the atom remains unchanged through time. All of its value for scientific explanation lay precisely in its assumed self-identity and permanency. When Boltzmann, at the end of the last century, toyed with the idea of "changing atoms," Emile Meyerson rightly observed that such atoms would change *without cause*, which is impossible; if, however, their change were really observed, then it would only indicate that they are not simple units but complex aggregates, and that the true units, i.e., unchangeable units, should be looked for in the finer particles of which the alleged "changing atoms" are made.[12] This actually happened, as we shall see, several times in the history of atomistic thought: the observed change in the allegedly ultimate particles led to the assumption of their complexity and stimulated a search for more minute and more basic units which would not vary in time. This seemed to be the only way to avoid a *causeless change* of atomic properties, whether mass, volume, or shape.

The concept of the rigidity of atoms, that is, of the constancy of their mass, volume, and shape, may be approached fruitfully from another angle, complementary to, rather than different from, our previous approach: from the principle of the *causal passivity* of space and time. This has already been extensively covered in Chapters II and III and may therefore be dealt with briefly here.

We have seen that the doctrine that space and time are homogeneous means that a cause for every physical change, that is, every change observable in physical bodies, whether simple or compound, should be looked for in physical bodies and their physical actions; we should never regard any change as an effect of particular regions of space, as Aristotle believed, or of a particular moment of time, as probably nobody ever believed. But then it is manifestly absurd to believe that an ultimate material unit would change its properties simply by moving in space. If we do not want to accept the notion of causeless change, then the only possibility is to ascribe this effect to the change of position. Such assumption, however, would destroy the homogeneity of space. It would be equally absurd to assume that the elementary unit will change its characteristics (mass, volume, shape) by simply *persisting through time* while at rest;

then time would appear as the only entity that might be credited for the change, and we already know that this would lead to the conclusion that its moments are heterogeneous.

This logical correlation of the homogeneity of time and the permanency of material substances was clearly seen by Kant, who expressed it in his usual abstruse way by saying that "the transcendental unity of time" requires the persistence of the same quantity of substance in the phenomena. The passages quoted earlier from James Clerk Maxwell and Bertrand Russell concerning the homogeneity and causal inefficacy of space and time lead to the same conclusion as that of Kant. Russell's "axiom of free mobility" is nothing but one of the basic postulates of atomism according to which the rigidity of bodies is affected neither by their displacement in space nor by their persistence through time.[13] But the concept of rigidity implies constancy of mass, shape, and volume as well.

ATOMICITY IS UNDERIVABLE
FROM THE BASIC DEFINITION OF MATTER

At first it may appear paradoxical that while so many properties of atoms are derivable from the basic definition of matter as full space, the existence of atoms themselves is not implied in it. Once their existence is assumed, many of their properties follow logically from the basic definition, but the proposition that the volume of the particles must have a certain lower limit is not included among them. The claim that the particles of matter must have a certain finite volume appeared to be an arbitrary assumption, and the opponents of atomism took full advantage of this alleged weakness. Using the language of contemporary science: Why should the distance of 10^{-13} cm possess a privileged character in being the radius of the ultimate units of matter? Why not any smaller distance, for instance 10^{-40} cm, once hinted at by Eddington? [14] Or a larger one? Even Democritus was aware of the logical possibility of conceiving an atom as big as the universe.[15] This was something more than a reminiscence of Parmenides' indivisible world-sphere, although the underlying logic was the same: absolute fullness being the only basis for the indivisibility of atoms, there is no inconsistency in conceiving the world-atom. Thus the only justification for assuming the existence of minute atomic particles, since the time of Lucretius to the present day, has been of an empirical nature: our experience requires them. The definite value of the radius of the atom is an empirical constant which is logically underivable from the basic definition of matter.

This logically arbitrary character of the empirical constants, which prevents their derivation from some more general principle, is what Meyerson called *l'irrationnel* in scientific explanation; it is the stubborn resistance of certain features of experience to appearing as logical consequences of those logical principles which, because of their greater generality and their apparent self-evidence, should in our view possess the privilege of being the only true and ultimate explanatory principles. In a completely rational, that is, logically necessary, world the arbitrary character of the empirical coefficients should disappear and they should be incorporated into an all-embracing deductive system.[16] How strong this logical urge of our mind is has been demonstrated in our own century by the famous attempts of Eddington to link logically various cosmic constants, including the mass and radius of the electron.[17] The temptation was only strengthened by previous undisputable successes of this tendency. How many constants which the chemistry of the last century regarded as purely empirical, that is, logically arbitrary, were found to be simple consequences of the new electron theory! Yet there seems to be a certain limit set by nature itself to such complete rationalization of reality. It is certainly very instructive that this limit has already been encountered in the atomistic explanations, in which the logical ordering of experience has reached such an unsurpassed peak. Like the three-dimensionality of space, the finite volume and mass of the ultimate particles of matter were in the last analysis nothing but bare irreducible and stubborn data.

This empirical feature in atomism accounts for the fact that the theory of the finite divisibility of matter never imposed itself with the same logical cogency as the infinite divisibility of space; for while the latter followed from the homogeneity of space, the former did *not* follow from the definition of matter. The concept of infinitely divisible space is equally compatible with the atomicity and with the continuity (infinite divisibility) of matter. In the seventeenth century, when classical physics was born, Gassendi and Newton accepted atomism while Descartes and Hobbes rejected it; all of them, however, accepted the continuity of space. One century later Kant, though he favored the concept of continuous matter in his *Metaphysische Anfangsgründe der Naturwissenschaft* as well as in his Transcendental Analytic, adopted a neutral view in the Transcendental Dialectic, where he regarded the dilemma "atomism versus continuity" as an unsolvable antinomy.[18]

The defenders of the continuity of matter could always dismiss the empirical evidence for the existence of atoms as merely provisional and inconclusive; they could always hope that the further investigation would resolve the allegedly indivisible units into their component parts and these parts into still smaller parts and so on *ad infinitum*. They could point out with some satisfaction how spurious was the alleged indivisibility of the Daltonian atom. Why then assume that the empirical evidence for the indivisibility of the electron is final? This explains why Pascal's idea of the infinite chain of the worlds, embedded in each other like the Chinese boxes, was dying so hard, and why it cropped up even in Whitehead's mind at the end of his life in spite of all his previous emphasis on the atomicity of nature.

On the other hand, the theory of infinitely divisible matter led to some very serious difficulties which will be mentioned in due time, while the atomic theory, in spite of the logically underivable assumption of one definite radius and one (usually spherical) shape, possessed such remarkable logical simplicity that it became the ideal of explanation which concrete physical explanations tried to attain, with varying degrees of success. This ideal was *almost* reached when the corpuscular-kinetic interpretation of nature definitely prevailed. Ancient atomism as well as the atomism of Gassendi, with all its multiplicity of atomic shapes and volumes, was still far away from this ideal goal, which found its definitive formulation when one single radius and one single spherical shape were postulated. The electron theory in its original form was *almost* a realization of this ideal, as we shall try to show in Chapter VI.

NOTES FOR CHAPTER IV

1. W. Windelband, *History of Ancient Philosophy*, tr. by H. E. Cushman (New York, Dover, 1956), pp. 61, 89.
2. *Essai sur les données immédiates de la conscience* (Paris, 1889), pp. 65-66; English translation, *Time and Free Will*, by F. L. Pogson (New York, Macmillan, 1910), p. 88.
3. K. Lasswitz, *Geschichte der Atomistik*, Vol. I, pp. 235-252 and 257-258; Pierre Duhem, *Le mixte et la combinaison chimique* (Paris, 1902), Chapter I. On the rudimentary crystallography of Democritus cf. S. Sambursky, *The Physical World of Greeks*, tr. by Merton Dagut (New York, Macmillan, 1956), pp. 120-121.
4. Lucretius, *De rerum natura*, I, vv. 483-519.
5. Huygens's letter to Leibniz, July 12, 1692; in C. I. Gerhardt, ed., *Leibnizens mathematische Schriften*, Vol. II (Berlin, 1850), p. 139.
6. *Critique of Pure Reason*, tr. by Norman Kemp Smith, p. 215.
7. Lucretius (*op. cit.* I, vv. 149 f., 215 f., 483 f.) regards the indestructibility of matter as a necessary condition of the order in nature; Spinoza claims that the destruction of a single material particle would imply the annihilation of the whole physical universe (*Opera* IV, ed. by C. Gebbhardt, Heidelberg, 1924, Epistola IV); Kant regards substance as a necessary category which makes experience possible, while the permanence of substance is to him a consequence of the transcendental unity of time (cf. Notes 6 and 13); H. Spencer claims that the constancy of matter is presupposed in any experimental device to establish it (*First Principles*, 4th ed., New York, Appleton, 1896, Part II, Chap. IV).
8. W. Windelband, *op. cit.*, p. 90.
9. E. Meyerson (*Identité et Réalité*, 5th ed., Paris, 1951, pp. 176-177 and 184-190), points out that both J. Rey and A. Lavoisier were convinced about the validity of this law before their attempts at verifying it; furthermore, that their verifications were far from being accurate.
10. J. B. Stallo, *The Concepts and Theories of Modern Physics* (New York, Appleton, 1882), Chap. IV.
11. This was the case of Johannes Chrysostomus Magnenus in the seventeenth century, who assumed the existence of extensible atoms. Cf. Lasswitz, *op. cit.* I, 498-511.
12. Meyerson, *op. cit.*, p. 473.

13. Kant, *op. cit.*, p. 212; B. Russell, *An Essay on the Foundations of Geometry*, pp. 149-161.
14. P. W. Bridgman, *The Logic of Modern Physics*, New York, Macmillan, 1948), p. 93.
15. C. A. Bailey, *Greek Atomists and Epicurus*, p. 126; A. Hannequin, *Essai critique sur l'hypothèse des atomes dans la science contemporaine* (Paris, 1895), p. 141 n.
16. E. Meyerson, *De l'explication dans les sciences* (Paris, 1921), Vol. II, p. 211, "Le monde nécessaire et la disparition des coefficients."
17. Cf. E. T. Whittaker, *From Euclid to Eddington* (Cambridge University Press, 1947), Chap. V.
18. It is true that Kant's second antinomy is spurious because the continuity of matter is entirely compatible with the assumption of the pointlike monads.

V · THE CONCEPT OF MOTION

MOTION AND THE CONCEPTS
OF SPACE, TIME, AND MATTER

THE discontinuity of matter was originally postulated for one explicit purpose: to account for the reality of motion. Atomism and kinetism are one and the same thing since the atomic particles are supposed to be in perpetual motion. Motion as a change of spatial coordinates implies both space and time. Its basically relative character is thus immediately suggested, because the spatial coordinates presuppose a certain frame of reference, usually—but according to Newton, not necessarily—embodied in a certain material body, be it the earth, the sun, or some fixed star. Although the number of possible systems of reference is limitless, there is one among them which, according to the same Newton, has a privileged and unique character: absolute space, which supposedly was truly immovable and entirely independent of concrete physical bodies contained in it. Thus a body moving with respect to this absolute space is in *absolute motion*, while a body at rest relatively to absolute space is at *absolute rest*. It is important to be aware that even the concepts of absolute rest and motion possessed a certain character of relativity because their very definition contained a relation to a certain system of reference, no matter how unique and privileged this system was.[1]

Motion defined as a change of spatial coordinates in time shares with space and time their common property: mathematical

67

continuity or infinite divisibility. To a series of the successive moments of time corresponds another series of juxtaposed points; the second series constitutes a *path* of a particle. As both series are continuous, it is possible to trace a motion of a corpuscle even within the smallest intervals of space and time. For this task theoretical physics found an appropriate tool in calculus.

The task of experimental physics was considerably more arduous, since the technical difficulties of penetrating by experiment and observation into very small intervals of space and time were very great, especially when a particle was very minute and changing the direction of its motion very quickly. Nevertheless it was always assumed that the trajectories of particles were continuous even within very small intervals of space and time where a direct observation was impossible. Classical models of the microcosm were all based on this perfectly natural assumption. Even in the original Bohr model of the atom the planetlike electrons were imagined to move along continuous orbits according to the same Keplerian laws as ruled the motion of the planets around the sun. This was merely another aspect of the principle of relativity of magnitude which classical physicists believed to hold for both space and time.

But if motion implies both space and time, the converse is not true. We do not have to repeat what has already been said about the independence of space and time with respect to their physical content. Motion occurs *in* space, but cannot affect space itself; as John Locke stated it, in the true Newtonian spirit:

> The parts of pure space are immovable, which follows from their inseparability; motion being nothing but change of distance between any two things; but this cannot be between parts that are inseparable; which therefore must needs be at perpetual rest one amongst other.[2]

How little this argument changed in two centuries may be shown by a similar quotation from James Clerk Maxwell:

> Absolute space is conceived as remaining always similar to itself and immovable. The arrangement of the parts

of space can no more be altered than the order of the portions of time. To conceive them to move from their places is to *conceive a place to move away from itself.*[3]

Similarly, motion occurs *in* time without being identical with time itself. The very possibility of a body being at rest during a certain interval of time shows plainly the logical as well as the physical separability of time and motion. Space and time are *containers* of motion, but its *vehicle,* that is, a *thing which moves,* can only be a material body. As David Hume wrote in his *Treatise on Human Nature,* "The idea of motion necessarily supposes that of a body moving." [4] Even more emphatically the impossibility of imagining motion without matter was stressed by John Tyndall:

> But is it in the human mind to imagine motion without at the same time imagining something moved? Certainly not. The very conception of motion includes that of a moving body.[5]

In other words, movement is always a displacement of *something,* and this something can be only a stuff which, while existing in space and time, is not identical with them. This stuff is classical matter.

More specifically, the classical concept of motion required that of *discontinuous matter.* The truth of this proposition was obscured by a certain haziness associated with the term "continuous liquid" or "continuous aether." As we shall see below in Chapter VII, the alleged continuity of any hypothetical fluid, supposedly filling the whole of space, was either spurious or led to absurd consequences. Moreover, it was rarely upheld consistently.[6]

But if motion implies matter, the converse again is not true. Let us not be confused by the fact that the inseparability of matter and motion was vehemently proclaimed by materialists of all centuries from Leucippus to Büchner. What they had in mind was the *factual* correlation of matter and motion; but the eternal coexistence of matter and motion, usually stressed for polemical purposes against theologians and theologically minded scientists, does not necessarily mean a *logical* relationship between them. In the basic definition of matter the concept of motion is *not* contained and cannot be extracted from it unless it is introduced there surreptitiously. This was clearly realized by young Leibniz, who wrote in his letter to Thomasius in 1668:

> Cum enim corpus nihil aliud sit, quam materia et figura, et vero nec ex materia nec figura intelligi possit causa motus, necesse est, causam motus esse extra corpus.* [7]

The same argument was put forth two decades later by John Locke:

> Let us suppose any parcel of matter eternal, great or small, we shall find it in itself able to produce nothing. For example: Let us suppose the matter of the next pebble we meet with, eternal, closely united, and parts firmly at rest together; if there were no other being in the world, must it not eternally remain so, a dead, inactive lump? Is it possible to conceive it can add motion to itself, being purely matter, or produce any thing? Matter, then, by its own strength, cannot produce it itself so much; the motion it has must also be from eternity, or else be produced or added to matter by some other being more powerful than matter: matter, as is evident, having no power to produce motion in itself. [8]

The concluding deistic note is irrelevant to the validity of the conclusion. The same argument may be found in D'Alembert's preface to his *Traité de dynamique* [9] and is implicit in the law of inertia. If there were a necessary logical correlation of matter and motion, then the concept of a motionless body should be either self-contradictory or incompatible with the laws of physics. But neither assertion is true; such a concept is contrary neither to the concept of body in general, nor to the laws of

---

* Since body is nothing but matter and figure and since the cause of motion cannot be understood on the basis of either matter or figure the cause of motion must necessarily be outside body.

mechanics; on the contrary, those physicists of the last century who adhered most faithfully and consistently to the classical conceptual scheme insisted that there *must be at least one* absolutely motionless body in the universe, even if its existence were empirically unverifiable: such was the motionless "body-Alfa" of Carl Neumann[10] or the motionless aether of Lorentz.

THE SUBSTANTIALITY OF MOTION AND THE LAWS OF CONSERVATION

As soon as movement was recognized to be underivable from matter or from space and time, it automatically acquired the character of an independent and quasi-substantial entity. Motion and matter being mutually inconvertible, nothing but motion can be a cause of motion, and also nothing but motion can be an effect of motion. Thus the quantity of motion must be constant just as the quantity of matter is, and only its spatial distribution varies with time. It is perhaps an exaggeration to claim with J. B. Stallo that "the law of conservation of energy is coeval with human intelligence," [11] but it cannot be denied that ancient atomists came very close to anticipating it when they insisted on the causelessness and indestructibility of motion. The principle of constancy of being, that is, its indestructibility and uncreatability, was applied by Lucretius not only to material substances but to their motions as well.[12]

It is true that Lucretius was not fully aware of the significance of his own principle and that some of his other views even contradicted it. He claimed, for instance, that there are only *two* first principles, matter and void, without realizing that, according to his own view, motion, being indestructible and eternal, is in truth a *third* principle. An even more serious inconsistency was his belief that *weight*, that is, the tendency of bodies to move downwards, is an inherent property of atoms; he obviously did not realize that the motion thus conceived is *born out of something that is not a motion,* i.e., out of the intrinsic polarity of space which, though bottomless, still possesses the absolute difference between UP and DOWN. (We need say nothing of another even more striking discrepancy—the idea of spontaneous deviation—which is utterly incompatible with Lucretius' law of the conservation of motion and with the whole spirit of his mechanistic system.) In this respect early Greek atomism was far superior to its Epicurean descendants. By Leucippus and Democritus space was correctly regarded not only as infinite but also as homogeneous and isotropic, all its directions being equivalent. Their atoms move in *all* directions and change the direction of their motion only by clashing with one another; weight of atoms is *not* a primary property of matter, but an effect of the surrounding medium, that is, ultimately, of the impact of other atoms. Thus the only properties of the atoms of Democritus seem to be their impenetrability *and inertia*.[13] Certainly the early Greek atomists came as close as was possible to the modern kinetic and mechanistic conception of nature; and the laws of inertia as well as the law of the conservation of energy were, if not explicitly anticipated, then at least foreshadowed by them.

As it turned out, the exact quantitative formulation of these principles had to wait until the seventeenth century. Aristotle's influence is usually credited with this delay, together with the atheistic coloring of atomism to which the whole medieval period was so hostile. The whole philosophy of Aristotle is based on the denial of the constancy of motion: everything which is moving moves only because and as long as it is moved by some "mover." Even a projectile or a stone thrown from the hand moves not because of a certain acquired velocity, but because something—in this case the pressure of the air—keeps it moving. This applies even to the eternal celestial motions and to the universe as a whole. It is thus correct to say with Arthur Haas that the basic law of Aristotelian mechanics, when translated into modern terminology, would be $F = mv$, in contrast with Newton's formula $F = ma$, where $F = $ force, $m = $ mass, $v = $ velocity, and $a = $ acceleration.[14] In other words, force is needed to keep a body going in the Aristotelian universe, while this is not so in the world of Galileo and Newton. We have sufficiently emphasized how inferior Aristotle was in this respect to the early

Greek atomists, who lacked only more sharply defined kinematic notions to arrive at a correct formulation of the law of inertia and that of quantity of motion.

But behind Aristotle's opposition to the atomistic theory of motion was something more than a lack of insight and his teleological prejudices. Behind his reluctance to admit the substantiality of motion lay a deep-rooted metaphysical prejudice which is common to all periods of Western thought and of which even atomists were not entirely free. It was the prejudice that change cannot be something logically or ontologically self-sufficient and that therefore it needs an *explanation*. In other words, there must be some sufficient reason, some explanatory principle which accounts for the reality of change, and this explanatory principle, in order to avoid an infinite regress, must be something *beyond change*. This is the core of the Aristotelian proof of the existence of God, accepted by St. Thomas, and even by Neo-Thomism, without any significant modification. But was there not behind Lucretius' reluctance to list motion as the third basic entity alongside matter and void the same fundamental tendency? The logic of atomism required the explicit listing of *all* basic entities which are logically independent: space, time, matter, and motion. But only the first and the third were explicitly listed. Motion, though its substantiality was clearly recognized, was never listed among the basic entities. On the contrary, the existence of the "third principle" was, at least nominally, denied. Time fared even worse; it was rarely spoken of, and if mentioned, its existence was regarded as a derivative one, dependent on bodies and motions in the sense of the later relational theory.[15]

This tendency receded in the modern era, but rather among scientists than among philosophers; and even among early modern scientists it was clearly present. If material particles are constant in mass, volume, and shape, why not apply the principle of constancy even to their *positions?* As late as at the beginning of the seventeenth century the word *inertia* did not have its present meaning. To Kepler it meant a natural tendency of matter to *retain its position in space*, that is, to resist motion.

Only after Galileo and Descartes did it become clear that this is only *the first half* of the law of inertia and that its second half requires that matter, once moved, has the tendency to persist in its motion and that it *resists* the opposing forces which are slowing it down. But to Kepler the term *inertia materialis* meant a resistance to the change of position, not to the change of velocity. Meyerson rightly observed that what may be called "the principle of the conservation of position" has for unsophisticated common sense a greater plausibility than the law of inertia.[16]

This explains why even when inertia is recognized as the basic property of matter alongside of its impenetrability, the tendency to look for an *explanation* of motion, including rectilinear and uniform motion, does not altogether disappear. Thus Euler, though recognizing inertia as the fundamental attribute of matter distinct from its impenetrability, still was tempted to explain the reality of motion from the impenetrability of matter: two bodies cannot occupy the same space; therefore one of them must move out of it.[17] Similarly Descartes, though he helped to formulate the law of inertia and gave it an even more general form than Galileo, was still inclined to postulate for every motion its material mover which, by impinging from behind, keeps a moved body going. This was his famous theory of vortices, which in only slightly modified forms was still alive at the beginning of this century; as we shall see, this tendency is not entirely dead even today.[18]

Needless to say, all attempts to derive motion from the impenetrability of matter are circular; in order to explain a motion of a certain body, another body *already in motion* must be postulated, like the *already rotating* aether of Descartes, which drags along the planets around the sun. As the question "What keeps the mover moving?" may be raised repeatedly, we either have to face an infinite regress, which may be arbitrarily ended only in an Aristotelian fashion, or we have to accept squarely the reality of motion as a substantial constant quantity, as Descartes eventually did. Not to recognize it means not to recognize the law of inertia, and to return, unwittingly perhaps, to Aristotle. How strong the temptation is, even today, can be seen from the following statement of Viscount Samuel about a flying bullet:

> But the bullet is passive; it is no different after it has been fired off than before it; it has not thereby come to 'possess' anything; it does not 'carry' or 'convey' anything at all. The cause of the flight must be looked for in something other than bullet itself. If we wished to speak precisely we ought to say that *the bird moves*, but that *the bullet is moved*. Moved by what? For the reasons given, nothing would be there to do it if not an energic ether.[19]

This obstinate tendency to look for a mover behind every motion is merely a special instance of a more general urge to *explain* the reality of change, frequently to *explain it away*. Changelessness seems to be rational and logically self-sufficient, but any change requires justification. Bernard Riemann, who in other respects was remarkably free of the traditional influences, expressed this urge in a classically concise way:

> The thing would remain what it is if nothing else were added. Here lies the motive for searching out the cause for every change*[20]

Very well; but motion cannot be explained by adding to a body at rest another body unless the latter is already in motion. On a more general level this is true of change as well; by no logical effort can change be obtained from anything devoid of change. But though this undertaking is hopeless, it is too fascinating for philosophers not to repeat it again and again, and with the same result.

Even when the independence of motion with respect to matter, space, and time was finally recognized, it was expressed in conservation laws in which, semantically at least, the true nature of motion was almost obscured. Motion was regarded as a sub-

---

* Das Ding würde bleiben, was es ist, wenn nichts anderes hinzukömme. Hierin liegt der Antrieb, zu jeder Veränderung die Ursache zu suchen.

stantial quantity which is preserved through time while only its spatial distribution changes. This is especially true of both fundamental laws of mechanics, the principle of the conservation of the quantity of motion and the principle of the conservation of energy. Although both principles were qualitatively anticipated by the early atomists, their accurate formulation belongs to the greatest achievements of the seventeenth century when the foundations of mechanics were laid down. Ernst Mach showed how the idea of the impossibility of *perpetuum mobile*, that is, of uncreatability and indestructibility of motion pervades the whole history of mechanics; it was present in the early researches of Stevinus, Leonardo, and Galileo as well as in the general demonstration of the principle of virtual motions on which Lagrange based the whole of mechanics.[21]

The accurate formulation of both principles and their relations was found only after considerable groping. Galileo correctly formulated the law of inertia, that is, the law of the conservation of the quantity of motion for an individual body, but he failed to see all its consequences; in particular, he did not apply it to celestial motions.[22] Descartes generalized the law of inertia by extending the law of the conservation of the quantity of motion to the whole system of bodies and even to the whole universe, but he still failed to realize that the sum of moments should be taken in a *vectorial* instead of an algebraic sense.[23] Newton stated his axioms of motion without realizing that they are not all genuine axioms, i.e., mutually independent; but he came very close to the formulation of the principle of the constancy of energy.[24] Only Huygens explicitly stated this law implicit in Galileo's work and also saw its compatibility with Descartes' law of the conservation of momentum, correctly reformulated in the vectorial sense.[25] Other principles of mechanics, like D'Alembert's principle, Lagrange's equations, the principle of least constraint, the principle of least action, and Hamilton's principle did not bring anything essentially new; they were merely mathematical restatements of the principles discovered in the "century of genius," as the seventeenth century was called by Whitehead. At the beginning of the nineteenth century Gauss was already aware that no essentially new principle of mechanics can be discovered, although *new points of view* can be found from which mechanical phenomena may be fruitfully contemplated.[26] The successful extension of the principle of the conservation of energy to the whole physical world in the nineteenth century by Mayer, Joule, and Helmholtz was generally accompanied by the repeated triumphs of the mechanical—i.e., corpuscular-kinetic—explanation in all provinces of natural phenomena.

NOTES FOR CHAPTER V

1. This neglected aspect of absolute motion was rightly stressed by E. Cassirer in his *Substance and Function*, tr. by W. Curtis Schwabey and M. C. Schwabey (New York, Dover, 1953), pp. 172-173.
2. John Locke, *An Essay Concerning Human Understanding*, Book II, Chap. 13, § 14.
3. James C. Maxwell, *Matter and Motion* (Dover, 1953; 1st ed. 1877), Chap. I, § 18; cf. also B. Russell, *Principles of Mathematics*, p. 405.
4. D. Hume, *Treatise on Human Nature*, Part IV, § 4, "Modern Philosophy."
5. John Tyndall, *Light and Electricity* (New York, Appleton, 1873), pp. 123-24.
6. Cf. Chap. VII, below, under "Fluid Theories of Matter," for a more extensive discussion.
7. Leibniz's letter to Jacob Thomasius, Sept. 26, 1668 (C. J. Gerhardt, ed. *Leibnizens Philosophische Schriften*, Berlin, 1875, Vol. I, pp. 9-11).
8. Locke, *op. cit.*, Book IV, Chap. 10, § 10.
9. Jean le Rond d'Alembert, *Traité de dynamique* (1743), Discours préliminaire: "On voit d'abord clairement qu'un corps ne peut se donner le mouvement à lui-même. Il ne peut donc être tiré du repos que par l'action de quelque chose étrangère."
10. C. Neumann, *Über die Principien der Galilei-Newtonschen Theorie* (Leipzig, 1870).
11. J. B. Stallo, *Concepts and Theories of Modern Physics*, 2d ed. (New York, Appleton, 1885), p. 69.
12. Lucretius, *De rerum natura*, II, vv. 294-307. Haas quotes this passage in *Die Entwicklungsgeschichte des Satzes von der Erhaltung der Kraft* (Wien, 1909) as the earliest known anticipation of the principle of indestructibility of motion. This, however, is not correct; see Note 13.
13. The studies of H. C. Liepmann (*Die Mechanik der Leucip-Demokritischen Atome*, Leipzig, 1885) and A. Brieger (*Die Urbewegung*

der Atome und die Weltanschauung des Leukipp und Demokrit,
Halle, 1884) established the necessity of differentiating between the
mechanics of Democritus and that of Epicurus; while the latter
assumed anisotropic space and the downward motion of atoms, the
former assumed the rectilinear motion of atoms through isotropic
space. But even Liepmann did not recognize that the correct word
for what he calls "die passive Schwere" is inertia. Nor is the word
"inertia" used by C. Bailey, although his view is the same as that
of F. Enriques *Le Dottrine di Democrito d'Abdera* (Bologna 1948),
Chap. III where it is convincingly shown how closely Democritus
anticipated Galileo.

14. A. Haas, *Die Grundgleichungen der Mechanik dargestellt auf Grund
    der geschichtlichen Entwicklung* (Leipzig, 1914), Chap. V; Aristotle,
    Physica, VII, 5.
15. Epicurus's definition of time as "accident of accidents" ($\sigma \acute{v} \mu \pi \tau \omega \mu a$
    $\sigma v \mu \pi \tau \omega \mu \acute{a} \tau \omega v$), later adopted by Gassendi, clearly indicates that in the
    corpuscular-kinetic scheme time is *twice removed* from the basic
    reality which is matter and void; motion is merely an "accident"
    because it affects neither the constancy of matter nor the immutabil-
    ity of space; while time, being a function of motion, is thus nothing
    but "accident of accidents." Cf. Bailey, *op. cit.*, pp. 305-309; W. Genf,
    Die Philosophie des Raumes und der Zeit (Bonn, 1926), p. 24.
16. E. Meyerson, *Identité et Réalité*, pp. 123, 149, 534 f.
17. L. Euler, *Lettres à une princesse d'Allemagne sur divers sujets de
    physique et de philosophie* (Paris, 1866), partie II, lettre 9e, p. 261.
18. *Principia Philosophiae*, II, 37; III, 30.
19. H. Samuel, *Essay in Physics* (Oxford, Blackwell, 1951), p. 70.
20. B. Riemann, "Fragmente philosophischen Inhaltes," *Gesammelte
    mathematische Werke* (Leipzig, 1892), pp. 522 f.
21. E. Mach, *Die Geschichte und die Wurzel des Satzes von der
    Erhaltung der Kraft* (Prague, 1872), especially pp. 13, 15, 33-46;
    The Science of Mechanics, tr. from 9th German edition by T. J.
    McCormack (La Salle, Ill., Open Court, 1942), *passim*, especially pp.
    101, 110, 602.
22. E. Meyerson, *op. cit.*, p. 155.
23. E. Dühring, *Kritische Geschichte der allgemeinen Principien der
    Mechanik* (Berlin, 1873), pp. 105-114 and 162-163; A. Haas,
    Grundgleichungen, Chap. VI, p. 57; Pierre Boutroux, "L'Histoire des
    principes de la dynamique avant Newton," *Revue de Métaphysique
    et de Morale*, 18e année (1921), especially pp. 675 f.
24. About this cf. P. G. Tait, *Lectures on Some Recent Advances in
    Physical Sciences* (London, 1876), p. 33-36.
25. About the achievements of Huygens, cf. Dühring, *op. cit.*, pp. 120-
    174; E. Mach, *The Science of Mechanics*, pp. 192-226; A. Haas, *Die
    Entwicklungsgeschichte*, pp. 64-66; *Grundgleichungen*, Chap. XIII;
    K. Lasswitz, *op. cit.*, Vol. II, pp. 376-397.
26. *The Science of Mechanics*, pp. 322, 442.

VI · THE MAIN FEATURES OF THE CORPUSCULAR-KINETIC VIEW OF NATURE

THE mechanical scheme of nature may be summarized in the following five propositions:

1. Matter, which is discontinuous in its structure, that is, made of absolutely rigid and compact units, moves through space according to the strict laws of mechanics.
2. All apparently qualitative differences in nature are due to the differences in configuration or motion of these basic units or their aggregates.
3. All apparently qualitative changes are merely surface effects of the displacement of the elementary units or their aggregates.
4. All interaction between the basic corpuscles is due exclusively to their direct impact. Action at a distance is a mere figure of speech.
5. Qualitative variety as well as qualitative transformation are *psychic additions* of the perceiving human mind; they do not belong to the nature of things.

It is important to emphasize at once in order to prevent a possible misunderstanding that this scheme represented only an *ideal limit* which physics was continuously striving to approach and which it never completely attained. New discoveries again and again imposed new modifications and corrections. These spoiled the beauty and rigor of the consistent mechanical scheme, but they were unavoidable if a close contact with physical experience was to be preserved. But in spite of all compromises and repeated failures to attain the ideal kinetic explanation in its unspoiled self-consistent purity, the tendency to move in this direction was, for the majority of physicists, irresistible. The superiority of the mechanistic explanation was so overwhelming that no failure to apply it consistently to a certain specific group of facts was ever regarded as final and definitive; on the contrary, it was always hoped that the further progress of science would make a strict mechanistic explanation possible. Again and again this hope was fulfilled. There is no place here for even a brief historical sketch of the development of classical science; a few typical instances should suffice to demonstrate that classical physics and the mechanical view of nature, contained in the five propositions above, were identical.

THE UNITY OF MATTER

It is clear that the propositions listed above are not logically independent. The last proposition, which was usually tacitly assumed by physicists, but explicitly stressed by philosophers of the classical period, was a mere consequence of Propositions 2 and 3; for qualitative change and diversity must have some ontological status, and if they do not belong to the "nature of things," they must take a refuge in the perceiving human mind. But even Propositions 2 and 3 are not independent assumptions; they both follow from the basic claim of the homogeneity and constancy of matter; from the homogeneity of the basic material units followed the denial of qualitative differences in nature, while from their immutability followed the denial of any change other than *that of position*. Thus both statements are simple corollaries of atomism.

It is true that the Aristotelian idea of qualitatively diversified and qualitatively changing nature was dying hard. We have already mentioned that when the concept of natural place was

given up, the idea of four different elements was virtually
doomed; with the discovery of the infinity and homogeneity
of space, the unity and homogeneity of matter was implicitly
asserted. Yet, in spite of this, it is amazing to see how the Aristotelian elements in a disguised form obstinately persisted in the
minds of scientists. Chemistry did not get rid of the idea of
phlogiston until the times of Lavoisier; a whole century after
the discovery of Newton's law of gravitation the idea of a substance without weight or even possessing a negative weight was
still regarded as a respectable hypothesis, although its affinity
with the old Aristotelian concept of the intrinsically light element, whether air or fire, is quite obvious. It was also Lavoisier
who had to disprove experimentally that the alleged qualitative
conversion of water into earth does not occur; in 1770 he proved
that the total weight of the closed glass vessel and of the water
which had been boiling in it remained the same, but that the
weight of the "earth" deposited on the bottom of the vessel was
exactly equivalent to the loss of the weight of the vessel; consequently that the "earth" came not from the water, but from
the glass.[1] The alleged qualitative transformation of a lighter
substance into a heavier one was thus nothing but a *displacement* of different masses whose total weight remained the same.
Yet, in spite of his successful effort to free the incipient science
of chemistry from the remnants of disguised Aristotelian ideas,
Lavoisier's mind was not completely free of them. He retained
the idea of *caloricum*, a mysterious fluid postulated for the
explanation of the phenomena of heat, without apparently realizing the close kinship of this substance with phlogiston; to us it
is now clear that the caloric is, epistemologically speaking,
nothing but an objectified sensation of warmth, and Lavoisier
in this respect hardly went beyond Aristotle.[2]

Even in the nineteenth century, when the kinetic theory of
heat as a mode of motion removed this particular remnant of
Aristotelianism and when the atomistic theory was brought by
John Dalton from the heights of philosophical speculation down
to the solid ground of experiment, physics and chemistry were
still far from the ideal of mechanical explanation described

above. A striking feature of Dalton's atomism was its *qualitative* character; its philosophic ancestor was Anaxagoras rather than Democritus. In this respect the qualitative atomism of Dalton, in insisting on the irreducible qualitative diversity of the atoms of different elements, sharply contrasted with the basic tenet of philosophical atomism which from Democritus to Gassendi repeatedly claimed that all qualitative differences in nature were purely phenomenal. From the strictly mechanical point of view it was intolerable to admit that the physical and chemical differences between, for instance, hydrogen and oxygen, were ultimate and irreducible data. But mechanistic philosophers as well as philosophically minded scientists never gave up the hope that the qualitative differences between the atoms of chemical elements are not irreducible and ultimate, but are due in the last analysis to differences in configuration of more minute and more basic particles.

Thus Robert Boyle, who first clearly formulated the concept of chemical element, and who also insisted on the persistence of the elements in the compounds, believed nevertheless that the smallest particles of the elements (such as gold and mercury) are still *corpora manifeste mixta*[3] (clearly mixed bodies), that is, composed of the truly elementary and qualitatively homogeneous atoms strongly cohering together. Boyle thus two centuries before the discovery of radioactivity anticipated the complexity of the chemical atom and the possibility of the transmutation of the elements! In the nineteenth century the same idea was held by various philosophers and scientists like Dalton's contemporary Prout and later by Berthelot, Gibbs, Lotze, Wundt, and Herbert Spencer.[4]

What is remarkable is that these hopes and expectations, which were motivated exclusively by philosophical reasons, were *almost* fulfilled by the empirically established electron theory. Although this theory belongs to the modern era of physics, in a certain sense it may be regarded as a culmination of the classical tendencies, since it apparently succeeded in reducing nearly all qualitative differences in nature to the differences of complexity and aggregation of the homogeneous basic corpuscles. The simplest element, hydrogen, was pictured as made up of two elementary particles—the *electron* and the central *proton* around which it revolved. By increasing gradually the number of the peripheral electrons and the number of the nuclear particles, all ninety-two elements then known could be obtained. By combining these elements into compounds and the resulting compounds into minerals, there arose all the apparently inexhaustible variety of inorganic nature. Similarly, organic compounds were results of the association of the atoms of carbon (each of which is nothing but a system of six electrons revolving around the complex nucleus), with other elements, and in this way the apparently miraculous complexity of organic bodies was successfully explained.

It would be an enthusiastic overstatement to claim the Democritean ideal of explanation could not have been realized more fully and successfully; but nevertheless its success was spectacular enough to justify the optimistic hopes that the remaining gaps in the mechanistic picture of the world would eventually be filled. These gaps were represented by the irreducible polarity of electric charges as well as by the duality of matter and electricity; after so many brilliant successes of mechanistic explanation it was natural to hope that these last vestiges of qualitative diversity would be resolved in the all-embracing unity of aether. It is true that the simultaneous emergence of the theory of relativity and of the theory of quanta represented a jarring note which considerably cooled down the optimism of the mechanistic model makers (cf. Chapter X below). It remains true that the last triumph of the corpuscular-kinetic explanation of nature as embodied in the early electron theory of matter was the most spectacular and most impressive.

THE ELIMINATION OF ACTION AT A DISTANCE

The last essential feature of the kinetic-atomistic view of matter was the view that every interaction between bodies is due to a direct mechanical impact or pressure; *action at a distance* is only an appearance due to the limitation of our sensory perception. Every physical influence is in the last analysis *some kind of direct contact*, if not between macroscopic bodies, then at least between the elementary particles of the intervening medium. It is of secondary importance whether this contact is lasting, as in the case of cohesive forces, or temporary, as in the case of clashing bodies. From Democritus to William Thomson and Heinrich Hertz the fundamental idea remained the same. Models of action at a distance only became more and more complex and ingenious without ceasing to be essentially mechanical. Today we are inclined to smile when we read about the hooks by which Democritus explained the cohesive forces between atoms. Yet, was the major part of the nineteenth-century explanations *basically* different?

In the last century James Clerk Maxwell was one of a growing number of physicists who began to realize that there is, strictly speaking, no direct contact between physical bodies.[5] Does this mean that he gave up the mechanistic explanation by direct contact? Certainly not; he repeatedly emphasized the physical reality of the intervening medium,[6] and his famous model of the electromagnetic aether, whose close similarity to the Cartesian model of young John Bernoulli was pointed out by E. T. Whittaker,[7] seemed to be inspired by the famous maxim of Hobbes: *Causa motus nulla esse potest in corpore nisi contiguo et moto* (There can be no cause of motion in a body except from a body in contact and moved).[8]

There was nothing contradictory in Maxwell's attitude; he was merely aware that the absence of contact between the *visible* material particles does not exclude the presence of much subtler and imperceptible particles of aether which fill the interstices between material corpuscles and by which the direct physical influence is communicated from one body to another. For instance the effect of the electric current on the magnetic needle is explained by Maxwell in the following way: while the translatory displacement of the aethereal molecules in the conductors represents the electric current, the concomitant aethereal whirl accounts for the simultaneous formation of the magnetic field in the plane perpendicular to the direction of the current. An interesting engineering detail in Maxwell's model was the presence of the so-called "friction molecules" inserted between the elementary aethereal vortices; their function was to assure that the whirl-like disturbance in the aether is propagated with one definite sense of rotation; otherwise, adjacent aethereal whirls would revolve in opposite directions.[9]

Philosophically speaking, such a model is not too remote from the Cartesian models of the seventeenth century or even from the hooks of Democritus; the idea of direct contact of the adjacent parts of the postulated machinery is common to all these explanations, and it is of secondary importance whether the motion is communicated by means of the chains and hooks of Democritus or the "idle wheels" of Maxwell.

The reluctance of Maxwell to accept action at a distance is typical of the whole classical period. He exemplifies the general tendency toward the mechanistic explanation of physical interaction between distant bodies: when the direct material link between the distant interacting bodies seemed to be absent, it was readily supplied by the imagination of philosophers and scientists in the form of the intermediate mechanical agency consisting of particles too subtle to be perceived by human senses.

Thus all physical influences occurring between distant bodies were again and again, and often in spite of repeated failures, explained in terms of minute particles traveling from one body to another. Long would be the list of all kinetic-corpuscular explanations of various forms of action at a distance from the first crude emanation theories of the Greek atomists to the emission theory of Newton, from the imaginative aether theory of Leonardo da Vinci, who regarded light as an undulatory disturbance of the "luminous air," [10] to the wave theories of Huygens and Fresnel; from the vague but interesting account of the phenomena of weight by Leucippus and Democritus to various hydrodynamic or kinetic models of gravitation proposed by Descartes, Newton, Lesage, and their modern imitators;[11] from the first naive explanations of electric and magnetic phenomena by Gilbert and Descartes to the refined models of the electromagnetic aether proposed by Maxwell, William Thomson, Larmor, and others.[12]

The differences between the emission theories and the aether theories, important as they are from the physical point of view, are, epistemologically speaking, of secondary importance. The basic postulate is the same in both theories; direct mechanical impact is the only type of physical influence admitted by both. The only difference is that while Democritus' *eidōla* and Newton's particles travel directly from the source of light to other bodies, in the aether theories the vibratory motion is communicated by the contiguous particles of the intervening medium; but the last vibrating aether particle impinges on the eye or some other body as directly as the traveling particle of Newton.

The same is true of the mechanical models of gravitation: whether we explain the motions of gravitating bodies by the continuous bombardment of ultramundane corpuscles, postulated by Lesage in his *Lucrèce newtonien*, or by difference of density in the hypothetical aethereal medium, as postulated by Newton in his *Optics*,[13] the ultimate result is the same. In either hypothesis, gravitational motion is caused by some sort of push, *vis a tergo*, directly impinging on the bodies in question.

In certain provinces of natural phenomena the mechanical explanation of interaction has been established beyond any doubt; such was the explanation of the propagation of sound by longitudinal waves which replaced the naive concept of the "sound particles" of the early atomists. In other provinces, like optics, the kinetic explanation of light in terms of a periodic disturbance seemed to be reasonably secure before 1900, in spite of the hypothetical character of the postulated luminiferous aether. But to construct a satisfactory and consistent model of *all* electromagnetic phenomena, not only of the very special class of them which we call light, proved to be a much more arduous task. The difficulty seemed to be almost insurmountable if it was required that the model of aether should be comprehensive enough to account for the phenomena of gravitation as well. But the difficulty of this task made only more significant the obstinacy with which the mechanical models of the electro-magnetic and gravitational aether were again and again pro-posed.

There must have been deeper reasons behind such persistent faith, which in spite of repeated disappointments never ended in complete discouragement or resignation, and which, as we shall see, sporadically persisted even after the classical period was over. As a primary reason, the mechanical model of the *actio in distans* was an unavoidable consequence of the consistent corpuscular-kinetic view of physical reality and, in particular, of the kinetic interpretation of the law of conservation of energy. Once this is accepted, the question immediately arises: Where is the luminous or electromagnetic energy in the interval *between* its emission from one body and its arrival at the other? If it does not disappear temporarily, it must exist *somewhere* and in *some form;* the only assumption consistent with mecha-nism is that it exists in the kinetic energy of the postulated intervening medium. The aether hypothesis was, as Poincaré clearly saw,[14] a logical consequence of the law of constancy of energy, interpreted in a strictly kinetic way. The assertion that every form of energy is kinetic energy was an ever-present part of the consistent mechanical view of nature.

This claim may at first appear historically incorrect, as it seems to be contradicted by the wide use of the concept of *potential energy*. But a closer inspection will show that for the most outstanding classical physicists this concept was a mere convenient mathematical device invented for the explicit pur-pose of keeping the quantity of energy constant; as soon as the *real physical meaning* of this concept came into question, the view prevailed that the potential energy is only a disguised form of kinetic energy, that is, the kinetic energy of the invisible particles. The examples of Leibniz and Huygens are both in-structive in this respect. They share the merit of clearly formu-lating the principle of the constancy of energy; moreover, Leibniz was the first to introduce the concept of potential energy into physics.[15] Does this mean that he regarded potential energy as autonomous and irreducible to the energy of motion? This is at least doubtful, because he was a man who made most significant contributions to the kinetic interpretation of the law of the conservation of energy. It was Leibniz who recognized that in the clash of inelastic bodies the portion of the kinetic energy which apparently disappears is not destroyed but only distributed among molecular particles; the apparent loss of energy is in reality a transformation of the macroscopic perceptible motion into the microscopic invisible one.[16] In principle, this was an anticipation of the mechanical equivalent of heat which was discovered much later and which is one of the cornerstones of the kinetic theory of heat. But if thermal energy is only a special form of the energy of motion, is this not true also of other forms of energy, including the *energy of position?* This is what Leibniz believed when he favored the kinetic explanation of gravitation while rejecting the notion of the attracting force acting at a distance as a return to "occult qualities" of the scholastics.[17]

In this respect Leibniz's view was similar to that of Huygens, who in his *Dissertatio de causa gravitatis* also tried to explain gravity kinetically, that is, as a result of the motion of impinging atoms of the hypothetical aethereal medium. This means that if the pendulum gains potential energy in its ascending motion while losing its visible motion, this loss is only apparent; the kinetic energy is *not* destroyed but merely redistributed, being communicated to the atoms of the gravitational aether, which eventually enforces the descending motion of the pendulum. The situation is then basically the same as in the apparent loss of energy in inelastic bodies. In his *Additamentum ad dissertationem de causa gravitatis,* written after the publication of Newton's *Principia,* Huygens accepted the mathematical formalism of Newton's theory while insisting on the necessity of mechanical explanation. According to Huygens, the laws of the conservation of energy and momentum hold not only for macroscopic visible bodies, but also for atoms and aethereal particles. His view is a convincing illustration of the fact that *the rejection of action at a distance* and the assertion that *all energy is kinetic* are basically one and the same proposition.[18]

This proposition was, for two centuries after Leibniz and Huygens, the inspiration of all persistent efforts to account mechanically for *all* instances of apparent action at a distance. The concrete difficulties of this task were enormous, but precisely this makes the persistence of such efforts more significant and betrays the strength of the underlying motive. The majority of the outstanding physicists of the nineteenth century, such men as Gauss, Faraday, Maxwell, William Thomson, Helmholtz, Hertz, and J. J. Thomson, were opposed to the idea of force jumping instantaneously over the distance, whether this distance was of molecular or interplanetary dimensions.[19] How little this basic conviction varied may be illustrated by the two following quotations:

> In the true Philosophy we conceive the causes of all natural effects in terms of mechanical motions. And, in my opinion, we must admit this, or else give up all hope of even understanding anything in physics. (Chr. Huygens, *Traité de la lumière*, 1690.)

> It seems to me that the test of "Do we or do we not understand a particular topic in physics?" is "Can we make a mechanical model of it?" (W. Thomson, *Notes of Lectures on Molecular Dynamics*, 1884.)

But there was one additional reason for the continuing confidence in the ultimate success of mechanical explanation for all phenomena of nature in spite of temporary setbacks. This reason, though negative, was probably as strong as the positive mechanistic conviction from which it could hardly be separated psychologically: there simply was no rival theory which could successfully compete with mechanism by its intrinsic consistency or its empirical verification. This will become clearer if we briefly analyze some theories and philosophies of nature which appeared during the classical period concomitant with the prevailing mechanistic trend.

NOTES FOR CHAPTER VI

1. E. von Meyer, *A History of Chemistry from Earliest Times to the Present Day*, tr. by G. McGowan (London, Macmillan, 1891), p. 152.
2. Hélène Metzger, *La Philosophie de la matière chez Lavoisier*, Actualités scientifiques et industrielles, No. 218 (Paris, 1935) pp. 38-44.
3. Robert Boyle, *Chemista scepticus* (Geneva, 1680), p. 15; English translation, London, Everyman's Library, 1911, p. 32.
4. E. von Meyer, *op. cit.*, pp. 189-191; J. B. Stallo, *Concepts and Theories of Modern Physics*, 2d ed., Chap. III; E. Meyerson, *Identité et réalité*, pp. 266-269.
5. J. C. Maxwell, "Action at a Distance," *Scientific Papers* (Cambridge, 1890), Vol. II, pp. 313-315.
6. Maxwell, *op. cit.*, p. 322; cf. also his article "Ether," *ibid.*, pp. 763-775.
7. E. T. Whittaker, *A History of the Theories of Aether and Electricity* (New York, Philosophical Library, 1951), Vol. I, p. 248.
8. T. Hobbes, *Opera philosophica omnia* (Londini, 1839), I, pars 1a c. IX, p. 110.
9. J. C. Maxwell, "On Physical Lines of Force," *op. cit.*, I, pp. 451-513, especially p. 488.
10. G. Séailles, *Leonardo da Vinci: l'artiste et le savant* (Paris, 1919), pp. 246-7.
11. C. Bailey, *Greek Atomists and Epicurus*, pp. 92-97 and 143-146; F. Enriques, *Le dottrine di Democrito d'Abdera*, pp. 62 f., C. Isenkrahe, *Das Rätsel der Schwerkraft* (Braunschweig, 1879).
12. W. Gilbert, *On the Loadstone and Magnetic Bodies*, tr. from Latin by F. Mottelay, Chaps. II-III. On the influence of Gilbert's theory of *effluvia* on Descartes and Newton, cf. Whittaker, *op. cit.*, Vol. I, pp. 34-37; on the persistence of the Cartesian mechanical approach to the phenomena of electricity, cf. F. Rosenberger, *Die moderne Entwicklung der elektrischen Principien* (Leipzig, 1898), pp. 23-24; B. Cohen, *Franklin and Newton* (Philadelphia, The American Philosophical Society, 1956), *passim*, especially pp. 387-390. About Franklin's loyalty to the principles of mechanism, cf. Cohen, *op. cit.*, especially pp. 297-98. About the mechanical models of aether in the nineteenth century, cf. Whittaker, *op. cit.*, Vol. I.
13. Lesage, "Lucrèce newtonien" in: *Mémoires de l'académie de Berlin 1782* (Berlin, 1784); I. Newton, *Optics*, 4th ed. (London, 1730), Query 31. On Newton's views on aether, cf. E. A. Burtt, *Metaphysical Foundations of Modern Physical Science*, Chap. VII, § 5, pp. 265-280; E. Meyerson, *op. cit.*, Appendix I, pp. 513-527; B. Cohen, *op. cit.*, pp. 142-145 and 166-174.
14. H. Poincaré, "Science and Hypothesis" in *The Foundation of Science*, p. 146.
15. A. Haas, *Entwicklungsgeschichte*, pp. 20-21. Although the first indica-

tions of the concept of potential energy appear in Gassendi and Borelli, its first clear definition is in Leibniz's, *Dynamica,* pars II, sec. 1.

16. *The Leibniz-Clarke Correspondence,* ed. by H. G. Alexander, pp. 87-88 (Leibniz's fifth letter); Max Jammer, *Concepts of Force* (Harvard University Press, 1957), p. 167.
17. Leibniz's fifth letter to Clarke, *op. cit.,* p. 94.
18. Leibniz's letter to Huygens, April 11, 1682, and Huygens's answer on July 11, 1692 (*Leibnizens mathematische Schriften,* II, pp. 133-36).
19. Cf. numerous references in Meyerson, *op. cit.,* pp. 76-80.

VII · SOME COLLATERAL TRENDS: DYNAMISM, ENERGETISM, FLUID THEORIES

DYNAMISM

THE greatest advantage of the kinetic-corpuscular explanations seemed to be their great appeal to our imagination. Even today the idea of the direct mechanical impact appears to an unsophisticated mind as the most familiar and most natural. But since the time of Hume the question has been alive to what extent we have the right to confuse psychological familiarity with logical clarity. Is not the feeling of familiarity based on customary conjunction of ideas, that is, on association strengthened by repetition and habit? Do we really understand action by direct contact any better than action at a distance? Or is the only difference due to the fact that we are more *used* to the first kind? Is not action by contact, in the last analysis, just as puzzling as action at a distance? Such questions led some philosopher-scientists—e.g., Boscovich, Kant, J. S. Mill, Comte, Wundt, J. B. Stallo, E. Mach—to the conclusion that the aversion to action at a distance is merely a prejudice of our conditioned imagination. These tendencies were, in the last century, associated with empiricist positivism, which deliberately resigned from every attempt at explanation in insisting that the only task of science is to *describe*, not to *explain;* hence its critical attitude to atomism and kinetism, which were regarded by numerous positivists as the last remnant of metaphysics.[1]

On the other hand the positivistic attitude toward action at a distance was associated with the so-called *dynamic theories of matter,* according to which *forces,* acting immediately through the distance, either constitute the real physical essence of matter or, at least, are as primary as matter itself. This last view was a sort of compromise between atomism and dynamism; the existence of ultimate material particles was not denied, but they were endowed with forces emanating from them, by which the physical influences between bodies were conveyed. This hybrid combination of atomism and action at a distance was probably the most widely accepted view in the last century. It certainly pervaded the textbooks of physics and the heads of less sophisticated scientists. Ludwig Büchner's dualism of force and matter (*Kraft und Stoff*) belongs to this line of thought.

The dynamic view, which saw the ultimate essence of matter in forces emanating from pointlike centers and acting instantaneously through distance, was represented especially by Boscovich, Kant, and Faraday. Historically it may be traced to Newton's disciples rather than to Newton himself, whose view concerning the nature of force was uncertain and hesitant, oscillating between the agnosticism of a positivistic type (*Hypotheses non fingo*—"I do not fashion hypotheses") and the mechanistic explanation of gravitation by the pressure of the aether. In a certain carefully defined sense, dynamism had its roots also in Leibniz's metaphysics of unextended dynamic monads;[2] but keeping in mind the distinction between Leibniz metaphysician and Leibniz scientist, we should not forget that in all concrete physical problems Leibniz favored mechanical explanations and was, like Huygens, resolutely opposed to the reification of force, in which he saw a disguised return to the "occult qualities" of the Middle Ages. In this sense he differed from Kant who, though noncommittal about the ultimate essence of matter, was a resolute dynamist as far as its "phenomenal manifestations" were concerned.[3]

It is instructive to compare the merits of dynamism with those of atomism. Dynamism claimed that it is more in harmony with the principle of continuity than atomism. It does not have to accept the arbitrary finite radius for material particles. Unlike atomism, it does not lead to the consequence that the velocities of the impinging particles change abruptly on the rigid surfaces of the atoms. By accepting force as a primary physical entity whose magnitude and *sign* vary with distance, it accounts for impenetrability and gravity at the same time. Impenetrability results from the repulsive force in the immediate neighborhood of the dynamic center, while gravity is a consequence of the fact that the same force reverses its sign at a certain distance. There is therefore no need of cumbersome mechanical models. This, and the elimination of the distinction between the particle and the field of force surrounding it has an almost modern ring.

Yet, this should not hide from us some serious difficulties inherent in this view of matter. In spite of all the difficulties which mechanism began to face at the end of the last century and which became insurmountable in this century, it remained far superior to dynamism, logically as well as in its interpretation of empirical data. First, as shown above, mechanism avoided the difficult notion of action at a distance. The word "action," at least in its original and usual sense, is *dynamic* and *successive* in its character; the action unfolds itself gradually in space as well as in time, advancing with finite speed from place to place. This is certainly incompatible with the concept of instantaneous action which travels with an infinite speed. In truth, the word "traveling" is a mere figure of speech here; action at a distance is *simultaneously present* in all points of its "path." Physical action thus understood is rather a *static connection* than a dynamic influence; the very name "dynamism" is rather a misnomer. Besides, the growing physical evidence gradually relegated the self-contradictory concept of instantaneous velocity into the realm of fiction; first sound, then light, and finally electromagnetic disturbances were shown to travel with *finite* velocities.

It is true that gravitation seemingly did not have any finite velocity, and the authority of Laplace, whose error in computation was not discovered until 1901, greatly strengthened this belief.[4] But is it surprising that even after the empirical establishment of the finite velocity of electromagnetic vibrations the hope persisted that the action of gravity would eventually be shown to move from one place to another in a *finite* interval of time, no matter how short? The logical difficulty inherent in the notion of instantaneous velocity naturally strengthened this hope long before the advent of relativity, which showed that gravity is no exception in this respect. Herrmann Lotze wittily observed that action at a distance is taking place "behind the back of space"; he might have added that it takes place behind the back of time as well.[5] In this sense it is not only an anti-spatial concept, as Meyerson called it,[6] but an antitemporal one as well. But of what use is the allegedly physical entity which is by its definition *beyond* space and time? At least, of what use is it from the point of view of classical physics, for which the traditional concepts of space and time were regarded as the *containers* of everything physical?

This was not the only difficulty. According to the corpuscular-kinetic explanation of nature, every apparently new quantity of motion was merely a transformation of an equivalent quantity of the motion pre-existing in a hidden molecular form. Every apparent disappearance of motion was also regarded merely as a conversion of motion into its invisible equivalent distributed among the microscopic particles. Thus the laws of the conservation of energy and of momentum were regarded as quantitative descriptions of the *substantiality* of motion, that is, of its indestructibility and uncreatability. As was pointed out above, the inevitable corollary of mechanism was that all energy is in its nature kinetic, while "potential" energy is a mere figure of speech. When the dynamists were forced by empirical evidence to recognize the finite velocity of transmission of electromagnetic energy, they faced the question already mentioned: What is the status of traveling energy in the interval between its emission and its absorption? Only two alternatives were possible: either the emitted energy persists as kinetic energy of the aethereal particles or it acquires, temporarily at least, a new specific form altogether irreducible to motion. Mechanism accepted the first alternative and thus possessed the definite advantage of logical simplicity embodied in Occam's razor; while dynamism added to the duality of matter and force (a duality which, as we shall see shortly, it did not succeed in eliminating) the duality of two kinds of energy: kinetic and potential.

From the dynamist point of view the conversion of the kinetic energy into potential energy and vice versa had to be regarded as a true *qualitative* transformation, almost in the Aristotelian sense—a consequence which was not unwelcome to the Aristotelian-minded Pierre Duhem.[7] Thus, according to Boscovich and his followers, motion is born out of force, that is, out of something which is *not* a motion, and when it disappears, it is transformed into something which is *not* a motion. The law of the conservation of energy is formally preserved, but it is evident that when its kinetic interpretation is given up, we are almost back to Aristotle and his idea of qualitative transformation. While the homogeneity of cause and effect was preserved in the mechanistic scheme, it was clearly sacrificed by dynamism.

No wonder that the unsatisfactory character of dynamism was vaguely felt by the majority of physicists, even by those who were not clearly aware of the superiority of mechanism. Indeed, this was felt by some philosophers with distinctly dynamist leanings. Thus Kant in spite of his dynamism had to resort to a corpuscular explanation of the change of physical state;[8] Faraday, in spite of his sympathy for Boscovich's theory, by his opposition to action at a distance and his emphasis on the importance of the mechanical processes in the intervening medium, greatly contributed to the revival of the Cartesian tendency to construct a mechanical model of the aether.[9] Finally Spencer, who so much insisted on the primary character of force, indignantly rejected the suspicion that he recognized potential energy as an autonomous form of energy, irreducible to motion. Spencer was a dynamist more in his language than in his thought; this is so much the more significant because he may be regarded as an intermediate link between the dynamism of Boscovich and modern energetism.[10]

There was a third difficulty in dynamism which was just as

serious as the two just considered. Boscovich replaced the minute indivisible particles of atomism, which were still retained by Newton, by simple points with zero radius. From this simple dimensionless point the repulsive and attractive forces emanate, causing at different distances, according to which one of them prevailed, the phenomenon of impenetrability or gravitation. But did Boscovich really give up the idea of material particle? Did not this concept survive in some form? He certainly claimed that his material points are merely centers of force and that the alleged impenetrability of particles is due to the prevailing of the repulsive force within a certain radius. But this does not meet the basic objection. His material points, even when they are considered as simple centers of force, are capable of *motion in space*. Now *what* exactly is moving in space? How can a single mathematical point move in respect to other points of space *without being differentiated from the temporary positions* which it occupies in successive instants of its movement? Because the geometrical points constituting space do not move *by definition*, motion, at least in its classical sense, always implies the distinction between an underlying motionless position and its temporary occupant. By saying that it is the dynamical point which is moving, and not the geometrical one, dynamists are merely reintroducing under a different name the basic relation of *occupancy* which, as we have seen above, is the very core of atomism. The center of force then occupies a certain pointlike position in space; it is a true *material* point.

This was even explicitly admitted when the dynamists endowed their dynamical points with *inertia*, that is, the intrinsic resistance to any change of motion. In this respect dynamism differed from atomism only by reducing the atomic radii to zero; in other respects its dynamical points were hardly different from the particles with the finite radius. They were admittedly *inert* like atoms; they were in a certain sense *rigid*, since they preserved their identity through time; finally, they were even *impenetrable* because they were *ex definitione* indivisible; the repulsive force, being infinite at each center of force, prevents a fusion of two distinct particles. It is hardly surprising that some dynamists considered themselves atomists: such was the case of Boscovich himself as well as Faraday and Fechner.[11]

This was hardly an improvement over the classical atomism; on the contrary, the change was for the worse. Mathematically it is conceivable that certain continuous functions can at one point either become discontinuous or possess a singularity; but it is difficult to see how a geometrical zero, that is, a point without dimensions, can have concrete physical properties like the capacity of motion, inertia or resistance to acceleration, the repulsive force of infinite magnitude, and the magic power to produce motion either instantaneously at an infinite distance (as was still believed in the case of gravitation) or gradually, after a certain time lag as in other physical actions. Even in this last case when the finite velocity of propagation is conceded, the fundamental difficulty which has been already pointed out still remains. How can something which is *not* a motion produce motion? For it is the essence of the dynamist theory that motion is always an *effect* and never a cause; any material point moves because it is moved by a distant *force*, and moves any other material point by its own force; the homogeneity of cause and effect, which was an outstanding feature of mechanism, is thus sacrificed.

At first it looks as if Boscovich's idea underlay a large part of classical physics, especially mechanics and the theory of electromagnetism. The "material points" as well as the pointlike electric charges are apparently only recent versions of his "dynamical points." It is also true that there were many scientists and philosophers—Cavendish, Cauchy, Ampère, Poisson, Faraday, Fechner, Couturat, and Russell [12]—who took the existence of physical points with the zero radius quite literally. But is it not obvious that this is nothing but a naive *reification* of geometrical points, almost in the old Pythagorean sense? And is it not more natural to regard the alleged "material points" as mere approximations and idealizations permissible when the volume of particles, though different from zero, is small enough to be neglected? From this point of view the concept of pointlike masses or charges is merely a convenient methodological device suitable for certain theoretical tasks; but the hypostatization of such limit concepts leads, as we have seen, to enormous difficulties, philosophical as well as physical.

Even the desire to respect the law of continuity, which was one of the basic motives of Boscovich when he rejected the discontinuous transition from the zero density of the vacuum to the infinite density of the interior of the atom, is eventually frustrated by the fact that force itself becomes infinite at the center of force. The assumption of particles having finite radii avoided all these difficulties, was epistemologically more acceptable since it did not confuse an ideal mathematical entity with the physical reality, and was in agreement with the corpuscular-kinetic view of nature. What was even more decisive, this assumption was confirmed by physical experience, which showed more and more convincingly that the elementary particles underlying matter and electricity are neither simple points nor do they interact instantaneously. The discovery of the finite radius of the electron, coming only a few decades after the discovery of the finite velocity of electromagnetic vibrations, was the final blow to the surviving forms of Boscovich's theory.

ENERGETISM

In the period when the electromagnetic theory of light replaced the old mechanical theory of Huygens and Fresnel, and especially when the existence of electrons was established, a strong reaction against mechanistic physics took place. The development of physics itself greatly contributed to this reaction. If light is only a certain type of electromagnetic vibration, does it make any sense to persist in searching for a mechanical model of aether? Is not the original mechanical model of the aether replaced by a new electromagnetic aether? Moreover, if all matter is made of elements which are of an electrical nature, is not electricity instead of matter the fundamental physical reality? Are not the so-called impenetrability and inertia of classical matter merely peculiar manifestations of electromagnetic energy? Such were the questions which began to crop up in the last decade of the nineteenth and in the first decade of the twentieth century. They definitely reflect the tendency to regard classical mechanism, including atomism, as an obsolete view which must be replaced by the energetic, or more specifically, the *electromagnetic* view of nature.

This tendency was strengthened by the epistemological considerations of several scientists and philosophers who emphasized the economic and conventional character of the basic physical concepts and the biological conditioning of our thinking. To mention at least some representatives of this trend: In Germany Ernst Mach insisted that the preference for mechanical explanations in physics is nothing but a prejudice, in part excusable because of its historical origins and its past successes. According to him, the concept of the atom is a mental artifice, a hypothetical device which should not be regarded as a faithful replica of physical reality. In the United States, Mach's contemporary J. B. Stallo pointed out extreme difficulties which any consistent application of the principles of mechanism faced.[13] The tremendous prestige of the law of the conservation of energy, based on its fruitfulness in the interpretation of various natural phenomena, led several outstanding thinkers of the last century, in particular Herbert Spencer, to regard this law as the truest expression of ultimate reality, and thus contributed to the rise of energetism, in which Wilhelm Ostwald saw a definite overcoming of materialism and the final bankruptcy of atomism.[14]

Yet the whole noisy reaction against classical mechanism and atomism was premature, and today, from the distance of sixty years, we know why: prior to the coming of the theory of relativity and the theory of quanta it was impossible to challenge effectively the classical conceptual fabric. Moreover, the whole antimechanistic movement was far more ambiguous and heterogeneous than it appeared. It is instructive and even amusing to see how some basic ideas of mechanism were tacitly assumed even by some most resolute energetists. In this respect there is a certain similarity between modern energetism and eighteenth-century dynamism; in fact, the one can be regarded as a modified continuation of the other. The transition can be traced, especially in the thought of Robert Mayer and Herbert Spencer. The main difference was that *energy* and not *force* was made the fundamental substantial entity by modern energetists; the fact that they used the term "force" and were speaking about the "law of the conservation of force" was irrelevant; they meant energy.[15] But it is significant that some basic features of the classical corpuscular-kinetic view were clearly present in the mind of energetists. For Herbert Spencer the law of evolution is the law of continuous redistribution of matter and motion. In his own words:[16]

> The change from a diffused, imperceptible state, to a concentrated, perceptible state, is an integration of matter and concomitant dissipation of motion; and the change from a concentrated perceptible state, to a diffused, imperceptible state, is an absorption of motion and concomitant disintegration of matter. These are truisms. Constituent parts cannot aggregate without losing some of their relative motion; and they cannot separate without more relative motion being given to them. . . . When taken together, the two opposite processes thus formulated constitute the history of every sensible existence, under its simplest form. Loss of motion and consequent integration, eventually followed by gain of motion and consequent disintegration—see here a statement comprehensive of the entire series of changes passed through: comprehensive in an extremely general way, as any statement which holds of sensible existences at large must be; but still, comprehensive in the sense that all the changes gone through fall within it.

The ancient atomists could hardly have expressed more definitely their basic belief that every change is reducible to the process of redistribution of matter and motion. Spencer believed in the constancy of matter and the indestructibility of motion; so did the atomists. Spencer rejected the irreducible qualitative plurality of chemical elements recognized by Helmholtz and the majority of the nineteenth-century scientists. He rejected it because he believed in the basic unity of matter; so did the atomists. Spencer did not admit potential energy as an autonomous form because he regarded it as a disguised form of kinetic energy; so did the atomists.[17] He stressed the importance of the "law of persistence of force" (viz., energy) which he regarded as the supreme physical law. It is true that the concept of energy was unknown to the ancient atomists; but they at least foresaw it qualitatively, and it was one of the modern atomists, Christian Huygens, who made the most significant contribution to its exact formulation.

What then was the difference between mechanism and Spencer's dynamism? It consists in Spencer's claim that *energy* is the basic physical reality and that which we call matter is only its manifestation. Yet, in spite of this energetist claim, Spencer recognized the duality of "space-occupying force," which is "passive and independent," and the "force which moves," which is "active but dependent on its past and present relations to other atoms." [18] What is the difference between this space-occupying force of Spencer and the *vis insita* of Newton or the *impenetrability* of atomists? The difference is purely semantic. In any case, Spencer's claim that the reduction of the data to their lowest terms will yield *"the unit of matter, or atom, and its motion"* [19] is undistinguishable from classical mechanism of the least compromising type.

The example of Spencer is instructive because he unquestionably was one of the most influential philosophers at the turn of the century. It shows how much philosophical thought was pervaded by the influence of classical physics. In comparison with Herbert Spencer, Wilhelm Ostwald is certainly less philosophical. Spencer always emphasized the phenomenal character of his physical "force," which was for him only a symbol of the ultimate unknowable reality. It is true that this subtle epistemological distinction is nearly obliterated by another passage in which it is claimed that for practical purposes "the absolute reality" and its phenomenal manifestations are equivalent;[20] this explains why the main orientation of Spencer's thought remains, in spite of some verbal precautions, physicalistic if not materialistic. But in Ostwald even such verbal precautions are missing, and his energy is identified with the ultimate metaphysical reality. In this respect his "energetism" is a thinly disguised materialism, as Driesch noticed.[21] For the material substance of Lamettrie and Büchner there was substituted the no less physical concept of substantialized energy. But as far as the view of the physical world is concerned, there is hardly any difference between Spencer and Ostwald; both believed that matter is merely a manifestation of energy and cannot be perceived except in its energetic manifestations. In this sense they philosophically paved the way to the later relativistic fusion of matter and energy; but as they did not depart from classical mechanics, their attempt was necessarily premature and ineffective. For in the thought of Ostwald, like that of Spencer, the basic presuppositions of mechanism, including the concept of material substance, were tacitly preserved. Pierre Duhem, who could hardly be suspected of a promechanistic bias, and who belonged to the group of energetists, pointed out convincingly that Ostwald's reasoning instead of excluding the concept of material substance really presupposes it.[22] For every movement presupposes a thing which moves, and *kinetic energy*, by definition, presupposes the mass. As long as the validity of the formula $E = \frac{1}{2}mv^2$ is recognized, the concept of the material substrata of motion is implicitly admitted.

The discoveries of the late nineteenth century, which raised fresh doubts about the sufficiency of the mechanistic world view, were far more ambiguous than the opponents of mechanism were willing to admit. Thus the electromagnetic theory of light did not do away with the concept of aether; it only joined the adjective "electromagnetic" to the old noun of Huygens and Fresnel. The question of fundamental importance, then, was: Can the properties of such an aether be described in terms of classical mechanics or not? The history of the aether theories in the second half of the nineteenth century shows that nearly all attempts at explaining the phenomena of light and electromagnetism were inspired by the hope that a satisfactory mechanical model of aether could be constructed. The very term "vibration" was taken over from mechanics and naturally suggested the idea of an elastic medium in which the waves of various lengths may arise. The mechanics of the aether seemed to be nothing essentially different from the mechanics of the elastic medium.

As late as 1881 William Thomson stated in the true Cartesian spirit that, like heat, elasticity is probably a "mode of motion." [23] The Cartesian inclinations of James Clerk Maxwell, the author of the electromagnetic theory of light, have already been mentioned; the same inclinations are present in Heinrich Hertz, who successfully tested his theory by experiment. According to him, the basic and sufficient concepts in physics are *space, time*, and *matter in motion;* the concept of energy is derived from these basic ones and the concept of force is altogether superfluous. It is true that in order to explain certain phenomena it is necessary, according to Hertz, to postulate "hidden masses" and "hidden motions," but their *only* difference from the visible masses and visible motions is that they are not perceived by human senses. It was difficult to reject dynamism and energetism more explicitly and to state the program of mechanistic explanation more clearly.

This program, as Duhem observed, remained largely just a program,[24] and the finding of a satisfactory model of the aether which would account for *all* dynamical interaction between visible bodies proved to be extremely difficult; but this only makes the persistence of the search epistemologically more significant. Certainly the electromagnetic theory of light, at least in its classical form, was regarded as a continuation of the tendencies of classical mechanism rather than as opposed to them.

The same is true of the electron theory which, at least in its first stage, was a definite vindication of atomistic thought. It is true that the Daltonian solid atom was broken into much smaller particles—electrons and protons—which seemed to be the ultimate constituent elements of matter as well as of electricity. Apparently, then, matter was reduced to electricity. But when the nature of the electron and proton was looked into more closely, a question arose which was similar to that faced by physicists in regard to the constitution of the aether: Was matter reduced to electricity or vice versa? Are not the electrons after all *rigid* particles, possessing the same basic features as the indivisible particles of classical atomism except on a much smaller scale? It is certainly significant that the first name given to the electron by one of its discoverers, J. J. Thomson, was *corpuscle*.[25] This seemed to indicate that electrons were regarded as having the same basic properties as the particles of classical atomism: space occupancy, inertia, indivisibility. The empirical evidence apparently pointed in this direction: the electrons, though exceedingly small, seemed to possess a finite radius different from zero, that is, 10^{-13} cm; J. J. Thomson measured the ratio of their mass to their charge and found it constant; the search of Ehrenhaft for the existence of *subelectrons*, that is, of particles having only a fraction of the electronic charge, proved to be futile.[26]

On the other hand, the notion of the electron, still retained by Abraham, as a rigid material particle to which its electric charge adheres, was hardly satisfactory. It was a hybrid notion, incongruously combining the atomistic idea of the rigid material particle with the dynamist idea of force. This was as unsatisfactory as when the majority of the nineteenth-century physicists accepted Newton's idea of hard particles from which the forces *à la* Boscovich mysteriously emanate; or when John Dalton imagined the irreducible qualitative properties of chemical elements sticking to the hard atoms. It remained not only unexplained but inexplainable how and in what sense the electric charge "sticks" to the surface of Abraham's atom, and Hermann Weyl was right when he called such a notion a "grotesque naïveté." [27]

It is naive not only from the point of view of modern physics, but from the classical standpoint as well. For a consistent mechanist the whole notion of the basic and irreducible distinction between matter and force (in this case between mass and electricity) was intolerable. It contradicted the basic assumptions of mechanism expounded in Chapter VI. For a consistent mechanist there was only one possible way out; to remove the alleged

duality of matter and electricity and regard them both as particular manifestations of one and the same all-pervading mechanical
medium—the *aether*. In other words, the aether was to explain
not only all instances of dynamical interaction between bodies
themselves *but the individuality of the basic physical particles
as well.*

FLUID THEORIES OF MATTER

The tendency to dissolve the individuality of the basic particles
of matter into the unity of an all-pervading cosmic medium has
a long tradition in classical thought. It is connected with the
so-called *fluid theory of matter*, which may be traced to Descartes and Hobbes. Descartes refused to regard solidity as the
ultimate property of matter; this was one of the reasons why he
remained opposed to atomism. His successors Malebranche and
Papin explained the apparent solidity of atoms by a *motus
conspirans*, that is, by the pressure of the surrounding medium;[28]
in such a view the term "atom" was no more than a figure of
speech. More recently, William Thomson's theory of "vortex-
atoms," which was proposed in 1867 and attracted a great deal
of attention, remained Cartesian in spirit.[29] On this theory the
universe is filled with a homogeneous, uniformly dense, and
perfectly mobile liquid endowed with inertia. Its movement is
ruled by Euler's equations, which in turn follow from D'Alembert's principle; what we call atoms are only steady gyrostatic
formations within this cosmic fluid. The theory was based on
Helmholtz's mathematical discovery that such vortex-rings
within the perfect fluid are *permanent*, that is, indestructible
and uncreatable: that their volume is *constant*; that they are
mutually *impenetrable*; that their shape may vary even when
their volume is constant; consequently, unlike the atoms of
Lucretius and Gassendi, they are capable of *internal vibratory
motion*. With the exception of the last property, the "vortex-
rings" simulate the most important features of the solid atoms.

It would be beyond the scope of this chapter to describe the
hopes which were stirred by this theory and the subsequent

disappointment; suffice it to say, the spirit of William Thomson was very much alive even at the time of his death forty years later. After the discovery of the electron, the problem was merely shifted. Granted that matter is reduced to atomistically conceived electricity, the question still remains: Is not the electron, which is the ultimate unit of electricity and matter at the same time, merely a certain configuration within the continuous mechanical medium of aether? As late as 1909 Oliver Lodge in a book altogether Kelvinian in spirit, *The Ether of Space,* quotes approvingly the following words of J. J. Thomson:

> The whole *mass* of any body is just the mass of ether surrounding the body which is carried along by the Faraday tubes associated with the atoms of the body. In fact, all mass is the mass of the ether; all momentum, momentum of ether; and all kinetic energy, kinetic energy of the ether [p. 116].

Oliver Lodge's later book, *Ether and Reality*, is animated by the same spirit. In the chapter significantly called "Matter as One of the Forms of Ether Energy" he again stated the same view:

> Electrons and protons are the building stones of which matter is made. The atom of matter is composed of them, and all matter is composed of atoms. Electrons are evidently composed of ether, because whatever mass they may have is represented by the energy of their electric field, which is certainly an etherial phenomenon: and apart from this field they seem to have no other existence [p. 137].

The fact that this was written as late as 1925 merely shows how persistent the mechanistic tendencies were, even when the reputation of the mechanical models of the aether was seriously impaired by the theory of relativity. In Lodge, as in Maxwell and William Thomson, we can trace the old Cartesian idea of the all-pervading subtle medium, homogeneous and fluidlike, of which ordinary matter is only a particular structural or kinetic modification. The mechanistic idea of the homogeneity of matter has been fully and consistently upheld by such theories, in which the duality of matter and electromagnetism has been only apparent and superficial, being absorbed into the unity of the aethereal medium underlying them both.

But did not the concept of the continuous fluidlike aether threaten two other fundamental properties of classical matter, that is, its *discontinuity* and its *solidity?* Are not the solid particles, whether they are called atoms or electrons, dissolved into the continuity of the all-pervading aether? Is not the fundamental distinction recognized by classical mechanism—the distinction of the *full* and the *empty*—done away with by all hydrodynamical theories of aether and "vortex theories" of matter? At first glance the answer to this last question seemed to be in the affirmative; in particular, numerous British physicists thought so. Some of them were influenced by theosophical speculations and their aether mysticism was only a modified version of the space mysticism of Newton's disciples, Clarke and Bentley.[30] But the main reason which led them to believe this was that they failed to analyze sufficiently the term "fluid." There are two possible views: the continuity and fluidity of the aethereal liquid may be regarded either (1) as an ultimate and irreducible quality of nature or (2) as a macroscopic effect of the swiftly moving extremely small particles. The first view would imply a thinly disguised return to Aristotle, for whom "liquidity" was one of the basic and ultimate qualities of nature, like "warmth," "coldness," and "dryness." A similar idea was present in Giordano Bruno's theory of the aether which, according to him, was comparable to water and whose adhesiveness accounts for the cohesive forces between the material atoms.[31]

The second view was adopted by Democritus and his seventeenth-century followers. It accepts the discontinuous structure of matter, including the aethereal matter together with the reality of the void between the aethereal atoms. Borelli had already stated explicitly that the individual particles of any liquid are themselves *not* fluid: *partes fluidum corpus componentes fluidae non sunt;*[32] in other words, the liquids are ultimately made of minute discrete corpuscles. Even more significant was Richard Hooke's experimental demonstration that when the tiny particles of some solid substance—for instance, grains of sand—are set into violent vibratory motion, the total mass will acquire all known properties of a liquid substance.

> By this means the sand in the dish, which before lay like a dull and inactive body, becomes a perfect fluid; and ye can no sooner make a hole in it with your finger, but it is immediately filled up again, and the upper surface of it leveled. Nor can ye bury a light body, as a piece of cork under it, but it presently emerges or swims, as 'twere on the top; nor can ye lay a heavier on the top of it, as a piece of lead, but it is immediately buried in sand, and (as 'twere) sinks to the bottom. Nor can ye make a hole in the side of the dish, but the sand shall run out of it to a level. Not an obvious property of a fluid body, as such, but this does imitate; and all this merely caused by the vehement agitation of the containing vessel, for by this means, each sand becomes to have a vibrative or dancing motion . . .[33]

Similarly Descartes pointed out, in anticipating the kinetic theory of matter, that the difference between the solid and the liquid substance is in the difference of the internal motion of the respective molecules, the particles of the latter having a greater mobility than those of the solid substance.[34] It is true that Descartes did not accept, as Gassendi did, the existence of the void; and we have seen that those who viewed the aether as a liquid filling continuously the whole of space followed in his footsteps. But as we shall see, neither Descartes nor his followers were consistent in this respect. Descartes in his concrete explanations always used the corpuscular language and he definitely failed to reconcile it with his denial of the void. His language betrayed him; within his complete *plenum* no motion and no differentiation is possible, as some of his modern critics convincingly pointed out and as even some of his disciples recognized. This was the case of Gerard de Cordemoy, who turned away from the Cartesian idea of continuously filled space to atomism.[35] But it was Christian Huygens who applied the strict

corpuscular-kinetic interpretation of the liquid state of matter
to the aether itself and who explicitly insisted on the solidity of
the aether-atoms separated by the minute interstices of the real
vacuum. Similarly, one century after Huygens, Lesage in his
Lucrèce newtonien postulated the discontinuous aether consisting of the fast flying particles whose impact on the bodies of
ordinary matter supposedly accounted for the fact of gravitation.[36]

In the nineteenth century, physicists were less inclined to
speak about the atomic structure of the aether, and many of
them took the expression "continuity of aether" quite literally.
This is certainly true of William Thomson. Yet it should not be
overlooked that at the end of the century the molecular constitution of liquids and gases was generally recognized; practically
nobody dared to deny that the molecules of H_2O are the same in
ice, liquid water, and water-vapor. It was accepted that the alleged continuity of water or of any liquid was merely a mathematical device enabling us to deal with huge molecular aggregates instead of the individual molecules, which are too numerous
and moving too rapidly to be traced individually. The same
method was applied in the kinetic theory of gases and the electronic theory of the electric current.

In all provinces of natural phenomena various fluids, which
were merely disguised descendants of one or another of the
Aristotelian elements, were rapidly disintegrating into their real
corpuscular constituents. The kinetic theory of matter replaced
the mysterious caloric by moving solid particles and thus reduced the differences between the three physical states to purely
quantitative differences of the internal molecular motion and of
intermolecular distances. The alleged fluidity of liquids and gases
and of the electric current was recognized as a surface phenomenon hiding from our senses the true discontinuity of discrete
and fast moving particles. I am not mentioning another fluid—
phlogiston—because its replacement by the discontinuous particles of oxygen and of other elements had already been achieved
at the beginning of the nineteenth century. It certainly would
be strange after such general bankruptcy of all fluid theories to

treat the aethereal fluid as an exceptional case. It was incomparably more plausible to interpret its alleged fluidity and continuity in the same corpuscular-kinetic sense as for all other "fluids."

This point was seen more clearly by philosophers than by scientists, especially by those philosophers who were aware of the suspicious historical roots of the term "fluid" and who saw its incompatibility with the consistent mechanistic scheme. This was especially true of the historian of atomism, Lasswitz, who pointed out correctly that even vortex theories of atoms did not necessarily entail abandoning the discontinuity of matter; they merely enormously reduced the size of the true atoms by identifying them with the particles of the aethereal medium.[37] Hydrodynamical models of gravitation proposed at the end of the classical era in physics differed from Huygens' or Hooke's hydrodynamical model of aether, proposed two centuries before, in detail rather than in substance: for while Huygens explicitly postulated the atomicity of his aether, the same postulate was implicitly present in the very term "liquid" used by James C. Maxwell, William Thomson, C. A. Bjerknes, Korn, and others.[38] Maxwell was even more explicit about this matter when he conceded, though hesitatingly and with a great deal of caution, the discontinuous structure of aether;[39] but there were also some physicists who accepted it in the true spirit of classical atomism, explicitly and unambiguously. Such a one was, for instance, Osborne Reynolds, whose *Sub-Mechanics of the Universe* appeared as late as in 1903 when classical physics was already dying.

Physicists who insisted rigorously on the continuity of the aethereal fluid, filling gaplessly the whole of space, faced another serious difficulty: How is motion possible in the *plenum?* This problem emerged at the very dawn of Western thought. The school of Elea as well as the atomists agreed that motion in the plenum is impossible; but while the Eleatics Parmenides and Zeno concluded that motion does not exist, the atomists Leucippus and Democritus inferred the existence of the void from the same premise, in order to make motion possible. Although since the seventeenth century the atomistic tradition had been prevailing in general, a considerable number of physicists and philosophers claimed that the existence of the *plenum* is compatible with the existence of motion. The attitude of young Bertrand Russell in his book about Leibniz is fairly representative of this group:

> On one minor point, however, namely the possibility of a motion in a plenum, Leibniz is unquestionably in the right. Locke had maintained that there must be empty space, or else there would be no room for motion. Leibniz rightly replies . . . that if matter be fluid, this difficulty is obviated. It should indeed be obvious, even to the non-mathematical, that motion in a closed circuit is possible for a fluid. It is a pity philosophers have allowed themselves to repeat this argument, which a week's study of hydrodynamics would suffice to dispel. The complete answer to it is contained in what is called the equation of continuity.[40]

Russell's view is characteristic of those physicists to whom advanced mathematical training is a handicap rather than an advantage because it is not supplemented by the willingness to analyze historically and epistemologically certain conceptual tools of theoretical physics. The concept of a perfect fluid is such a conceptual tool whose usefulness should not make us blind to its fictitious and artificial character. The modern defenders of the *plenum* were naturally reluctant to follow their Greek philosophical ancestors in denying the reality of motion; they were too empirically minded to go to such an extreme. But failing to realize that the continuity of any fluid is a macroscopic and superficial phenomenon which hides from our senses its corpuscular microstructure, they naturally also failed to realize that, as John Locke pointed out, the motion of the fluid particles is possible because of tiny interstices of void between them; consequently, their main effort was directed toward establishing the compatibility of the absolute plenum with the reality of motion. The solution of the difficulty which they proposed was very old, much older than Russell realized; it was proposed twenty centuries before Leibniz by Aristotle, who in his *Physics* pointed out that a circular whirl-like motion within fluid is possible without the necessity of postulating empty space. The same claim was made later by Descartes, who in his opposition to the atoms and the void followed Aristotle closely.[41]

Now it is true that in the abstract the concepts of plenum and of whirl-like motion appear compatible; nothing is easier to imagine than a portion of fluid moving within a ring-shaped channel between a stationary liquid core and an equally stationary outward ocean. But as soon as we begin to analyze the concrete examples with which Descartes tried to illustrate the compatibility of the plenum and of vortical motion, the inferiority of his view with respect to classical atomism becomes obvious. Not only can Descartes' illustrations be equally well explained by corpuscular models, but his plenist interpretation leads to the consequences which even the experience of the seventeenth century plainly refuted.

Descartes' famous illustration of his claim that motion is possible without the void is a fish swimming in an ocean; the liquid being incompressible, its portions enter the space behind a moving fish *at the same time* as other portions of the liquid are displaced in front of the moving body.[42] In other words, the pressure exerted by the motion of a moving fish is *instantaneously* transmitted along the whole body from the head to the tail. Thus the plenum theory inevitably implies the existence of instantaneous physical actions, that is, of actions spreading in space with infinite velocity. Descartes was only consistent when he claimed that light, which, according to him, consists of pressure in the aether, is being propagated with infinite velocity.[43] Only a quarter of a century had elapsed after Descartes death when Olaf Roemer showed this consequence of Cartesian physics to be wrong. On the other hand, the corpuscular theory of matter not only had no difficulty in explaining the motion of a fish in water but also correctly anticipated the finite velocity of *all* physical actions at a distance; for it is obvious that only the finite interstices of void within a spuriously continuous liquid can account for the finite velocity of propagation; in substances rigorously continuous, any transmission must be instantaneous.

Even more serious is the fact that Descartes did not always uphold his own concept of plenum consistently. Kurd Lasswitz called attention to one strange passage of his *Principia Philosophiae*, in which Descartes maintains the continuity of matter filling all interstices of space and at the same time accepts the necessity of tiny intervals between all particles of this allegedly continuous liquid:

> . . . necesse est omnes imaginabiles ejus particulas, quae sunt revera innumerae, a se mutuo aliquantulum removeri, & talis quantulacunque remotio vera divisio est.* [44]

It is clear that no such intervals can ever arise as long as space is filled in an absolute sense; thus Descartes, though he does not admit it explicitly, in fact concedes the existence of the void. For no matter how tiny the intervals separating the particles of the fluid—even if they are, speaking with John Locke, as tiny as the 100,000,000th part of a mustard seed—they constitute a real void.[45] The reason Descartes was not aware of such a serious inconsistency was that in his mind two very different concepts were fused together: geometrical divisibility of space and physical separability of particles. This was merely another unfortunate consequence of his ambiguous identification of matter with space. But this very ambiguity enabled him to use corpuscular models for the explanation of concrete natural phenomena while upholding, verbally at least, the existence of absolutely full space.

Closely related to his unfortunate confusion of *divisio* and *remotio* is the vicious circle which underlies Descartes' treatment of motion. He claims that matter must be divisible *ad infinitum* so that any interstice and corner between macroscopic bodies could be gaplessly filled; but this division of matter is operated by motion, which is the only differentiating principle

---

* All imaginable particles of it—and they are indeed countless—must keep very slightly distant from one another; and such distance, however slight, constitutes a genuine separation.

admitted by Descartes. Thus motion appears at the same time as the *condition* and the *result* of the infinite divisibility of matter!

Such uncertainties and inconsistencies seem to be characteristic not only of Descartes but of all modern defenders of the absolute plenum. Thus Leibniz, in the passage referred to approvingly by Russell, defends the Cartesian claim, according to which vortical motion within the plenum *is* possible. But Russell is evidently unaware that Leibniz in his letter to Des Bosses in 1706 criticized the same basic principle of Cartesian physics which eight years later he defended in his *Nouveaux essais sur l'entendement humain* against John Locke.[46] Leibniz pointed out that a rotational motion within a perfectly homogeneous fluid would produce no observable difference because the successive states of such liquid would remain completely undistinguishable. Thus the Cartesian theory of vortical motion within the plenum is dismissed by Leibniz as an utterly useless hypothesis unable to account for the observed variety of the physical world. The very same criticism may be applied to Willam Thomson's theory of vortex-atoms, which is so obviously Cartesian in its spirit; indeed, J. B. Stallo in his book *The Concepts and Theories of Modern Physics* raised the same objection againt Willam Thomson's theory that Leibniz raised against Cartesianism:

> There would be no phenomenal difference or change. A fluid both destitute and incapable of difference is as impossible a vehicle of real motion as pure space.[47]

Similarly Bergson, who on this point was almost certainly influenced by Stallo:

> But, if you will notice that this fluid is perfectly homogeneous, that between its parts there is neither an empty interval which separates them nor any difference whatever by which they can be distinguished, you will see that all movement taking place within this fluid is really equivalent to absolute immobility, since before, during, and after the movement nothing changes and nothing has changed in the whole.[48]

This failure to account for both phenomenal diversity and change will appear less surprising if we remember the basic Eleatic premise on which the fluid theories are based: Everything is full. From such an Eleatic premise it is extremely difficult to derive anything but the Eleatic conclusions which exclude both change and diversity, no matter how unwelcome such implications were to the empirically minded physicists who did their best to avoid them. This was easier for the physicists of the last century because they were much less dogmatic than Descartes in their insistence on the absolute plenum. Thus after insisting so vigorously on the complete absence of the void in the universe, William Thomson later accepted the hypothesis of the vortices with "vacuous cores." [49] Philosophical defenders of the plenum also showed a greater flexibility than their seventeenth-century philosophical ancestors; thus Bertrand Russell, who, as we have seen, sided with Leibniz against Locke's affirmation of the void in 1900, only three years later shared Locke's belief in the existence of empty space. [50]

All the preceding considerations lead to one conclusion: the aether theories did not represent any serious threat to the basic propositions of atomism. The basic distinction between the "full" and the "void" on which the concept of discrete particle is based, seemed to be entirely compatible with the idea of the interplanetary or intermolecular medium. A corpuscular-kinetic interpretation of such a medium remained an open possibility as long as the classical era in physics was not over. Whitehead was fully aware of it when he characterized the spirit of classical physics in the following concise paragraph:

> The answer, therefore, which the seventeenth century gave to the ancient question of the Ionian thinkers, "What is the world made of?" was that the world is a succession of instantaneous configurations of matter— *or of the material, if you wish to include stuff more subtle than ordinary matter, the ether for example.* [Italics added.] [51]

In other words, the introduction of the concept of aether did not add anything basically new to the four basic concepts already analyzed: space, time, matter, and motion.

NOTES FOR CHAPTER VII

1. Roger Boscovich, *Philosophiae naturalis redacta ad unicam legem virum in natura existentium* (*Venetiae, 1763;* English-Latin edition by J. M. Child, Chicago, Open Court, 1922), I; Kant, "Die metaphysische Anfangsründe der Naturwissenschaft," *Werke*, Bd. IV (Berlin, 1911); John Stuart Mill, *An Examination of Sir William Hamilton's Philosophy* (New York, 1874), Vol. II, pp. 242-246; J. B. Stallo, *Concepts and Theories of Modern Physics*, p. 145; E. Mach, *Science of Mechanics*, pp. 589-590 (against mechanism and kinetism in general). There is an important difference between the physical dynamism of Boscovich and Kant and positivism of Mach; Mach rejected even the concept of force, which the dynamists regarded as the very essence of matter (Mach. *op. cit.*, pp. 308, 317). But Mach was closer to dynamism than he was willing to concede; when he spoke about the "mutual dependence of bodies," did he not reintroduce action at a distance under a new name? W. Wundt (*Die physikalische Axiome und ihre Beziehungen zum allgemeinen Kausalprincip*, Erlangen, 1866, p. 32) is hardly consistent when he accepts action at a distance in spite of his general sympathy for kinetic explanations.
2. Boscovich, *op. cit.*, I, where he characterizes his own philosophy of matter as a synthesis of the views of Leibniz and Newton.
3. Cf. Chapter VI, above, Note 18.
4. Laplace's computation of the speed of gravitation as *at least* 50,000,000 times the speed of light was based on wrong assumptions. Cf. W. Wien, *Wiedemann's Annalen* (1901), pp. 501 f.
5. H. Lotze, *Grundzüge der Naturphilosophie*, 2d ed. (Leipzig, 1889), p. 26. Nevertheless, Lotze did not reject the action at a distance; in this respect his attitude is similar to that of dynamists Mill, Stallo, and Mach (*Metaphysic*, pp. 316 f.).
6. Meyerson, *Identité et Réalité*, p. 85.
7. In his resolutely antimechanistic book *L'Evolution de la Mécanique* (Paris, 1905) Duhem recommends a return if not to the letter, at least to the spirit of the Aristotelian physics. Cf. the chapter "La physique de la qualité," pp. 197-208; also pp. 218-19.
8. Kurd Lasswitz ("Die Rechtfertigung der kinetischen Atomistik," *Vierteljahrschrift für wissenschaftliche Philosophie*, IX, 1885, pp. 145-47), speaks about *latent atomism* of dynamists. He points out how Kant in his book *Vom Übergange von den metaphysischen Anfangsgründen zur Naturwissenschaften* used corpuscular views for concrete explanations—for instance, for explaining the solidification of liquids.

9. Cf. M. Faraday, "A Speculation Concerning Electric Conduction and the Nature of Matter" in *Experimental Researches in Electricity* (London, Taylor, 1839-55), Vol. II, pp. 284 f., especially p. 290. On the other hand in his essay "Some Thoughts on the Conservation of Force" he approvingly quotes Newton's third letter to Bentley in which the basic idea of dynamism that gravity is an inherent property of matter is rejected, and he adds: "I do not oppose Newton at any point; it is rather those who sustain the idea of action at a distance that contradict him." In *The Correlation and Conservation of Physical Forces*, by Grove, Helmholtz, Mayer, Faraday, Liebig and Carpenter (New York, Appleton, 1871), p. 378.

10. Spencer's view that matter is a manifestation of force has an obvious similarity to Boscovich's theory, to which Spencer explicitly refers (*First Principles*, 4th ed., pp. 54-57). Spencer, however, rejected Boscovich's idea of action at a distance. This is at least implied in his interpretation of gravity as an "ethereal strain" (p. 190) and his refusal to regard potential energy as autonomous and irreducible (Appendix, pp. 598-599).

11. Faraday, *Experimental Researches*, Vol. II, pp. 284 f.; G. T. Fechner, *Über die physikalische und philosophische Atomenlehre* (Leipzig, 1855). About the development of dynamism from Leibniz to Spencer cf. M. Jammer, *Concepts of Force*, Chap. 9.

12. M. Jammer, *loc. cit.*; L. Couturat in his review of A. Hannequin's book *Essai critique sur l'hypothèse des atomes dans la science contemporaine* in *Revue de métaphysique et de morale*, Vol. V (1897), p. 106; B. Russell, *Principles of Mathematics*, p. 468: "A simple material unit occupies a spatial point at any moment." The same hypostatization of geometrical points is contained in the following passage of G. Cantor: quoted approvingly by A. Grünbaum in *Analysis* XII (1951-52), p. 146: "In order to achieve a more satisfactory description of nature, the ultimate or genuinely simple elements must be postulated as *actually infinite in number* and they must be regarded *as completely devoid of extension* and strictly pointlike" ("als völlig ausdehnungslos und streng punctuell zu betrachten sind"). Cantor is aware of the similarity of his view with those of Ampère, Faraday, Weber, and Leibniz. Cf. G. Cantor, "Über verschiedene Theoreme aus der Theorie der Punktmengen," *Acta Mathematica*, VII (1885), pp. 105-124.

13. E. Mach, *The Science of Mechanics*, pp. 590, 597-98; J. B. Stallo, *op. cit., passim.*

14. W. Ostwald, *Die Überwindung des wissenschaftlichen Materialismus* (Leipzig, 1895).

15. It is not entirely fair to accuse Spencer of "extreme vagueness and almost unparalleled laxity in the use of the term force" as M. Jammer does (*op. cit.*, p. 186). It is true that Spencer uses this term in three different senses, but they are all carefully defined and differentiated: (*a*) "space-occupying force" which is "passive and dependent"; this is clearly only another term for impenetrability; (*b*) force manifest-

ing itself in motions whether molar or molecular. Spencer is perfectly aware that this kind of force is also called "energy" (*op. cit.*, p. 195). (*c*) The third meaning is philosophical: "Force" or "Ultimate Power" is a designation for the noumenal correlate of all phenomenal manifestations and as such it is irrelevant for physical considerations. If we accuse Spencer of using the term "force" for what we call today "energy," we should be equally severe to a number of outstanding physicists of his time who did the same thing even in the very titles of their books: R. Mayer, *Bemerkungen über die Kräfte der unbelebten Natur* (1842); H. Helmholtz, *Über die Erhaltung der Kraft* (1847); M. Faraday, "Some Thoughts on Conservation of Force" (1871) and as recently as 1909 A. Haas's historical study *Die Entwicklungsgeschichte des Satzes über die Erhaltung der Kraft*.

16. H. Spencer, *op. cit.*, p. 291.
17. H. Spencer, "M. Martineau on Evolution," *Contemporary Review*, XX (June 1872), p. 143. About Spencer's view of potential energy, see above, Note 10.
18. See above, Note 15.
19. A. Spencer, *op. cit.*, p. 196.
20. *Ibid.*, p. 165.
21. H. Driesch, *Naturbegriffe und Natururteile* (Leipzig, 1904), p. 106.
22. P. Duhem, *L'Evolution de la mécanique*, p. 179.
23. W. Thomson, "Steps toward Kinetic Theory of Matter," *Popular Lectures and Addresses* (New York, Macmillan, 1891-94), I, pp. 218-252; especially pp. 243-44.
24. H. Hertz, *Die Principien der Mechanik* (Leipzig, 1884), p. 30; P. Duhem, *op. cit.*, pp. 157-168.
25. N. R. Campbell, *Modern Electrical Theory* (Cambridge, 1914), p. 110; E. T. Whittaker, *A History of the Theories of Aether and Electricity*, Vol. I, pp. 361-66.
26. About Ehrenhaft's experiments, cf. R. Bär, "Der Streit um das Elektron," *Naturwissenschaften*, Bd. 10 (1922), pp. 344-350.
27. H. Weyl, *Was ist Materie?* (Berlin, 1924), p. 18.
28. Huygens, *Œuvres complètes*, Vol. IX (Hague, 1901), p. 429; Paul Mouy, *Le Développement de la physique cartésienne* (Paris, 1934), pp. 282-92.
29. W. Thomson, "On Vortex Atoms," *Proc. Royal Soc. Edinburgh* (Feb. 18, 1867). About the Cartesian character of W. Thomson's theory, K. Lasswitz, "Über Wirbelatome und stetige Raumerfüllung," *Vierteljahrschr. f. wissenchaftl. Philosophie*, III (1879), p. 275; E. Meyerson, *Identité et Réalité*, pp. 279-80; P. Duhem, *op. cit.*, p. 177.
30. O. Lodge, *Ether and Reality*, Chap. X, "Life and Mind and Their Use of the Ether," with the characteristic quotations from Newton, Larmor, and Maxwell.
31. Lasswitz, *Geschichte der Atomistik*, I, pp. 377-80.
32. Quoted by Lasswitz, *ibid.*, II, p. 307; I. Newton, *Opticks*, Book III, Quest. 31; "All Bodies seem to be composed of hard Particles; otherwise fluids would not congeal."

33. Quoted by W. Bragg, *Concerning the Nature of Things* (New York, Harper, 1925), pp. 16-17.
34. Descartes, *Principia Philosophiae*, II, 54, 56.
35. Lasswitz, *Geschichte der Atomistik*, II, pp. 417-19; P. Mouy, *op. cit.*, 103.
36. Cf. Note 13 in Chapter VI, above.
37. Lasswitz, "Über Wirbelatome . . .", pp. 206-215; 275-294, especially pp. 279 f.; A. Hannequin, *Essai critique sur l'hypothèse des atomes dans la science contemporaine*, p. 245; "La particule d'éther apparaissait donc bien, au terme de l'analyse, comme l'atome véritable. . . ."
38. On Hooke's theory of gravitation, cf. J. C. Maxwell, "Attraction," *Scientific Papers*, II, p. 490. About Bjerknes's and Korn's theories of gravitation, cf. E. T. Whittaker, *op. cit.*, I, pp. 284-85.
39. Maxwell, "Ether," *op. cit.*, II, p. 774: "The ether, if it is a medium of electromagnetic phenomena, *is probably molecular*, at least in this sense" (i.e., it contains molecular vortices. Italics added). Cf. Mary B. Hesse, "Action at a Distance in Classical Physics," *Isis*, Vol. 46 (1955), p. 337.
40. B. Russell, *The Philosophy of Leibniz* (Cambridge University Press, 1900), p. 93, note. Leibniz's replies are found in the *New Essays on the Human Understanding*, pp. 53-54; *Monadology* (edited by R. Latta), p. 385; and Gerhardt's collection, *Philosophische Schriften*, Vol. V, p. 52.
41. Aristotle, *Physica*, IV, 7; Descartes, *Principia*, II, 33.
42. Descartes, *ibidem:* "Hocque facile intelligimus in circulo perfecto, qui videmus nullum vacuum, nullamque rarefactionem aut condensationem requiri, ut pars circuli A moveatur versus B, modo *eodem tempore* pars B moveatur versus C, C versus D, ac D versus A." [We see this easily in the case of a perfect circle, when no void and no rarefaction or condensation are needed for part A of the circle to move toward part B, if only *at the same time* part B moves toward C, C toward D, and D toward A.] (Italics added.) Cf. also *Le Monde ou le Traité de la Lumière*, Chap. IV.
43. *Ibid.*, III, 63.
44. K. Lasswitz, *Geschichte der Atomistik*, II, 97-109; Descartes, *Principia Phil.*, II, 34.
45. J. Locke, *Essay*, Book II, Chap. XIII, § 23, "Motion proves vacuum."
46. Leibniz, in C. J. Gerhardt, *Leibnizens Philosophische Schriften*, V, p. 52.
47. Leibniz, *Phil. Schriften*, II, p. 295; J. B. Stallo, *op. cit.*, p. 44.
48. Bergson, *Time and Free Will*, p. 206.
49. E. T. Whittaker, *op. cit.*, I, p. 303 note.
50. Russell, *Principles of Mathematics*, p. 449: "Both being and existence belong, I believe, to empty space."
51. *Science and the Modern World* (New York, Macmillan, 1926), p. 73.

VIII · THE IMPLICIT ELIMINATION OF TIME IN CLASSICAL PHYSICS

THE LAPLACIAN TIMELESS FORMULA

IT IS obvious that succession is not the only relation between different configurations of material. As Whitehead says in the passage immediately following the one quoted at the end of Chapter VII, "the configurations determined their own changes, so that the circle of scientific explanation was completely closed." In other words, any instantaneous configuration of an isolated system logically implies all future configurations of the system. Its future history is thus virtually contained in its present state, which, in its turn, is logically contained in its past states. What is true of any isolated system must be true of the whole universe, provided that the universe itself possesses the character of an isolated system. The last supposition was more or less tacitly accepted in the classical science no matter whether the total mass of the universe was believed to be infinite or finite. In this respect there is no difference between the infinitist philosophy of Giordano Bruno, Descartes, Spinoza, and others, and the finitism of Eugene Dühring and Friedrich Nietzsche. They all adhered to rigorous determinism, which found its most precise expression in the famous and frequently quoted passage of Laplace:

121

An intellect which at a given instant knew all the forces acting in nature, and the position of all things of which the world consists—supposing the said intellect were vast enough to subject these data to analysis—would embrace in the same formula the motions of the greatest bodies in the universe and those of the slightest atoms; nothing would be uncertain for it, and the future, like the past would be present to its eyes.[1]

Underlying this Laplacian concept of causality, which has become an article in the orthodox creed of classical science, is the claim that the history of the physical universe can be represented as a mathematically continuous series of instantaneous states, each state being represented by an instantaneous configuration of a fantastically large number of simultaneous corpuscular entities with sharply definable positions and velocities; each of these configurations is implied by any previous one while in turn it implies any future one.

Thus the classical concept of causality presupposes the whole set of already analyzed classical ideas: (*a*) spatiotemporal continuity, (*b*) absolute simultaneity of even the most distant events, and (*c*) corpuscles with their positions and velocities sharply definable. This is basically the *corpuscular-kinetic view of reality*, which in its broader sense includes even the so-called dynamic theory of matter, as well as the energetic and electromagnetic theories. The basic scheme remains the same no matter whether the ultimate entities are atoms, electrons, aether-particles, simple points of force or pointlike energetic states which, though without any finite volume, still are by their own nature differentiated from the geometrical positions they occupy. This is why Whitehead's term "material" is so comprehensive that it applies to all physical entities, whether they are punctual as in the fluid-theories or have a definite finite radius as in various kinds of atomism.

It is hardly surprising that the first precise formulation of rigorous determinism appeared together with the first clear outline of the corpuscular-kinetic view of nature. The historical connection is not accidental; it exhibits a logical relation.

Twenty-two centuries before Laplace, Democritus unambiguously stated that "by necessity are foreordained all things that were, are, and will be." [2] The only difference between Greek atomism and nineteenth-century physics was that the latter had incomparably more efficient technical and conceptual tools at its disposal than Democritus and Leucippus; the vague necessity (ἀνάγκη) of Greek atomism has been replaced by the precise conservation laws of modern dynamics.[3] Fundamentally, however, the basic conceptions were the same. This was the deep historical reason why the birth of modern science occurred simultaneously with the revival of atomism by Bruno, Bacon, Gassendi, and others.[4]

Physical reality was regarded both by ancient and modern atomists as made of homogeneous particles which, though moving through space, remained eternally the same. Only their distances, i.e., their relations in empty space, were changing; but it is highly significant that the empty space was called Non-Being in opposition to the solid Being of matter. Thus the change of distances in empty space was regarded as taking place in Non-Being. As this Non-Being was regarded as existing in a certain sense, it is clear that the reality of change was not completely eliminated; but as the void did not possess a reality of equal rank with that of solid and substantial matter, motion shared with the void its spectral and half-real character. In other words, change, though not completely abolished, was only admitted in a halfhearted and innocuous way; motion being defined as a change of relation in Non-Being evidently did not affect the eternal sameness of the basic material reality. Thus change and succession retained merely a shadowy existence, a sort of half-existence, hovering hesitatingly between the full Being of matter and pure nothingness, sliding as it were on the smooth surfaces of hard and impenetrable atoms. Or in Whitehead's less metaphorical terms:

> This fact that the material is indifferent to the division of time leads to the conclusion *that the lapse of time is an accident, rather than of the essence of the material.*

> The material is fully itself in any sub-period however short. Thus the transition of time has nothing to do with the character of the material. The material is equally itself at an instant of time. Here an instant of time is conceived as in itself without transition, since the temporal transition is the succession of instants. [Italics added.] [5]

In this passage, Whitehead shows how the indifference of matter to time, that is, its quantitative constancy and qualitative unchangeability, is related to the infinite divisibility of time. We have already discussed this point in showing how the unity of matter in time was a consequence of the homogeneity, i.e., the mathematical continuity of time. Thus the lapse of time is a mere accident: matter and its laws are the same whether we consider them within cosmic aeons or within excessively minute intervals of time. We have seen that this was the basic postulate of classical physics.[6]

This accidental and superficial character of time in the mechanistic scheme can be demonstrated in another way. Causes imply their effects; but conversely as well, from effects causes can be derived. The causal relation is not only a logical implication but also a tautologous implication (equivalence). From any particular state of the universe, not only any of its future states but also any past state is derivable. In virtue of the law of causality not only is it possible to anticipate the future in all its details, but even the past can be reconstructed completely, provided all the features of the present state are fully known.

Thus the Laplacian timeless formula is the key to the knowledge of both the future and the past. For an astronomer who desires to know the past positions of the moon, it is sufficient to substitute a negative sign for time in his equation.[7] But if this is so, then the direction of time has hardly any meaning in rational mechanics, which in the classical era had become an ideal model for other sciences to imitate. Causal relation being logically symmetrical, there seems to be no intrinsic difference between the two directions of time, or, if there is any difference, it seems to be unaccountable for by the definition of causality as a tautologous implication. According to our sensory perception, the direction "from the past to the future" is qualitatively different from the opposite one; according to classical mechanics, the difference is comparable to the conventional difference between a plus and a minus sign in analytical geometry.

But if the asymmetry of time is abolished, is not time itself eliminated?

THE REVERSIBILITY OF CLASSICAL TIME

We face the same question when we approach the problem of reversibility of time from a more concrete angle. We have seen that the logical equivalence of cause and effect obliterates or tends to obliterate the distinction between the past and the future. It is equally significant that this distinction (the "direction of time") loses its objective meaning in the corpuscular-kinetic model of the universe with which the doctrine of causal necessity has been traditionally associated. If the differences between the successive phases of the world history are due merely to the differences between the spatial configurations of the immutable particles, then the so-called "irreversibility of time" becomes nothing more than an extremely small probability that an identical configuration, representing the state of the world at a given instant, will recur again. But even such an extreme improbability is not an impossibility; on the contrary, with unlimited time at our disposal, it becomes a *necessity*, at least if we rigorously adhere to the view of the finite atomistic universe. Nietzsche, who was greatly influenced by the dynamic atomism of Boscovich, expressed the idea of eternal recurrence in words of unsurpassed eloquence in various passages of the book *Also sprach Zarathustra* and in a less colorful form in his *Wille zur Macht*:

> If the universe may be conceived as a definite quantity of energy, as a definite number of centers of energy— and every other concept remains indefinite and therefore useless—it follows therefore that the universe must go through a calculable number of combinations in the

great game of chance which constitutes its existence. In infinity, at some moment or other, every possible combination must once have been realized; not only this, but it must have been realized an infinite number of times. And inasmuch as between every one of these combinations and its next recurrence every other possible combination would necessarily have been undergone, and since every one of these combinations would determine the whole series in the same order, a circular movement of absolutely identical series is thus demonstrated: the universe is thus shown to be a circular movement which has already repeated itself an infinite number of times, and which plays its game for all eternity.[8]

Or, as Bergson says in a clear and concise way:

Now, we say that a composite object changes by the displacement of it parts. But when a part has left its position, there is nothing to prevent its return to it. A group of elements which has gone through a state can therefore always find its way back to that state, if not by itself, at least by means of an external cause able to restore everything to its place. This amounts to saying that any state of the group may be repeated as often as desired, and consequently that the group does not grow old. *It has no history*. [Italics added.] [9]

In its radical form the idea of eternal recurrence was defended not only by Nietzsche but by some other thinkers who certainly cannot be suspected of having an excess of poetic imagination: Henri Poincaré in 1890, Ernst Zermelo in 1896, Abel Rey as late as in 1927.[10] According to Poincaré's "theorem of phases" a mechanical system, no matter how complex it may be, given a sufficiently long time, must pass an infinite number of times through a configuration which is infinitely close to a configuration through which it has already passed. From the nature of the probability laws it follows that even the least probable combination will eventually occur; or, in the recent words of Reichenbach:

This is an essential feature of probability sequences: every combination of attributes that has a non-zero probability must occur with that non-zero frequency. When we throw a die often enough, a run of a thousand throws showing face 6 on top must eventually occur, because the probability of such a run, though very low, is larger than zero. When we shuffle a deck of cards just after putting all the red cards on top of the black ones, we shall transform this ordered state into a mixture; but if we shuffle long enough, we must by pure chance eventually come back to the original state, because the probability of arriving at such an arrangement is larger than zero.[11]

The assumption is, of course, that the universe is a pack of cards, that is, an aggregate of distinct entities persisting through time without any intrinsic change. This, as we have seen, is the very essence of the corpuscular-kinetic model of nature. In a less radical and more diluted form the reversibility of time was upheld by the rest of the nineteenth-century thinkers who were imbued by the spirit of classical physics. It is sufficient to mention two once famous men—Herbert Spencer and Svante Arrhenius. According to the former, cosmic history as a whole is without any definite direction; periods of evolution will endlessly alternate with periods of dissolution:

And thus there is suggested the conception of a past, during which there have been successive Evolutions analogous to that which is now going on; and a future during which successive other such Evolutions may go on—*ever the same in principle but never the same in concrete results*. [Italics added.] [12]

Similarly, Svante Arrhenius in conscious agreement with Herbert Spencer insisted on the cyclical character of cosmic "history." [13] In agreement with nearly all the nineteenth-century cosmogonists he claimed that the universe is an eternally running mechanism, developing "from nebula to nebula" in a never-ending series of cycles.

This idea of the periodicity of worlds, which again in its essential features was anticipated by some pre-Socratic philosophers, faced one serious obstacle: the second law of thermodynamics, according to which the universe is moving inexorably toward the state of "heat death" in which all differences of temperature will be leveled, and cosmic energy, though indestructible and quantitatively the same, will be uniformly dissipated throughout space. It is significant how persistently the majority of the classical scientists, especially those who were philosophically minded, tried to escape the consequences of the second law of thermodynamics. Various devices were postulated by which, to use Arrhenius' term, "the clockwork of the universe" could be rewound; more specifically, by which a sufficiently high temperature, prevailing in the original Laplacian nebula, could be produced. It would be useless to survey *all* these hypothetical constructions, some of which were ingenious, some plausible, and some queer; one specimen for each category will be sufficient for illustration.

The most plausible way to "rewind the universe," at least on a local scale, was by means of cosmic clashes. Spencer mentioned that under certain conditions a clash of dark cold bodies is sufficient to transform them into a gaseous mass. Croll and Ritter tried to find more specific mechanical conditions for such occurrences by which the origin of nebulae may be explained. Croll found that velocities of 200 miles per second would be sufficient to convert the clashing bodies into vapors creating heat which would last 50 million years.[14]

More ingenious was the hypothesis of Arrhenius. In order to support the classical idea of the reversibility of cosmic history, he used a timely discovery whose significance really pointed *beyond* the classical conceptual framework: the pressure of radiation. According to him, the universe would tend to form a single huge cold body if the concentrating effect of gravitation and the dissipating effect of the law of entropy increase were to go on unchecked; but fortunately the pressure of radiation counteracts the concentrating effect of gravitation, while at the same time it carries fine cosmic dust into distant nebulae and raises their temperature, creates new nuclei of condensation processes, and thus produces a local decrease of entropy.[15] The queerest hypothesis was proposed by Rankine. Its purpose was the same, as is clearly indicated by the title of his paper: *On the Reconcentration of the Mechanical Energy of the Universe.*[16] But his idea of the "reflecting walls of the universe" which would prevent the radiation from escaping into the infinite void surrounding the cosmic mass, was evidently too artificial and adventurous to be regarded seriously.

By its very queerness Rankine's attempt showed to what desperate expedients some physicists were willing to resort in order to escape the idea of irreversible cosmic time. In one chapter of his classical work Emile Meyerson showed convincingly that underlying this reluctance to accept the consequence of the law of entropy-increase for the whole universe was a deep-seated philosophical rather than scientific conviction about the *cyclical* character of cosmic time, the character which is implied in the very essence of the corpuscular-kinetic scheme.[17] This explains the great satisfaction felt among philosophically minded scientists when it was fully realized that the law of entropy is merely a *statistical law* which indicates only the probability of occurrences. Probability laws by their very nature do not exclude even the most improbable occurrence; consequently a decrease of entropy, though improbable, is not impossible. The study of Brownian motion showed that on the molecular level it is meaningless to speak about the law of entropy because the elementary mechanical processes are reversible, and a slower particle may gain kinetic energy at the expense of the particles with a greater amount of kinetic energy.[18] This would be a violation of the second law of thermodynamics *if* the latter were not a probability law. In other words, the second law of thermodynamics is meaningful only on a *macroscopic* scale where processes containing an enormous number of elementary particles occur; on the molecular scale it is of no use because the very concept of temperature is a macroscopic one.

But this is not the only limitation. If the very nature of probability laws implies that even the most improbable events must occur, it is possible that even on a macroscopic scale some extremely improbable processes not only can but eventually *must* occur: not only may there be regions where there *is* a local decrease of entropy; there may even exist, according to Boltzmann, regions where even on a macroscopic scale entropy decreases, and time, so to speak, is "running backwards." It is true that such regions must be enormously far away in space from our world where the entropy increases; but even if that distance were, for instance $10^{10^{10}}$ times the distance of Sirius from our solar system, it would be a *finite* distance and it would not make a "backwards running time" less real.

By the same probability considerations it was also concluded that even our region of the universe must eventually pass through an improbable stage in which entropy would decrease and time would move in the opposite direction. Thus, the law of entropy underlying the irreversibility of time not only is meaningless on a molecular level, but even on a cosmic scale cannot be universally valid. In Boltzmann's words, "for the whole universe the two directions of time are indistinguishable" in the same sense as in cosmic space itself there is no intrinsic distinction between up and down.[19] Although Boltzmann was less explicit on this point, his abolition of the distinction between the past and the future is, implicitly at least, as radical as that presented in the magnificent Nietzschean vision of eternal recurrence.

There was one silent assumption underlying all the claims about the reversibility of time and the possibility of the identical repetition of one particular moment of the world history. This assumption is known by the name of *the relational theory of time*. A brief reference to it has already been made in Chapter III. The relational theory states that the moments of time are differentiated only by *observable differences* between the corresponding states of the universe. In other words, if there are two states of world history which are in *all* respects identical, then their difference and even their "twoness" is *merely verbal*; there are only two different names for one and the same state. Because in the corpuscular-kinetic scheme of the universe "the states" are defined in the terms of configurations and velocities of particles, it is evident that two states of the universe characterized by the same distribution of particles possessing the same velocities are only verbally two; they would be one and the same state. In other words, the universe would in such a case run a full circle and it would literally, not only metaphorically, return into the previous state.

The contrast with the absolutist theory of time, represented by Barrow and Newton, is obvious. In Newton's theory two successive moments of time remain successive *even if all physical events occupying these moments are completely identical.* Even if the universe were to return into the same state, characterized by a very improbable but not impossible recurrence of the same configuration of its basic units, time itself would not return; the two moments, though having the same physical content, would remain incurably successive. This naturally follows from the separation of time from its content in the absolutist theory. In the relational theory the *relation of succession itself* is defined by recognizable (in principle at least) physical differences; applying Leibniz' *principium indiscernibilium* [the identity of indiscernibles], the adherents of the relational theory claimed that two states which are identical in *all* respects cannot be different and consequently cannot even be successive.

The relational theory of time was first clearly formulated by Lucretius, undoubtedly under the influence of his Greek teacher Epicurus:

> So, too, time hath no being by itself,
> But 'tis from things we grasp a sense of that
> Which in the past was set, or what for us
> Today doth hold, tomorrow hath in store.
> Then too, thou must perforce confess that none
> Can e'er perceive time by itself, apart
> From things which move or stand in quiet rest.[20]

The substance of the argument has not changed through the centuries, and when Boltzmann at the end of the last century insisted that the "direction of time," i.e., the distinction between the past and the future, is inapplicable to the whole of the universe and that even on a local scale is defined only in terms of the passage from a less probable to a more probable state, he only restated in modern language Lucretius' claim about the inseparability of time from "things," to wit, from the elementary material particles. But with equal emphasis, the defenders of the absolutist theory from Newton to young Russell[21] claimed the independence of time from its content or, more specifically, the independence of *the direction of time* from the direction and orientation of concrete physical processes, which may be reversed without causing a reversal of the time-direction. This conflict, sometimes latent, sometimes acute (as in the famous Leibniz-Clarke controversy), remained unresolved throughout the whole classical era and in a different form is present even after the foundations of classical physics have been swept away.

Although the relational theory of time has never definitely prevailed over the absolutist theory, its influence was sufficiently strong to account for the general tendency *not* to include time among the basic physical entities. This explains the fact that even the absolutists were wavering in their defense of absolute time. An instructive example of such hesitation may be found at the very dawn of the classical era. In his views about space and time, Pierre Gassendi was a predecessor of Newton and was regarded as such by Newton himself.[22] The Newtonian independence of space and time from their concrete physical content was clearly expressed by him when he stated that, while matter was created in time, space was *always* in existence; in other words, space and time are not only logically, but even temporally prior to the material universe. It is therefore even more startling to hear from the same author the statement which reduces time to a mere mode of thought, and characterizes it as a mere *accidens accidentium*.[23]

But this obvious contradiction will become less surprising when we remember that the roots of the relational theory of time are in the atomistic-kinetic scheme of Epicurus and Lucretius which Gassendi was reviving. If, as Lucretius wrote, "time is nothing by itself," being merely a function of shifting and, in this sense, accidental configurations of particles, it is no wonder that it was called "accident of accidents" by the disciple of Epicurus. As long as the universe is regarded as an aggregate of the immutable elements, merely changing their positions in space, it cannot possess any real history; thus what we call the direction of time is a local phenomenon which loses its significance on the cosmic scale. When in the twentieth century Russell, Reichenbach, and others expressed doubts about the existence of cosmic time,[24] they merely pursued the path opened by the classical relational theory of time. From regarding time as an accident of accidents to its complete denial there is only one small step.

NOTES FOR CHAPTER VIII

1. Laplace, *Introduction à la théorie analytique des probabilités, Œuvres Complètes* (Paris, 1886), p. VI.
2. C. Bailey, *The Greek Atomists and Epicurus*, pp. 120-21.
3. Cf. Chapter V, above, especially notes 12 and 13 about the foreshadowing of the law of inertia and conservation of momentum by the early atomists.
4. Many modern scientists who are proud of their empirical verifications of atomism tend to exaggerate the differences between the "speculative" atomism of the Greeks and "empirical" atomism of the nineteenth century. But the continuity between the two forms of atomism is undeniable, and the difference between them is only that of degree; the seventeenth-century atomism of Gassendi, Boyle, and Newton represents an intermediate, half-empirical, half-speculative stage between Democritus and Dalton. Cf. K. Lasswitz, *Geschichte der Atomistik*, II, *passim*; F. A. Lange, *The History of Materialism* (New York, Humanity Press, 1950), II, p. 240; E. Meyerson, *Identité et Réalité*, p. 87; *De l'explication dans les sciences*, II, pp. 321-2 (against the doubts of L. Büchner and M. Smoluchowski concerning the continuity between ancient and modern atomism).
5. A. N. Whitehead, *Science and the Modern World*, p. 73.
6. W. Thomson, "The Size of Atoms," *Popular Lectures and Addresses*, I, p. 150 (about the impossibility of any limit to the divisibility of space and time).
7. This was stressed by E. Du Bois Reymond, "Über die Grenzen des Naturerkennens," *Wissenschaftliche Vorträge*, ed. by J. H. Gore (Boston, Ginn, 1896), p. 38.
8. *The Will to Power* in *The Complete Works of Friedrich Nietzsche* (Edinburgh and London, Foulis, 1913), Vol. IX, p. 430.
9. Bergson, *Creative Evolution*, p. 11.

10. H. Poincaré, "Sur le problème des trois corps et les équations de la dynamique," *Acta mathematica*, XIII (1890), especially pp. 69-72; E. Zermelo, "Über einen Satz der Dynamik und die mechanische Wärmetheorie," *Ann. der Physik u. Chemie*, Bd. 57 (1896), pp. 485-94; A. Rey, *Le retour éternel et la philosophie de la physique* (Paris, 1927).

11. H. Reichenbach, *The Direction of Time*, ed. by Maria Reichenbach (University of California Press, 1956), p. 111.

12. H. Spencer, *First Principles*, p. 550.

13. Svante Arrhenius, *Worlds in the Making*, tr. by H. Borns (New York, Harper, 1908), p. 209.

14. S. Arrhenius, *Die Vorstellung der Weltgebäude im Wandel der Zeiten* (Leipzig, 1908), p. 169. About similar computations of Ritter, cf. *Worlds in the Making*, p. 162.

15. Arrhenius, *Worlds in the Making*, pp. 194-195.

16. *Phil. Mag.* IV, 4 (1852), pp. 552 f.

17. Meyerson, *Identité et Réalité*, Chap. VIII, especially pp. 301 f.

18. E. Meyerson, *op. cit.*, p. 313; Jean Perrin, *Les Atomes*, 2d ed. (Paris, 1927), pp. 121-22.

19. L. Boltzmann, *Vorlesungen über die Gastheorie* (Leipzig, 1898), II, pp. 257-58.

20. Lucretius, *De rerum natura*, I, vv. 459-465. A new translation by C. A. Bennet (W. J. Black, New York, 1946).

21. Cf. B. Russell, "Is Position in Space and Time Absolute or Relative?", *Mind*, Vol. X (1901), pp. 293-317.

22. Cf. Chapter III, above, Note 7.

23. Cf. Chapter V, above, Note 15 and Chapter III, Note 7.

24. B. Russell (*Outlines of Philosophy*, London, Allen & Unwin, 1927, p. 114) speaks of the "abolition" of cosmic time. Reichenbach agrees with L. Boltzmann in his view about "the sectional nature of time direction": "It follows that we cannot speak of a direction for time as a whole; only certain sections of time have directions, and these directions are not the same." (*The Direction of Time*, p. 127.)
directions are not the same." (*The Direction of Time*, p. 127.) A similar view was expressed by M. Schlick, *Grundzüge der Naturphilosophie* (Wien, 1948), pp. 105-107.

IX · THE ULTIMATE CONSEQUENCES OF MECHANISM

In the classical model physical reality was constituted by four fundamental entities: space, time, matter, and motion. All other concepts, including that of energy and momentum, were derived ones; similarly, attempts to reduce the number of basic entities to fewer than four were not successful. The Cartesian attempt to reduce matter and motion to purely spatial characteristics had as little success as the attempt of the relational theory of time to reduce time to motion. For psychological reasons, the concept of matter sometimes obscured the concept of void, or both concepts obscured that of motion; and nearly always the concepts of space, matter, and motion tended to obscure that of time. The void appeared as a diaphanous entity in contrast to tangible matter, but it still retained visual and geometrical characteristics, which to the Cartesian school and its modern descendants appeared as the only reality. Likewise, matter and space, in virtue of their constancy and immutability, seemed to be less elusive than motion. Tactile sensations disclosed the reality of matter, visual sensations the reality of space. Since visual and kinesthetic sensations disclosed the reality of motion, motion, too, was a sensory datum.

But to what sensory datum did the reality of time correspond? It can neither be touched nor seen; it manifests itself most con-

135

spicuously in the auditory sensations which, since the times of the ancient atomists, have been excluded from physical reality; or in the emotional introspective qualities which by definition do not belong to the physical world. It is true that in the sensory perception of motion we concretely experience succession and that the concept of motion presupposes the concept of time; but it is psychologically understandable that this logical order was forgotten and, as motion in the form of spatial displacement was more accessible to perception and imagination, it was made the very basis of the concept of time in the relational theory.

This tendency to eliminate time or, at least, to degrade it to a secondary and derived entity, was strengthened by certain in-grained features of our conceptual thinking. The *tendency to spatialize time* may be traced to the very dawn of Western thought and reached its culmination in classical Newtonian physics. Though at the beginning of the classical era, time was still regarded as ultimately or even divinely real, nearly all of its attributes were believed to be comparable to the attributes of space. Time was believed to share its homogeneity, infinity, and mathematical continuity with space. The only differentiating feature was a different number of dimensions and the difference between the relation of juxtaposition and that of succession; but as the relation before-after was again symbolized by spatial juxtaposition, the very essence of temporality was unconsciously, and sometimes against the explicit denials of philosophers and scientists, converted into a timeless and spatial entity, into "the fourth dimension of space" in the sense of D'Alembert and Lagrange.[1] In this fourth dimension, so-called future events literally pre-exist, and only the limitations of human knowledge prevent us from perceiving them as *coexisting* with the present moment instead of as *not yet existing*. It is thus significant that two bolder contemporaries of Newton—Spinoza and Male-branche—dropped time from the basic properties of the divine, that is, of the ultimate reality, although they continued to list space among them.

The example of Spinoza shows that parallel to the tendency which subordinated time to space ran the tendency to explain

change in terms of substance, or *becoming in terms of being.*
Indeed, the spatialization of time was merely a special form of
this second tendency. If Parmenides was the first to propose
a radical conversion of becoming into being, his disciple and
defender Zeno was the first to treat temporal intervals as geometrical segments. It would be repetitious to dwell on the genetic
relation between the Eleatic and corpuscular-kinetic model of
reality. Although less radical than the school of Elea, atomism,
ancient as well as modern, retained the basic Eleatic belief in
the constancy of being which in its quantity as well as quality
is not subject to any change; change, though not completely
denied, retained a half-spurious character, as it did not affect the
ultimate units of material substance. It would be equally repetitious to stress again how, when motion itself became an object
of scientific study in the seventeenth century, it was explained
as a logical consequence of the laws of conservation; in other
words, how motion itself became substantialized under the names
of momentum and energy. Various conservation laws are different variations of the same basic theme: a certain substantial
quantum remains constant while its constitutive parts change
their places in space. The quantity of matter remains the same,
but its parts change their spatial relations; the quantity of motion
is preserved, but its spatial distribution changes; the quantity of
energy remains constant, but its spatial distribution varies.

Thus in both the laws of conservation, and in particular in
the law of the conservation of energy from which the law of the
conservation of momentum may be derived,[2] we detect the
basic inspiration of *static determinism:* Being—viewed as a substantial unchanging quantum whose superficial change, appearing
as a succession of causes and effects (or more accurately, as a
succession of energetic equivalents)—is a mere unfolding of its
eternal identity. This energetic interpretation of causal relation
is based on the assumption that the cause and effect are at bottom
identical, being merely two successive designations for one and
the same reality. This basic identity of cause and effect explains
the necessary character of the relation between them; what we
call a necessary causal relation is nothing but a transformation

of the causes into their effects, a transformation which, as Lucretius already saw, follows from the basic constancy of being, its indestructibility and uncreatability. The necessary causal relation is merely a manifestation of the underlying identity of material or energetic substance.[3]

This means that every present state of the world is contained in any past state and contains all future states. In terms of the corpuscular-kinetic model of reality, it means that if each state of the universe is represented by an instantaneous configuration of the basic atomic elements (whether they are called atoms, electrons, or aether particles), then each such configuration is logically deducible from any previous configuration, while it contains logically any future one. There is no novelty in the universe; contingency is, as Democritus observed centuries before Spinoza,[4] nothing but a symptom of human ignorance. The displacements of atoms and "redistribution of motion" (to use Spencer's words) by which a transition is made from one configuration to the next is going on according to the strict laws of dynamics, which may be summed up in the laws of the conservation of momentum and energy. Successive states of the world are bound together by the iron link of necessity, whose uncompromising character had been anticipated by ancient atomism and whose specific mathematical form was discovered by Newtonian dynamics. The only differences between the successive states of the universe are in different spatial distributions of matter and energy; but even this difference may be lacking if sufficiently large intervals of time are taken into consideration, because there is no logical absurdity in assuming that the very same configuration of matter and distribution of energy may recur. Moreover, if we suppose that the universe is made of a finite number of elements, the identical state of the universe eventually *must* recur. Thus, in the corpuscular-kinetic scheme, time loses its irreversibility and the idea of eternal recurrence appears as its logical consequence. The essential difference between the past and the future thus disappears.

In a more abstract way, the same conclusion may be derived from the concept of causality. If cause and effect are logically equivalent, it means that not only from the present state of the universe can any future state be derived, but also any past state. Thus the principle of logical equivalence of cause and effect, *causa aequat effectum*, means that all successive states of the universe imply each other regardless of their temporal order; thus what we call the direction of time becomes meaningless, and the past, present, and future merge into one huge single timeless pattern. If we say that the future *follows* from the present and the present *follows* from the past, the word "follows" should not be understood in a temporal sense; it is less misleading to speak about the past logically *containing* or *implying* the present or the present *containing* or *implying* the future. But as this implication is mutual, it is correct to say, no matter how paradoxical it may sound, that not only does the present *imply* the past but also that the future *implies* the present. Thus the very succession of temporal phases is, virtually at least, lost.[5]

It is true that this elimination of time in classical physics was only implicit and that physicists in general were speaking of natural *processes*, of *transformations* of causes into their effects, of causal determinations of *future* events, of the present *following* from the past or the future *following* from the present. All this seemed to indicate that they believed in the genuine reality of succession in the physical world.[6] Was this anything more than a simple *façon de parler*, a mere concession to common-sense modes of speech? It was the very ambiguity of the words "it follows" which enabled the majority of scientists to believe that temporality and necessity are compatible. Words like "antecedent," "consequent," "sequence," "it follows" can indeed be understood in either a logical or a temporal sense, but never in both senses at the same time. Every logician is aware that these two meanings should not be confused. When we say that a certain conclusion *follows* from the premises, it would be absurd to claim that the word "follows" should be understood in a temporal sense. Yet it was precisely this inconsistent fusion of these two meanings which served as the basis of the claim that rigorous necessity and genuine succession are compatible.

Only a few consistent minds—significantly, the greatest and most philosophical—saw clearly the ultimate consequences of mechanism and realized that time in the sense of genuine succession has no place in the consistent necessitarian scheme. Time which possesses no direction except on a local scale; time which "moves" from the "past" (which will return) to the "future" (which has already been); time whose "movement" or "flow" is only apparent because its "future" is merely a concealed and disguised present; time in which no novelty emerges and whose successive phases are fused into one huge simultaneous pattern—such time obviously lacks all essential features of temporality as we experience it and should not be called time at all.

NOTES FOR CHAPTER IX

1. D'Alembert, *Traité de dynamique*, p. 7; Lagrange, *Œuvres* (Paris, 1867-92), Vol. IX, p. 357.
2. Provided we assume that the law of conservation of energy holds in *all* inertial systems. Cf. J. R. Schütz, "Princip der absolutem Erhaltung der Energie", *Nachrichten von d. Königl. Gesellschaft der Wissenschaften zu Göttingen, Math.-phys. Klasse* (1897), pp. 110-125.
3. The interpretation of the causal relations in the terms of transformations of energetic equivalents was proposed by Herbert Spencer (*First Principles*, Chaps. VII and VIII) and upheld by W. Ostwald (*Vorlesungen über Naturphilosophie*, Leipzig, 1902, p. 296; *Grundriss der Naturphilosophie*, Leipzig, 1919, p. 144).
4. C. Bailey, *The Greek Atomists and Epicurus*, pp. 142-43; Spinoza, *Ethica*, I, prop. 33, schol. 1.
5. B. Russell wrote as late as 1914: "We shall do better to allow the effect before the cause or simultaneous with it, because nothing of any scientific importance depends upon its being after the cause" (*Our Knowledge of the External World*, Chicago, Open Court, 1914, p. 226).
6. About the peculiar but quite common fusion of two contradictory ideas in the mind of an average determinist—that of temporal process and that of timeless implication—cf. H. Bergson, *Essai sur les données immédiates de la conscience*, pp. 161-164.

PART II · THE DISINTEGRATION OF THE CLASSICAL FRAMEWORK AND THE SIGNIFICANCE OF NEW CONCEPTS

X · THE NEGATION
OF INSTANTANEOUS SPACE

THE difficulties inherent in the Newtonian concept of absolute motionless space became conspicuous when physicists of the second half of the last century began to face seriously the question of *absolute motion*. A body at rest with respect to Newtonian space is in absolute rest, while a body moving with respect to Newtonian space is in absolute motion. In other words, Newtonian absolute space was a frame of reference which was required if we were to differentiate sharply and unambiguously between absolute or real motions and relative or apparent ones. But some questions remained unanswered in classical physics. Which of the infinite number of inertial systems coincides with Newtonian motionless space? By what empirical means can the absolute system of reference be identified? According to classical dynamics, a body at rest with respect to Newtonian space reacts against an external acceleration by the so-called "inertial forces"; but so does any other body which moves with respect to motionless space with constant velocity and along a straight line. All inertial systems are *dynamically equivalent* and it seems to be a matter of convention to regard any of them as identical with the absolute system of reference. This means that if absolute motionless space exists, its existence is unverifiable.

Newton was well aware of these difficulties, but he believed that he had a decisive experimental proof of the existence of absolute space. His famous experiment with a rotating bucket of water was intended to demonstrate the difference between absolute and relative rotations.[1] While absolute rotations manifest themselves by the rise of centrifugal forces, which produce the characteristically concave shape of the rotating liquid, relative rotations remain without such dynamical effect: the surface of the liquid which rotates *with respect to the walls of a vessel only* remains entirely flat. This indicates, according to Newton, that the liquid in the question is at rest with respect to absolute space. All rotating systems thus fall into two dynamically distinct classes: those accompanied by the rise of centrifugal forces, and those marked by their absence. The only interpretation of this fact is, according to Newton, that the rise of centrifugal forces is an effect of the absolute rotation of bodies with respect to absolute space; the absence of such forces is an indication of absolute rest. Absolute space and absolute motion thus become meaningful and physically verifiable physical concepts.

But is this the *only* possible interpretation? Ernst Mach and J. B. Stallo[2] showed that the result of Newton's experiment may be interpreted equally well if the expression "with respect to absolute space" is replaced by "with respect to the great stellar masses of the universe." This objection against Newton's interpretation of his experiment may be found already in George Berkeley's little essay *De motu* written during Newton's lifetime; Berkeley also anticipated Mach and Stallo in radically rejecting the Newtonian idea of absolute space.[3] Even if Newton's interpretation of the rotating-vessel experiment is retained, it does *not* help us in answering the earlier question: Which one of all inertial systems coincides with absolute space? The experiment does not furnish any criterion by which the privileged inertial system can be found; the effect of centrifugal forces which appear in one system would equally appear in *all other systems* which are in a uniform translatory motion with respect to the first system. This is a natural consequence of the dynamical equivalence of all inertial systems; this equivalence was recently named the *classical* or *Galileo's principle of relativity*, in order to differentiate it from the modern Lorentz-Einstein principle of relativity.

But would it not be possible to identify the privileged inertial system, coinciding with the Newtonian space, by *optical* means? If all the inertial frames of reference are equivalent dynamically, are they also equivalent *optically?* To this question classical physics answered unhesitatingly no. For, according to classical physics, no matter what the nature of light may be, whether it consists of corpuscles or waves, its behavior was ruled by the laws of classical kinematics. More concretely, its velocity, its direction of propagation, and its frequency must be different in different frames of reference. Doppler's principle established the dependence of the frequency on the relative motion of a source and of an observer. Bradley's discovery of the aberration of light established that the apparent direction of propagation is affected by relative motion. What was more natural than to expect that the velocity of light is similarly affected by the same cause? For, according to the wave theory, whose ultimate success seemed to be definitely assured by Foucault's experiment in 1850, light consists of periodical disturbances in an elastic medium, later identified with the electromagnetic aether; the velocity of these disturbances must naturally be different for observers moving at different velocities with respect to aether. The velocity of a disturbance as measured by an observer at rest in aether would have a privileged value. It would coincide with the *true* velocity of light; it would be a velocity with respect to the absolutely motionless aether, that is, absolute space. The luminiferous aether thus became a concrete physical embodiment of Newtonian absolute space; its existence, once verified, would furnish a definite clue for distinguishing absolute or "true" motions from relative or "apparent" ones. This line of reasoning had to be accepted as long as the classical law for addition of velocities was retained; prior to the advent of the special theory of relativity nobody even remotely suspected that this law might be overthrown.

The situation was ripe for the crucial experiment which was undertaken by Michelson in 1881 and repeated several times by him and other physicists. The experiment showed conclusively that the motion of the earth through the hypothetical aether does not have the slightest influence on the velocity of the electromagnetic waves; the theoretically anticipated effects of such motion, though well above the limits of experimental errors, have *not* been observed. The same result was obtained by other less known and historically less famous experiments which demonstrated that no "aether wind," resulting from the relative motion of the hypothetical aether in respect to the earth, exists.[4] It is true that at first glance it looked as if the negative results of Michelson's and similar experiments could be explained by a hypothesis according to which aether is dragged along by the bodies moving through it; thus no "aether wind" could arise, since the moving bodies and the surrounding medium would be at relative rest. This explanation, proposed first by Michelson himself, reappeared much later in the books of some opponents of the relativity theory—for instance, Hans Driesch—who were not sufficiently acquainted with other physical facts which made the theory of complete "aether drag" unacceptable.[5] The aberration of light, discovered by Bradley, and a *partial* drag of light in transparent moving bodies are obviously incompatible with the hypothesis of the *total* drag of aether. This was only the last, though the most serious difficulty which the theory of the mechanical aether faced; as we shall see, it was a *coup de grâce* to the hypothesis of an interplanetary medium which would possess dynamical and kinematic properties comparable to those of ordinary bodies.

How serious the predicament was into which physics had got is illustrated by the attempt of G. F. FitzGerald to explain the negative result of Michelson's experiment. He assumed in 1892[6] that the dimensions of the moving bodies which are parallel to their motion are contracted in a definite ratio while the dimensions perpendicular to the direction of motion remain constant. Thus the equality of two optical paths in Michelson's interferometer was restored and the reflected rays arrive at the same phase; consequently, no shift in the interference fringes occurs. Today this explanation is usually presented as a perfect specimen of an *ad hoc* hypothesis, artificially postulated in order to save the appearances; it is overlooked that there is a certain inherent logic in it because, were it true, it would provide a definite criterion by which absolute rest could be differentiated from absolute motion. For, according to this hypothesis, a body which is *really* moving, that is, moving in respect to absolute space, is contracted, while a body *really* standing still, that is, at rest with respect to absolute space, retains its shape and volume. This, within the framework of the absolutist theory of space, is hardly paradoxical: for if positions in space have absolute significance, as Russell still believed at the beginning of this century,[7] it is only natural that change of place must be *physically distinguishable* from staying in the same place. In other words, if absolute motionless space is truly real, there is nothing surprising about the fact that it reacts in a verifiable physical way against displacements occurring in it.

This also was the view of Lorentz.[8] If the hypothesis of the real FitzGerald contraction were true, it would mean a definite vindication of the absolutist theory of space. This in turn would relegate the law of inertia into the category of merely approximate, that is, not basic laws. For there would really be a *dynamical difference* between rest and motion, a difference which escapes our attention only because of the extremely minute value of the ratio v^2/c^2. If this appeared queer, it did so only because physicists after two centuries had become used to the law of inertia; but we must not forget how persistent was the tendency to rediscover the dynamical difference between rest and motion, including uniform and rectilinear motion.

It is needless to repeat what has been said about this tendency in the first part of this book; it is sufficient to recall that in all such attempts from Kepler to Viscount Samuel we may discern the inclination to regard *the principle of the conservation of rest* as the basic law of dynamics while every motion, even including the inertial motion, was regarded as requiring a mechanical explanation. But is this not really consonant with the absolute theory of space? If space is made of motionless absolute positions, is it not logical to believe that it is *not* indifferent to *any* change of absolute place, including the change which is caused by inertial motion? The Lorentz-FitzGerald contraction would be precisely a form of physical reaction by which absolute space reacts to the change of absolute position.

This seems to be in conflict with the alleged *causal inertness* of space which was one of the basic features of classical space. It was pointed out in Chapter II how the relativity of position is logically tied with the homogeneity of space from which the causal inertness of space naturally follows. But against this objection the defenders of the absolutists theory of space may retort that the idea of complete passivity of space is unattainable and that even for those who insist on the relativity of position, space is not indifferent to certain types of motion. Cannot the rise of inertial and centrifugal forces be regarded also as a sort of *reaction against vectorial acceleration*, a reaction by which space manifests its existence? This was the meaning of the rotating vessel experiment, at least in the eyes of Newton.

This argument only shows how difficult any sharp separation is of the "purely physical" from the "purely geometrical" properties of space, even within the framework of classical physics. Moreover, we must not forget that the Lorentz-FitzGerald contraction takes place not with respect to empty space, but rather with respect to space filled by the electromagnetic aether; thus the principle of the causal inertness of space is preserved as long as we keep this distinction between the geometrical container and the material filling it. For it is plausible to assume that it is the material and not space itself which is responsible for concrete physical effects like the FitzGerald contraction or, according to Viscount Samuel and others, even for inertia itself.

We shall see later that there was no lack of attempts to construct concrete mechanical models for explaining even such recently discovered phenomena as the increase of mass with velocity or the impossibility of a material body having the velocity of light. In such a way it would have been possible even to save the rigidity of the basic elements of matter—a basic dogma of classical physical thought. If the electrons themselves are regarded as complex, made of much smaller aethereal atoms,

then the FitzGerald contraction is explained as a change of the
aethereal configuration which constitutes the electron; but the
contraction itself does not affect either the shape or volume of
the ultimate material elements which compose the aethereal
medium. Thus, appearances notwithstanding, neither the passivity of space nor the rigidity of the ultimate physical elements
was fatally endangered by the postulate of longitudinal contraction.

But there was another, probably even more serious difficulty to
which the contraction hypothesis led. In order to account for
the fact that all observers, moving or not with respect to the
alleged motionless aether, find always the same velocity of light,
it was necessary to introduce another independent postulate,
according to which *absolute motions affect even the flow of
time itself*. More specifically, in the moving frames of reference
time is flowing at a *slower* rate, which means that its units are
dilated; the ratio of the time intervals associated with systems
at rest to the intervals within moving systems, is

$$\frac{t}{t^1} = 1 : \frac{1}{\sqrt{1 - \frac{v^2}{c^2}}}$$

Again, the postulated modification is very small, owing to the
extreme minuteness of the ratio v^2/c^2, but this does not diminish
the revolutionary character of the hypothesis. The unity and
uniformity of the temporal flow was one of the basic presuppositions of classical science, and it was explicitly stressed by
Newton in his definition of time. Newtonian physics equally
stressed the independence of time from its concrete content.

All these three features of classical time—unity, uniformity
and independence from concrete physical events—are challenged
by the dilatation theory of Lorentz, according to which there
is a *plurality of local times*, each of them being dependent on the
mechanical velocity of its own system. Such dependence would
mean the possibility of *causal interaction* between time and the
events occurring in it: in the contraction hypothesis not only is
the rate of the time flow affected by mechanical velocity, but

also time thus slowed down slows in the same ratio all physical processes within the moving system. In other words, time is subject to causal action by physical processes and in its turn affects physical processes; both its independence and its causal inertness are gone. We have seen how much classical physical thought insisted on both the independence and causal inefficacy of time, which are both challenged by the Lorentz dilatation hypothesis.

There seemed to be one possible way out of this difficulty. The absolutist theory still could claim that it is not the time flow itself, but merely physical events *in* time, which are slowed down. Such a distinction is, of course, meaningless for the relational theory of time, but for an absolutist of the Newtonian type it remains *the very essence* of his view. In such a view there is an irreducible ontological distinction between the homogeneous one-dimensional container which we call time and its concrete content, made of physical events, which fills it. The dilatation theory may then be interpreted in the following way. The flow of absolute time remains everywhere unchanged and its rate is truly and objectively measured by clocks in the stationary frames of reference, that is, stationary with respect to absolute space. In all other systems, moving with respect to the motionless absolute space, clocks are slowed down in a definite ratio, though time itself remains undisturbed and continues to flow at the same uniform and constant rate in accordance with Newton's definition, independently of all physical changes. In other words, in any other system than the stationary one, there is a discrepancy between the absolute flow of empty time and the rate of concrete physical changes; this discrepancy grows with mechanical velocity and it reaches its maximum when mechanical velocity reaches the velocity of light ($v = c$). In this limit case all clocks would stop; but, according to the absolutist theory, this does not mean that time ceases to flow; even then it would continue to "flow equably without relation to anything external," to use the words of Newton. Even if all motions came to a standstill, the flight of time would not be suspended.

This possibility was envisaged by classical physics before the unattainability of absolute zero temperature was discovered. According to the relational theory, the elimination of all motions and changes would eliminate time as well; but it has been already shown how much classical physical thought was leaning toward the absolutist theory. This is why both absolute space and time have become almost extraphysical entities in the thought of Newton and his disciples, for the fate of these entities, in virtue of their absoluteness and independence, did not depend on the fate of the material world contained in them. This, again, was the view of Lorentz.[9]

If such an interpretation of the dilatation of time is accepted, then it is necessary to explain why absolute motions slow the movement of the clocks or, more generally, all periodical processes by which time is measured. Such an explanation was not impossible in principle; as in the case of the contraction hypothesis it is again the concept of aether which may help. Absolute motion is a motion through the aethereal medium; it is, in principle at least, conceivable that there is a braking effect which the resistance of such a medium would exert on the motion of a pendulum or vibratory motions taking place within the moving system; the fact that the slowing effect is proportional to mechanical velocity apparently only increases the temptation to look for this sort of explanation. Thus neither the contraction hypothesis nor the assumed dilatation of time stand in irreconcilable opposition to the classical concepts of space and time, if we are not discouraged by the arduousness and complexity of the task which such an effort of reconciliation requires.[10]

But this was not the path which physics of the twentieth century chose. Although modern physics retained both FitzGerald's contraction formula and Lorentz's formula for time dilatation, both formulae are now interpreted in a sense *altogether different* from the original naively realistic meaning. The main difference between the attitude of Einstein and that of Lorentz and Fitz-Gerald was that Einstein regarded the negative result of all experiments establishing the constancy of the velocity of light as one of the ultimate and irreducible features of physical reality, while Lorentz and FitzGerald hoped to *explain* the constancy of light velocity as a kind of happy or unhappy coincidence which may be derived from the unchanged laws of classical mechanics. We have shown above how strong the temptation was to choose the second way; the whole tradition of physical thought weighed heavily in its favor. The bold originality of Einstein lay in resisting this temptation. By accepting the fact of a constant velocity of light as a primary principle, Einstein had no other choice than to draw all consequences from it; only gradually did it become evident that this implied a complete reconstruction of the foundations of classical dynamics and kinematics.

There is no place here for a detailed treatment of the special theory of relativity; for our purpose it will be sufficient to point out how the basic classical concepts of space, time, matter, and motion have been radically transformed in it. For reasons which will be discussed later, the revolutionary character of this transformation has not always been fully noticed, in particular as far as the concept of space is concerned.

RELATIVITY OF SIMULTANEITY

The acceptance of the principle of the constant velocity of light implied a rejection not only of the idea of aether but of *every absolute frame of reference which would serve as a means for differentiating between "apparent" and "real" motions;* in other words, *a rejection of the absolute motionless space of Newton.* This may be shown by analyzing the relativization of simultaneity which is one of the most conspicuous consequences of the principle of constant luminous velocity.

Classical physics regarded the whole history of the physical world as a continuous succession of instantaneous material configurations. Every such configuration represented a "state of the world at a given instant," each being an instantaneous cross section of the spatiotemporal world process. The terms "instantaneous cross sections" and "instantaneous cuts" are more than simple metaphors. Even classical physics had its idea of the four-dimensional spatiotemporal continuum which was nothing but a graphical representation of the way in which space and time were then believed to be related. Needless to say, classical space-time is profoundly different from the space-time of the theory of relativity, but the structure of both concepts as well as their differences are most conveniently studied on the corresponding three-dimensional models. Such models are necessitated by our inherent inability to imagine the fourth dimension. Although this procedure involves, as will be shown later, certain risks from the epistemological point of view, it has the definite advantage of exhibiting more clearly the relation of space to time in their respective synthesis, whether classical or modern. A similar procedure was successfully used when the properties of curved non-Euclidean spaces were visualized by their two-dimensional models.

In the three-dimensional model of classical space-time its spatial component is represented by a Euclidean plane, either vertical or horizontal, while the "fourth dimension of time" is symbolized by a straight line perpendicular to this plane. Indeed there is an infinite number of successive instantaneous spaces symbolized by parallel planes, all perpendicular to the time axis; each of these spaces contains an instantaneous configuration of material elements which represents "nature at a given instant." One of these instantaneous cross sections of the world process symbolizes the present state of the universe. All points contained in each instantaneous cross section are simultaneous in an absolute sense; in other words, each instantaneous space is an objective substrate of simultaneous events.* The close connection between absolute space and absolute simultaneity can hardly be exhibited more clearly; the two concepts are so intimately related that the question arises whether they are really different. If space is defined as juxtaposition of points, it is evident that the terms in question are regarded as *coexisting*, that is, existing

---

* See the diagram on p. 217.

simultaneously and never in succession. We have seen how Kant, who was so profoundly imbued by the spirit of classical physics, did not fail to notice this timelessness of classical space.[11] Bergson, too, insisted on the same point in his first book when he drew a sharp dividing line between juxtaposition and succession. Whitehead, while distinguishing between "timeless" and "instantaneous" space, emphasized equally strongly that no successive relation is possible in each instantaneous space; from this he even inferred that the concept of "instantaneous velocity," useful as it may be as a methodological device, is, philosophically speaking, devoid of meaning.[12] On the other hand, when we apply the principle of the identity of indiscernibles, it is difficult to see any difference between the class of simultaneous events and the "instantaneous space" of classical physics; the latter is merely a collective term applied to the former. Instantaneous space (*Momentraum* in Carnap's terminology)[13] is *constituted* by simultaneous events. What sounds misleading is the expression "events," which in ordinary language has a dynamic connotation and refers to finite stretches of duration; but we must not forget that moments of classical time are regarded as strictly instantaneous, that is, devoid of any temporal thickness. This was why the term "world points" (*Weltpunkte*) was frequently substituted for the term "events." Consequently, there is merely a semantic difference between the expression "class of simultaneous events" and "space at a given moment."

The space of classical physics was *the* absolute frame of reference which made possible not only a true and objective differentiation between absolute and relative motions, but also between "apparent" and "real" simultaneity of events. More concretely: to every instantaneous event on the earth correspond instantaneous events on all distant stars which are exactly simultaneous with it. We do not know about such events immediately and, at best, we infer their existence later from luminous messages received sometimes centuries after the event itself. Before the discovery of the finite velocity of light, there was no difference between apparent and real simultaneity; no distinction between "seen now" and "real now" existed. The belief in the finite velocity of light, anticipated by ancient atomists, was regarded in the Middle Ages as a heresy and the University of Paris in 1348 forced Nicolas d'Autrecourt to renounce publicly such a view.[14] When the famous new star was discovered by Tycho Brahe in 1572, it was mostly believed that the date of its observation and the date of the event itself coincided; such a belief was only natural a century before Olaf Roemer's epoch-making discovery.

When the velocity of light was finally established, the distinction between the "seen now" and "is now" had to be drawn, at least in astronomical observations. A starry sky seen in a bright summer night is an instance of such *spurious* simultaneity of an *apparent* space; the fixed stars which appear as luminous spots distributed simultaneously in our present perceived sky are seen not as they *are* now existing in the depth of absolute space, but as they *were* some time ago. How long a time ago? The answer is easy if we know the distance of an observed object and also its relative velocity in respect to the earth; then we have simply to divide the corresponding distance by the velocity of light, diminished or augmented by the relative velocity of source and observer. The result would represent an interval of time separating an observed past event from the date of our present perception. By subtracting this interval from the present date, we finally obtain the truly objective date of an observed event in absolute Newtonian time.

This means that our perception makes appear simultaneous events which are of very different age and have only one thing in common: that their, so to speak, posthumous messages reach our eyes at the same time. While the luminous message from the moon is only one second old, that from Polaris is fifty years old. But there are real events, on the moon and Polaris as well as on all distant celestial bodies, which are *truly* and *objectively* simultaneous with our present perception of the summer sky. In other words, it was believed that there is an absolute world-wide instant, stretching through the whole universe, containing all truly simultaneous events. This instantaneous cut across the world process is merely another term for absolute instantaneous space; it contains all the events having the same date in the stream of Newtonian time.

But such retrospective dating was possible only because it was believed that the classical addition theorem for velocities can be applied to light, that the velocity of light may be treated in the same way as the velocity of sound or any other mechanical velocity. But this is precisely impossible if we accept the constancy of the luminous velocity imposed by experience: mechanical velocity of moving bodies cannot be vectorially added to the velocity of the electromagnetic waves. This means that the whole procedure by which the "true" simultaneity of the past events was reconstructed is deprived of its foundation. We may still indulge in computing the date of any distant past event, for instance the date of the explosion of the nova which appeared on our earthly sky in 1572. But we cannot expect that observers moving with different velocities with respect to our frame of reference will find the same result. In other words, "instantaneous cross sections" of the universe are different for different inertial systems: the "now" inferred by me is generally different for other moving observers. And by denying the objective existence of the universal cosmic "now," or, in Eddington's words, of a "world-wide instant," [15] we implicitly deny the objective existence of the instantaneous spaces each of which is regarded as a three-dimensional layer in the four-dimensional world-process, a layer on which all "truly simultaneous events" are located. Such instantaneous classical spaces literally do not exist; in less provocative language, they are embedded in the dynamic spatiotemporal continuum out of which they are carved only by artificial operations. Such operations were possible in classical physics where space and time were united only in a loose way; the structure of classical space-time yielded naturally to the separation of the two components because four-dimensional becoming was defined as a continuous succession of instantaneous spaces. But the impossibility of a cutting operation by which the spatial component would be separated from the temporal one precisely measures the enormous difference between classical and the relativistic space-time.

NOTES FOR CHAPTER X

1. I. Newton, *Mathematical Principles*, scholium IV, pp. 10-11.
2. J. B. Stallo, *The Concepts and Theories of Modern Physics*, pp. 190-200; E. Mach, *The Science of Mechanics*, pp. 280-288.
3. G. Berkeley, *De motu*, § § 60-65.
4. No effect of the hypothetical "aether wind" was found on a vertically suspended charged condenser by Trouton and Noble in 1903, nor by Tomaschek and Chase in 1926.
5. H. Driesch, *Relativitätstheorie und Weltanschauung*, 2d ed. (Leipzig, 1930), p. 13.
6. E. T. Whittaker, *A History of the Theories of Aether and Electricity*, Vol. I, pp. 404 f.
7. B. Russell, "Is Position in Time and Space Absolute or Relative?" *Mind*, N.S., Vol. X (1901); reprinted in part in *The Principles of Mathematics*, Chap. LI, pp. 445 f.
8. H. A. Lorentz, "Michelson's Interference Experiment" in: *The Principle of Relativity*, A collection of original memoirs on the special and general theory of relativity by H. A. Lorentz, A. Einstein, H. Minkowski, and H. Weyl with notes by A. Sommerfeld. Translated by W. Perret and G. B. Jeffrey (London, 1923), pp. 6-7.
9. H. A. Lorentz, "La Gravitation," *Scientia*, Vol. XVI (July 1914), p. 35.
10. The enormous difficulties of the mechanical models of aether were listed by H. Witte, *Über den gegenwärtigen Stand der Frage nach einer mechanischen Erklärung der elektrischen Erscheinungen* (Berlin, 1906); cf. also the same author, *Annalen der Physik*, Vol. 26 (1908), p. 235.
11. See Chapter III, above, Note 24.
12. H. Bergson, *Essai sur les données immédiates de la conscience*, p. 81; A. N. Whitehead, *An Enquiry Concerning the Principles of Natural Knowledge*, 2d ed. (Cambridge University Press, 1925), p. 2.
13. R. Carnap, "Über die Abhängigheit der Eigenschaften des Raumes von denen der Zeit," *Kant-Studien*, Bd. 30 (1925), pp. 339-340.
14. K. Lasswitz, *Geschichte der Atomistik*, I, 157-158.
15. A. Eddington, *The Nature of the Physical World* (Cambridge University Press, 1933), pp. 42-47.

XI · THE FUSION OF SPACE
WITH TIME AND ITS
MISREPRESENTATION

THE FALLACY OF SPATIALIZATION

THE impossibility of separating space from time was for the first time clearly formulated by H. Minkowski in 1908.[1] It was then that the concept of the relativistic space-time continuum was explicitly formulated, although mathematically it was implied in Lorentz's transformation.

As soon as this fusion of space and time was proposed, certain psychological influences (which will be discussed in detail below) came into play and peculiarly distorted its true meaning. The very choice of the word which Minkowski used for designating this fusion was characteristic: the four-dimensional continuum of point-events was called by him "the world" (*die Welt*). This indicated that he understood this fusion as an operation in which the temporal component was absorbed by the spatial. In this respect Minkowski was not alone. Emile Meyerson in his philosophical commentary on the theory of relativity gives a long list of thinkers, both philosophers and physicists, who regarded the proposed fusion as a *spatialization of time;* according to them, time itself has become an additional fourth dimension of space on which all events, "past," "present" and "future" were juxtaposed. According to Einstein himself, "becoming" in the three-dimensional space has been transformed into "being" in the world of four dimensions; according to Hermann Weyl, "the objective world *is*, it does not become"; it appears to become only to our "blindfolded consciousness" (*abgeblendete Bewusstsein*) which creeps along its "world line" into the future.[2] According to Cunningham:[3]

> With Minkowski space and time become particular aspects of a single four-dimensional concept; the distinction between them as separate modes of correlating and ordering phenomena is lost, and the motion of a point in time is represented as a stationary curve in four-dimensional space. Now if all motional phenomena are looked at from this point of view, they become timeless phenomena in four-dimensional space. The whole history of a physical system is laid out as a changeless whole.

It is hardly surprising that Cunningham relates this static conception of space-time to the Laplacian type of determinism:[4]

> Such a view of the universe is inseparable from a mechanical determinism in which the future is unalterably determined by the past and in which the past can be uniquely inferred from the present state of the universe. It is the view of an intelligence which could comprehend at one glance the whole of time and space.

Nor is it surprising to find among the representatives of this view the belief that the theory of relativity was anticipated by H. G. Wells in his famous novel *The Time Machine* in which a fictitious traveler moves along the "fourth dimension" as freely as along the three spatial dimensions. In a recent essay Kurt Gödel seriously considers the Wellsian idea of a round trip "into any region of the past, present and future and back again." It is even more significant that Einstein's own comment about it was not unfavorable.[5] The very same idea was expressed by Ernst Cassirer when he claimed that in the theory of relativity the anisotropy of time disappears as the distinction between the "past" and "future" is purely conventional, comparable to the difference between "plus" and "minus" signs in space. Both Weyl and Cassirer saw in the theory of relativity a confirmation of Kant's view about the ideality of time: time, being only a form of our perception, cannot be applied to "things-in-themselves." [6]

There were some important dissenting voices, both among physicists and philosophers. Paul Langevin was one of the first who protested against calling time "the fourth dimension of space." Einstein himself admitted that the asymmetry of time is preserved even in its relativistic fusion with space when he recognized that "we cannot send wire-messages into the past." When Meyerson in the session of the French Philosophical Society of April 6, 1922, insisted on the distinction of space and time even in the theory of relativity, Einstein, who attended the session, explicitly agreed. Meyerson's argument was fully developed in his book, *La Déduction relativiste*, and Einstein in his highly favorable comment about it again praised Meyerson's criticism of spatialization of time. According to Einstein, the spatialization of time is a misinterpretation of the theory of relativity, a misinterpretation committed not only by popularizers, but even by many scientists, though it is often present in their mind only implicitly.[7] Weyl, when he was in a less Kantian mood, warned against a facile confusion of space and time and claimed that it is more accurate to speak of the 3 + 1-dimensional continuum than of the four-dimensional entity.[8] In the same decade, Eddington, Bridgman, and G. N. Lewis among the physicists and Whitehead, Bergson, and Reichenbach among the philosophers issued similar warnings.[9]

What then is the true meaning of the relativistic fusion of space and time? The very fact that there was a disagreement about it not only among philosophers but also among physicists, and that even the founders of the theory, like Einstein and Weyl, were not always consistent in their interpretations, shows the need for a clarifying analysis. In the pages that follow we intend to show, first, that the spatialization of time is a perennial philosophical illusion which has its roots in the modes of thought characterizing the major part of the philosophical and scientific tradition; second, that this spatialization of time, instead of being a correct interpretation of the theory of relativity, is precisely a distortion of its true meaning, a distortion which was made possible by the persistent influence of the intellectual habits referred to above; third, that an attentive interpretation of the same theory shows that the fusion of space and time is more accurately characterized as a *temporalization* or *dynamization* of space than as a spatialization of time; and finally, that this dynamization of space does not mean a fanciful negation of space or its fanciful reduction to a one-dimensional continuum of time, but only its incorporation into a type of becoming which, together with its dynamical temporal unfolding, still possesses a certain, so to speak, *transversal* extent or *width*.

The nature of the fallacy of spatializing time and its far-reaching disastrous influence is still largely misunderstood, in spite of repeated warnings by Bergson, Meyerson, Whitehead, and their followers. Yet, it is certain that what may be called the *Eleatic tradition* is one of the most persistent strains in philosophical thought. Although Parmenides and his immediate successors remained isolated in their radical and extreme denial of change and succession, they were followed by many philosophers in their insistence that the true reality is timeless, and that change and succession belong merely to the realm of shadowy and shifting appearances. This belief in the contrast between the true and changeless reality and the half-real realm of becoming is common to Plato, Plotinus, the medieval philosophers, Spinoza, Kant, Schopenhauer, Bradley, and McTaggart, to name only a few, and the fact that it is present under various terminological garments in such widely different thinkers in widely different periods makes it even more significant. The tendency is present not only in philosophers with idealistic leanings but equally, though less explicitly, among naturalistically minded philosophers and philosophically minded scientists.

In this second group the Eleatic twist of mind takes precisely a less conspicuous but in its implications an equally radical form of the spatialization of time. It is hardly accidental that the earliest attempts to symbolize time by a geometrical, infinitely divisible line resulted in Zeno's denial of change and motion and in his defense of the immutable Parmenidean One. The elimination of time and its spatialization are closely related, the latter being merely a more concrete form of the former. But the spatialization of time took a more systematic form only in the modern period simultaneously with the development of analytical geometry and classical mechanics. Descartes, who was the founder of the first and a cofounder of the second, was only consistent when he called time a "dimension" and when he followed the analogy between a geometrical point and an instant of time to its logical, though ultimately absurd, consequences. For Descartes, following in this respect the Arabian atomists and realizing that no dynamical link can logically be obtained between passageless and purely external instants, was perfectly consistent in concluding that our world is perpetually perishing and continually being re-created. Thus the divine *creatio continua* supplied a missing dynamical link joining durationless instants.[10]

In symbolizing time by the axis t (of independent variables) there was at first no conscious attempt at spatializing time. The dynamic and progressive character of time was symbolized by an ideal motion of the pointlike present sliding along the time axis from the past to the future. But in contemplating a spatial diagram of temporal process it is easy and psychologically natural to forget its underlying dynamic meaning. Any spatial symbol contemplated at a given moment is *completed*, i.e., all its parts are given *at once*, simultaneously, in contrast with the temporal reality which is by its own nature *incomplete* and whose "parts"—if we are justified in using such a thoroughly inadequate term—are by definition successive, i.e., nonsimultaneous. The spatial symbolism leads us to forget the essential difference between juxtaposition and succession and to reduce the differences between the past, present, and future to simple *differences of position:* "past" events are symbolized by the positions lying to the left of the point representing the "present," while "future" events lie to the right of the same point on the same already drawn "temporal axis." Thus the spatial diagram suggests the wrong idea that the successive moments already *coexist* and that their pastness and futurity is not genuine, but only "phenomenal" or "apparent."

From such a point of view future events already exist, and what we call their future occurrence is only an unimportant formality, unavoidable for a finite human consciousness, but not for a superhuman intelligence free of human limitations. It is true that when Laplace spoke of such a superhuman intelligence he did not mean the medieval God, but only the impersonal order of nature in which past, present, and future occurrences are timelessly contained; but his strictly deterministic point of view was, after all, not basically different from medieval and early Protestant ideas of predestination. The God of St. Thomas and Calvin shared with the impersonal order of nature of Spinoza and Laplace the property of embracing in one timeless act the whole history of the universe. This is what was called by Charles Hartshorne "a secret alliance" between theological and naturalistic determinism.[11]

Thus the tendency to spatialize time was entirely consonant with the idea of classical determination or rather predetermination. When Descartes and D'Alembert called duration "the fourth dimension" and when Lagrange characterized mechanics as a "geometry of four dimensions," they were only preparing the way for the Laplacian vision of reality, which belongs to the same tradition as the classical views of Parmenides and Spinoza. The universe with its whole history is conceived as a single huge and timeless bloc, given at once. In such a scheme, time itself, as Bergson wittily observed, is reduced to "our incapacity to know everything at once." [12]

It is precisely by this persistent Eleatic tendency, cropping up again in the spatialization of time, that the true meaning of the relativity theory was peculiarly distorted. Sometimes those who interpret relativistic space-time in the sense of the timeless four-dimensional entity are aware of their affinity with the Eleatic tradition; this is true, for instance, of Kurt Gödel, who sees in the theory of relativity a confirmation of the views of Parmenides, Kant, and McTaggart.[13] If this were true, the theory of relativity would be a simple continuation and even a culmination of the main tendency of classical physics which, as we have had opportunity to see, pushed the reality of time into the background. Could the Laplacian ideal of the elimination of time have been realized more completely and more accurately than in the idea of all future events *already existing* on the *already drawn* fourth dimension of space, which only our ignorance interprets as a process of successive unfolding? Though the word "space-time" is still used, the component "time" is a mere word; it stands for the static fourth dimension which in virtue of its completed character is something essentially timeless, and in which there is no "before" and "after." Spinoza, who also excluded succession from the attributes of the ultimate reality and who, more than a century before Laplace and Kant, reduced time to "confused and inadequate knowledge," would certainly be pleased.[14]

We shall deal only briefly with an extremely serious epistemological difficulty which arises when time is deprived of an ontological status and reduced to a mere appearance. For in relegating time into the phenomenal world an intolerable dualism is created between the realm of appearances, occurring in time, and the realm of timeless noumena. All static systems from Parmenides to Bradley and McTaggart are plagued by the same problem: If true reality is timeless, *where does the illusion of succession come from?* If time has no genuine reality, why does it appear to be real?

No solution can be found which would not introduce surreptitiously the reality of time *somewhere*. If the illusory reality of time is nothing but a gradual rising of the curtain of ignorance which separates our mind from a complete and timeless insight, then at least *this process of rising is still a process which unfolds itself gradually without being given at once;* but, by conceding this, we admit the reality of time either in our mind or *between* our mind and the allegedly timeless reality.

In the light of this it is not difficult to see that the historically latest attempt to eliminate time and succession fails in its ultimate purpose as much as all previous ones. Even if we consider the spatialization of time as the indisputably correct interpretation of the relativity theory and even if we admit with Cassirer that in the physical world the distinction between the past and the future is as arbitrary as the distinction between the positive and negative directions of a straight line in space, succession is *not* eliminated, because it remains unchallenged in its last refuge—consciousness itself.[15] When Hermann Weyl claims that the objective world *is* and does not become, he has to admit that at least our "blindfolded consciousness" *creeps* along the world line of its own body into the area of the universe called "future"; or when it is said that we meet the pre-existing future events *on our way to the future*, we concede that even if the future is completed, our way to the future is *still going on.* It is evident that although the world scheme of Minkowski eliminates succession in the physical world, it recognizes at least the *movement of our consciousness* to the future. Thus arises an absurd dualism of the timeless physical world and temporal consciousness, that is, a dualism of two altogether disparate realms whose correlation becomes completely unintelligible. The future in such a view becomes a merely *distant present* which is separated from our so-called present by the segment of the fourth dimension which we call time; it means, for instance, that we are already dead without realizing it now; but our consciousness creeping along the world line of its own body will certainly reach any pre-existing and nominally future event which in its completeness *waits* to be finally reached by our awareness. But our future awareness will create this event as little as Columbus's discovery created the American continent. To such strange consequences do both spatialization of time and strict determinism lead; they have a common root—the early Greek substitution of Being for Becoming.

THE IRREVERSIBILITY OF THE CAUSAL LINKS AND RELATIVITY OF JUXTAPOSITION

But is time really spatialized in the relativity theory? It is not. The alleged spatialization of time occurs merely in the imaginations of some interpreters who in retaining the classical habits of thought follow the path of the least psychological resistance. To show this, we need not resort to the ultimate epistemological argument in order to defend the reality of time and change; a detailed and attentive analysis of the *physical* content of the special relativity theory will be sufficient for this purpose.

Apparently the most convincing argument for a static mis-interpretation of the fusion of space and time is the relativity of simultaneity. A pair of events appearing simultaneous in one frame of reference is no longer simultaneous in other inertial systems. What seems to be even worse, some events appearing in succession in one system may even appear in a reversed order of succession in some other systems. As there is no privileged system which would impart a mark of objectivity to one of these systems, what objective status may time and succession still possess? Does not the theory of relativity thus substantiate the Kantian and idealistic view about a purely phenomenal nature of time? We have seen how strong was the temptation to draw this conclusion, especially for Neo-Kantians.

The main defect of this reasoning is that it starts with a wrong assumption. It is simply not true that the simultaneity and suc-cession of events are purely and unqualifiedly relative. Even a cursory inspection of Lorentz's and Minkowski's formulae dis-closes three cases which are rarely analyzed, if they are men-tioned at all, in popular expositions of relativity:

(*a*) The simultaneity and succession of the isotopic events, that is, events occurring at the same place.

(*b*) The simultaneity of *heterotopic* events, that is, of events occurring at different places.

(*c*) The succession of heterotopic events *causally related*.

(*d*) The succession of events which *are not* causally con-nected.

(*a*) Both simultaneity and succession of isotopic events are *topologically invariant* with respect to all possible frames of reference. In other words, the simultaneity and succession of the events occurring at the same place remains a simultaneity and succession for any conceivable observer. In Paul Langevin's words, the world lines, which by definition are constituted by a succession of isotopic events, are *irreversible* in all systems of reference. The irreversibility of the world lines is thus in the full sense of the word absolute.[16]

(*b*) What became fully relative in modern physics is the simultaneity of *distant*, i.e., heterotopic events. Such events appear simultaneous in one "consentient set," i.e., in such inertial systems as are at rest with respect to each other;[17] in all other systems the same pair of events is *not* simultaneous. In other words, with the exception of consentient sets, different observers will disagree what "space at a given instant" is; their instantaneous three-dimensional cuts across the four-dimensional process will *not* coincide. This statement is merely equivalent to the aforementioned assertion that there is no absolute space which would serve as an objective substratum for the "truly simultaneous" events. Thus the relativity of simultaneity can equally well be called a *relativity of juxtaposition*.

(*c*), (*d*) Contrary to a widespread belief, the succession of distant events is *not* made relative. Only the order of events which are *causally unrelated*, i.e., those whose distance in space is greater than their interval of time multiplied by the velocity of the fastest causal action, may appear reversed in a suitable frame of reference; the succession of causally *connected* events, remains topologically invariant, i.e., it retains its character of succession for all possible observers.

Misunderstanding on this point was due to the confusion of *metrical invariance* with *topological invariance*. It is true that in relativity, in contradistinction to classical physics, the *length* of the temporal interval even between two causally related events depends on the choice of the system of reference. But it cannot become zero in any system, and *a fortiori* cannot become negative.[18] The transformation of succession into simultaneity or a reversion of temporal order may occur when the corresponding events are *not* causally related. But in no conceivable system can an effect appear *before* its cause. Such a case, though possible in classical physics, is impossible in the relativity theory in virtue of the fact that *no causal action can move faster than the electromagnetic disturbances.*

Philosophically the most significant result is that *while there is no juxtaposition of events which would be a juxtaposition for all observers, there are certain types of succession which remain such in all frames of reference.* These types of succession are represented by causal series, i.e., by the world lines, including the world lines of photons. In other words, unlike spatial juxtaposition, the irreversibility of the world lines has an *absolute* significance, possessing genuine and objective reality independent of the conventional choice of the system of reference.

The ontological priority of time over space could hardly have found a more convincing illustration.

Thus it is more accurate to speak of *time-space* than of space-time; and while the term "temporalization of space" is not completely accurate, it is not so radically false as "spatialization of time." The reason why it would not be entirely accurate to speak about "temporalization of space" will be set forth later. Here it is sufficient to say that if space and time are fused into one single dynamic reality, we have to expect such a synthesizing operation to modify not only the classical concept of space but that of time as well. This modification of the concept of time is not so profound and radical, to be sure, as the modification of the concept of space. This is evident from what has just been said, i.e., that while the relation of juxtaposition has been completely relativized, the successive character of the universe—the irreversible character of the causal chains—is preserved in a full and absolute sense. But this does not mean that the character of spatiality is completely spurious or entirely reducible to relations of succession. For this reason it will be less misleading to speak of *dynamization* than of *temporalization* of space.

DYNAMIZATION OF SPACE IN THE SPECIAL THEORY

If space is inseparable from time, it is certainly artificial and misleading to deal with its properties separately as if it were an independent entity. On the other hand, it is important to realize fully in what sense and to what extent all the features of classical space are being transformed by the contemporary evolution of physics. This is the reason (or rather the excuse) why we shall continue to deal separately with the properties of space in this section.

The meaning of a new and revolutionary concept can never be understood without first pointing out *what it is not;* otherwise misleading associations will interfere with its understanding. This is true of the new concepts of space and time, or, using a more adequate language, of the new concept of time-space. If we analyze the changes which modern physics imposes on the classical properties of space and time, perhaps the conditions will be created for a positive understanding of their relativistic merging into the dynamic unity of time-space. This ultimate gain is worth the certain risk involved in a provisional separate treatment of the attributes of space. This separate treatment is imposed by the necessity of clear and orderly discussion; it is not a concession to the old habits of thought, though it may superficially look so. On the contrary: in reviewing the classical properties of the Newtonian space in the light of modern discoveries, we shall gain an additional insight into the impossibility of space existing independently from time; we shall have additional reasons for designating the union of space and time by the term *dynamization of space* as proposed above.

The classical space of Euclid and Newton was an immutable and static entity, entirely foreign to temporal passage; the only relation which the points in such space may have is the relation of *juxtaposition*, which *ex definitione* is timeless, unless we consider *simultaneous juxtaposition* to be a temporal relation too. In any case, the concepts of distance and succession were defined as mutually exclusive; any distance between two points in space was by its own nature *instantaneous*, i.e., timeless. The immutability of space was explicitly emphasized by Newton's famous definition. A century later the author of *Critique of Pure Reason* expressed the same idea in a different form when he insisted on the mutual exclusivity of spatial and temporal relations; and as late as the beginning of the present century Bertrand Russell claimed that the independence of space from time cannot be denied "without falling into the grossest absurdities." [19]

Now the relativity theory boldly challenges this time-honored belief: as classical space is nothing but the totality of simultaneous events, its objective existence necessarily disappears as soon as the objective existence of absolute simultaneity is lost. Classical space conceived as a simultaneous juxtaposition of points simply *does not exist;* to admit the contrary would mean to admit the absolute simultaneity of distant events, which is precisely what the special theory of relativity denies. As already stated, absolute space and absolute simultaneity imply each other; the denial of one implies the denial of the other. Newtonian static space is nothing but an artificial instantaneous cut across the cosmic becoming. Such cuts, in spite of their artificiality, have their *approximate* validity and *practical* justification for small distances and velocities—small in comparison with the velocity of light—but they do not have any objective counterpart in the structure of reality. Since the advent of relativity, according to Whitehead, "the spatial relations must stretch across time"; for there are no instantaneous timeless relations in the universe any longer.

We saw in Part I how nearly all classical features of space were related to its homogeneity and how this homogeneity implies the independence of space from any physical content and its changes. No causal interaction was admitted between classical space and its physical content: space was regarded both as *causally inert* and as *indifferent to any physical action;* its only function was that of a passive immutable container. This separation between space and its physical content is challenged not only by the general theory of relativity but even, though perhaps less explicitly, by the special theory. Chapter VI pointed up the tendency in classical physics to eliminate the self-contradictory concept of instantaneous physical action and showed how gradually all sorts of action at a distance were excluded from the model of the physical world. But although the belief in the occurrence of infinite velocities was continuously retreating, *no upper limit* was imposed on any velocity. New-tonian mechanics admitted *all* possible values of velocity, and the velocity of electromagnetic waves was only one of many possi-ble finite values. There was nothing apparently absurd in Laplace's computation (which we know today was false) ac-cording to which the velocity of propagation of gravitation was 50,000,000 times larger than the velocity of light; on the con-trary, any claim that there is a certain finite upper limit for the velocity of physical actions would have appeared not only as an arbitrary stipulation but as a violation of the law of causality. For, suppose a body is moving with the velocity of light; sup-pose that it is then subjected to some accelerating physical influence; then it is inconceivable that such body could some-how "ignore" a force acting on it or, in different words, that a certain physical action could remain *without* physical effect and that the velocity of the body would *not* increase. Newtonian space was thus indifferent to *any* increase of velocity.

In this respect there is an important difference between the Newtonian and relativistic mechanics: the latter insists that the velocity of propagation of the electromagnetic waves is *the upper limit* which no physical action can surpass. A full insight into this important difference will lead to the same conclusion concerning the dynamization of space which we have already reached, though it will show it from a different angle.

It had not been fully realized before the advent of relativity that even those classical physicists who rejected the idea of infinitely fast physical actions unconsciously accepted the idea of instantaneous propagation. A. d'Abro pointed out that the totality of events simultaneous in the classical, that is, absolute sense, *is located on the world line of a point moving with in-finite velocity*.[20] Instantaneous space of classical physics can thus be regarded as a physical realization of instantaneous propaga-tion. The word "propagation" used here is misleading; it suggests wrongly the notion of time-consuming action which is gradu-ally unfolded in successive stages, while "infinite velocity" is devoid of any successive character; any action "moving" with such velocity is *simultaneously present in all points of its path* and therefore is outside of time. For this reason the term "instantaneous connection" should be substituted for "instantaneous propagation" because it is free of unconscious or half-conscious temporal associations. Classical space was such a network of instantaneous relations or connections; *spatial distances*, separating juxtaposed points, constituted precisely such an instantaneous network of relations.

For this reason it is understandable that the Newton-Galileo transformation follows automatically from the equations of Lorentz if we substitute for the velocity of light *c* an infinite value; the Newtonian-Galilean transformation is a limit case of the relativistic transformation. Physicists are well aware of this important relation between the two transformations; they are generally well aware of the physical import of the difference between Newton's and Einstein's dynamics; but what they are rarely, if at all, aware of is that the rejection of the notion of instantaneous propagation implies the rejection of the concept of space in its classical sense as a juxtaposition of simultaneously existing points.

We cannot therefore overestimate the importance of the following conclusion of relativistic physics for the philosophy of nature. *In nature there are no infinite velocities, that is, instantaneous physical interactions with all their phases coexisting simultaneously; there are no instantaneous connections joining distant simultaneous points-events; there are only successive connections, characterizing concrete physical actions,* and there is no need to stretch the passive and static space underneath concrete interactions by which physical reality is exhausted. This is the meaning of the statement of Whitehead: with the coming of relativity the spatial relations must stretch across time, if we continue to use the term "spatial," so much tinged by classical associations.

One more word to complete our answer to the question of how it was possible for what was in truth a dynamization of space to be misunderstood and conceived as a spatialization of time. The answer has, in part, already been given: the habit of spatializing time is only one mode of the tendency to eliminate time, the tendency which is as old as philosophy. It was precisely this tendency which, consciously or unconsciously, led Minkowski to use the expression "four-dimensional world" (*vierdimensionale Welt*) instead of "four-dimensional becoming." A great many interpreters were misled, as we have seen, by the static connotation of the term "world"; what is in truth a dynamical unfolding process was mistakenly regarded as a completed whole. It was also overlooked that the relativization of succession was far from being absolute and that succession of causally related events remains absolute, i.e., independent of any frame of reference.

But there are also other reasons for the misunderstanding, not unrelated to the first one. The habit of spatializing time could not have survived without being, in part at least, sanctioned by experience. Transformation of relations of succession into timeless instantaneous connections does not begin at the level of abstract thought; it begins at the level of sensory, in particular visual, perception. Human perception is of such a nature that it discloses to us only the kinds of succession that manifest a rhythm approximately the same as its own. In other words, motions either too slow or too fast are not perceived at all, or —what is only a different way of saying the same thing—are transformed into immobilities. Hence the profound observation of Bergson that *"percevoir signifie immobiliser."* [21] Thus the slow motion of a pointer across a dial or of the sun across the sky is not observed, only inferred; we do not perceive it, but we conclude that it exists when we see its different positions at different moments. Similarly, when motions are too fast they are not perceived at all; the motion of a flying bullet is not perceived at all, only inferred from its effect at a distant place; the fast motion of a bright luminous body in darkness is registered by our slow-reacting retina as a motionless luminous trajectory.

If even moderately fast-moving bodies appear to our imperfect sense organ to be present simultaneously in all the positions of their trajectories, how much more inconspicuous is the successive character of such fabulously fast actions as light and gravitation! Their propagation is practically instantaneous; when we turn a switch, the room is filled with light at once, and the effect seems to be simultaneous with its cause. Today we know that this is not, strictly speaking, true; but mankind had to wait until the seventeenth century to know this. The corresponding time intervals are so minute on the human and even on the planetary scale that they may, for practical purposes, be safely disregarded: to assert that the luminous and gravitational interaction between the objects of our daily experience is instantaneous is a permissible inaccuracy.

What is a negligible inaccuracy from the practical point of view becomes a fundamental fallacy or philosophical inaccuracy if it is regarded as true without qualifications. Besides, the situation is at once different when we turn from our daily surroundings to our closest cosmic neighbor—the moon—and its relation to our planet. The gravitational and luminous links between the earth and its satellite are no longer instantaneous. They require a certain interval of time which, though still small, cannot be disregarded: one second. As the distance increases, the duration of causal links increases correspondingly: it is eight minutes for the sun, four hours for Neptune, about four years to the nearest star, fifty years to Polaris, a thousand years for the great nebula in Orion, one million years to the nebula in Andromeda.

But our reason—or rather our imagination—retains habits acquired by its perpetual contact with our immediate biological surroundings. Even when the finite velocity of light and of electromagnetic vibrations in general was discovered, the habit of postulating instantaneous connections between distant objects did not disappear; hence the distinction made between successive causal connections occurring *in* space and instantaneous geometrical connections which constitute *space itself*.

Even when this distinction is rejected by the relativity theory, it survives in our imagination and a great and continually renewed effort is required to overcome this habit. We still have a tendency to duplicate concrete dynamic links between distant physical events by static geometric connections which are, so to speak, stretched underneath physical actions. The assertion of such timeless connections between physical events was obviously another aspect of the separation of space from time in classical physics. With absolute space and absolute simultaneity swept away, every ground for such separation disappears. This means that the only links in nature are not of *geometrical*, but of *chronogeometrical type*. In one sentence: *concrete physical processes do not need any static container*.

DYNAMIZATION OF SPACE IN THE GENERAL THEORY

This dynamization of space becomes even more evident when we turn from the special to the general theory of relativity. There is no place here for a detailed analysis of the process of generalization by which Einstein arrived at his theory of gravitation in extending his principle of relativity to accelerated motions; for our purpose it will be sufficient to state the results and to contrast them with the assertions of classical physics. The general theory, while retaining the fusion of space and time, removes another classical distinction which was so fundamental in prerelativistic time: that between space and matter. The distinction between space and its physical content was implicitly abolished by the special theory as we have just seen; in Lorentz's equations the traditional separation of dynamics from kinematics disappears and space fused with time seems to acquire active physical properties which classical space did not possess, at least not to such a degree: for instance its resistance to an unlimited increase of velocity. We shall see in Chapter XIV how radically this particular consequence of Lorentz's equations transforms the traditional concept of matter. In the general theory this revision of the classical distinction between the passive geometrical container and the changing physical content is much more explicit and obvious; but its full significance will become clear only if we hold it against the contrasting backdrop of the traditional concepts of space, matter, and motion.

Classical space (see Chapters II and IV) was always *empty*, if not *de facto*, at least *de jure*; even in the fluid theories, which regarded space as continuously filled by the hypothetical aether, the distinction between space and the stuff which fills it was fully preserved. Matter, whether ponderable or aetherial, was always conceived as existing in *space*, superadded, so to speak, to the three-dimensional receptacle. Logically, even if not temporally, space was prior to matter. According to the atomistic scheme, which was implicitly present even in the fluid theories of matter, various bits of space occupy different regions of space in a temporary and accessory way, and the temporary character of space occupancy accounted for the reality of motion. The fundamental homogeneity and immutability of space remained entirely unaffected by the varying distribution of matter in it; every spatial position remained eternally the same, whether occupied by matter or not.

This distinction between matter and space disappears in the general theory of relativity—at least as long as it is properly interpreted, that is, purged of all Newtonian associations which hover reminiscently around certain words. There is no more distinction between the indifferent and passive container and changing physical content; both matter and space, formerly so sharply separated, are fused into one single dynamical reality: a non-Euclidean continuum with curvature varying from place to place and from one moment to another. The phenomena of gravitation and of accelerated motion generally, which were interpreted by classical physics as manifestations of *forces* located in space, follow naturally from the curvature of the four-dimensional non-Euclidean continuum. Just as a ship moving across the ocean moves along a curved path in virtue of the curvature of the earth surface, a physical body contained in a local curvature of time-space moves in accelerated motion.

It is true that this analogy is far from being accurate and, if it is taken literally, it may become dangerously misleading for at least two reasons. First, it does not express the nonintuitive character of the spatio-temporal curvature; it seemingly conveys the wrong idea that the effect of this curvature manifests itself necessarily in a *change of the shape of the path*. This, of course, is not true: a rectilinear accelerated motion is a result of basically the same spatiotemporal curvature as a parabolic motion of a projectile or an elliptical orbit of a planet. This becomes immediately clear as soon as we remember that the world lines of accelerated bodies are represented in the four-dimensional space-time diagram by *curved lines* even if their projections into the three-dimensional cross sections are straight lines. This shows plainly that the term "curvature" is essentially metaphorical, for it is based on an analogy with curvature of two-dimensional surfaces. For this reason the term "space constant" is less misleading and therefore preferable to that of "space curvature," as Bertrand Russell recognized as early as 1897.[22]

Before considering the second limitation of the two-dimensional illustration, it is important to realize all its positive sides. At first the analogy between a sailing ship and a moving body seems to be correct and very suggestive: in both cases it is the geometrical structure of the surroundings which determines the character of the motion. The "constraining" effect of the non-Euclidean structure of time-space is analogous to that of the spherical surface of the earth in the bodies moving on it. From this point of view the distinction between "natural" inertial motion and "enforced" accelerated motion vanishes completely in Einstein's dynamics. This distinction goes back to Aristotle, but in a modified form was retained by classical physics; in spite of the profound differences between the physics of Aristotle and that of Newton, the distinction between "enforced" and "forceless" motions was fully preserved by the latter. According to the general relativity theory the inertial motion is merely a *limit case* of the accelerated motion and the "inertial field" is a limit case of the gravitational field. The classical case of a "body free from all external actions" is, strictly speaking, never realized; stated in a relativistic language, the curvature of time-space is nowhere zero; only in the regions far away from material bodies is the curvature negligible, for practical purposes at least, and the corresponding motions are very approximately uniform and rectilinear.

The fundamental difference between Newtonian mechanics and the generalized theory of relativity is that in the former the world lines of material particles are straight lines either parallel to the time axis (i.e., the particles at rest) or *inclined* to the same axis (the particles in a uniform rectilinear motion); all deviations from rest or rectilinear uniform motions, that is, all curvatures of the world lines, are due to the action of some material—whether matter or "force"—present *in* space, but *different* from it. In the general theory of relativity *every* motion, accelerated or not, results naturally from the local structure of time-space. In other words, the law of inertia is a special case of the law of gravitation, or, what is the same, the law of gravitation is a generalized law of inertia. The dichotomy of natural and enforced motions is thus abolished because *every motion is natural*, that is, it occurs along a certain geodesic; but geodetic lines are generally of much more complex shape and only in regions of the spatiotemporal continuum in which the curvature is practically zero do they very approximately acquire the character of straight lines. This relativistic approach means an interesting reversal of the classical procedure. It is not inertia that explains gravitation, as in classical kinetic models, where the acceleration of gravitating bodies was ultimately due to the impact of inert masses; on the contrary, it is gravitation that, according to the relativistic mechanics, explains the phenomena of inertia.

But if gravitational action is thus reduced to a local deformation of the four-dimensional continuum, matter itself is reduced to the presence of some peculiarities in its spatiotemporal surrounding; for matter manifests itself by its gravitational field, from which it cannot be separated. If we eliminate the gravitational field, we eliminate matter itself and vice versa. It is true that classical physics maintains the distinction between the material substance itself and its action in space; or, in less philosophical and more physical terms, between the "inertial mass" and "gravitational mass." While inertial mass was regarded as a substantial core of matter, *vis insita* of Newton, *residing* in certain regions of space, gravitational mass was conceived as an action produced by inertial mass in surrounding space. Whether the propagation of gravitation was regarded as instantaneous or finite, whether it was explained dynamically *à la* Boscovich or mechanically, one assumption was always the same: that gravitation was something *intrinsically different* from, though invariably associated with, the substantial inertial nucleus of matter.

But precisely this distinction was abolished by the general theory. Einstein's principle of equivalence fuses the manifestations of inertia and gravitation into one single reality, and the numerical equality of the inertial and gravitational mass, which was a puzzling coincidence within the classical framework, is a mere consequence of their basic identity in the general theory. It is wrong to say that matter "causes" the corresponding curvature in space, as is sometimes vaguely suggested, for there is no relation of causality between matter and a local warping of space. The relation is that of identity: matter and local curvature of space are *one and the same reality*. Eddington's language is quite explicit on this point:

> On the Newtonian theory no explanation of gravitation would be considered complete unless it described the mechanism by which a piece of matter gets a grip on the surrounding medium and makes it the carrier of the gravitational influence radiating from the matter. Nothing corresponding to this is required in the present theory. We do not ask how mass gets a grip on space-time and causes the curvature which our theory postulates. That would be as superfluous as to ask how light gets a grip on the electromagnetic medium so as to cause it to oscillate. The light *is* the oscillation; the mass *is* the curvature. There is no causal effect to be atributed to mass; still less is there any to be attributed to matter. [Italics in the original.][23]

Or in the words of Emile Borel:

> All this is a consequence of the well-known fact that the Newtonian mass (or gravitational mass) and the mass of Galileo (inertial mass) are rigorously identical. It is therefore possible in the equations to substitute for the presence and action of matter the modifications cor-

responding to the displacements produced by the inertial forces; in mathematical language, this means that
*matter manifests itself only in the deformations of the
four-dimensional space-time.* [Italics added.][24]

Meyerson's philosophical conclusion that in the relativistic
theory of gravitation matter was "resorbed into space," [25] seems
to be entirely justified, if we do not forget that it is less misleading to speak of the resorption of matter into *time-space* rather
than into space. This necessary correction makes very questionable the view, defended by Meyerson and Bergson,[26] that the
general theory of relativity is a continuation and even a culmination of the Cartesian tendency to reduce matter to space. The
relativistic fusion of matter and space was made possible by
sacrificing nearly *all* features of classical space. The space of
the general theory of relativity not only is not Euclidean; it does
not even have the character of homogeneity which the special
theory of relativity seemingly preserved. Its different regions
are not qualitatively equivalent, since they differ by their local
non-Euclidean curvature. It is probably not infinite, though
still without limits. In it, unlike the infinite space of Bruno and
Newton, limitlessness and finiteness are compatible features.
It is indissolubly united with time, not only because of the special
theory of relativity, of which the general theory is an extension,
but in an even more striking sense: relativistic space-time does
not have a rigid structure because its curvature varies not only
from place to place, but also from one moment to another. This
is an inevitable consequence of the fact that there is a mutual
displacement of material bodies, or, in the language of the
general theory, a mutual displacement of local deformations of
space-time.

Moreover, not only is there a continuous change of local
curvatures due to the mutual displacement of bodies, but even
the total curvature of space-time varies in time. There is considerable astronomical evidence *for the expansion of space-time,*
that is, the continuous increase of the "radius of curvature." [27]

Can we imagine a more radical incorporation of the concept
of space into that of becoming? What is left of the classical

definition of space as "simultaneous juxtaposition of points"? Nothing but a word with misleading connotations.

This may sound like a rash statement; but such a conclusion is hardly escapable if we fully realize the contrast between the non-Euclidean heterogeneous, dynamic, variable continuum and the homogeneous, passive, rigid receptacle of Euclid and Newton. The latter is always implicitly or semiconsciously present in our mind when we use the term "space," and a considerable and constantly renewed effort is necessary to overcome this centuries-old habit. Even the mathematical mastery of the theory of relativity does not necessarily guarantee that the old habit will be overcome. The widespread misinterpretation of the union of space and time by many physicists and philosophers shows this very clearly. This misinterpretation has various degrees, ranging from the attitude of those who interpret the synthesis of space and time as a sort of four-dimensional hyperspace and who, like Jeans, see in it a confirmation of Bradley's elimination of time,[28] to those who in their conscious mind reject the fallacy of spatialization without getting rid of its subconscious residuum.

Our subconscious is far more conservative than we are willing to admit, and this is true not only of our emotional subconscious but of the intellectual one as well. That is why Newtonian-Euclidean habits of thought will—if not always, at least for a considerable time—appear more natural to mankind than the new modes of thought which require so much effort and vigilant analysis. The fact that we use the word "space-time" instead of "time-space" may appear innocent enough; but it is a significant symptom of our unconscious tendency to prefer space to time, a tendency which accounts for so much confusion about the true nature of the spatiotemporal synthesis.

It is equally significant that many expositors of relativity, after talking profusely about the union of space and time in dealing with the special theory of relativity, seem to forget about it when they begin to treat the general theory. Expressions like "Riemannian *space*" or "curvature of *space*" abound, and not only in popular expositions. Yet everybody who is aware of the fact that the general theory is an extension of the special theory should realize that such expressions are essentially incomplete and that the union of space and time is even *closer* in the general than in the special theory. Even such a serious scholar as Meyerson, who was publicly praised by Einstein himself for his understanding of relativity, speaks about "matter resorbed into space" instead of "space-time." This apparently harmless oversight very probably accounts for his erroneous view of relativity as a continuation of the Cartesian tendency to reduce matter to space.

The foregoing paragraphs really dealt with the second limitation of the sailing ship analogy, the limitation due precisely to its *static* character. The spherical sea surface of the earth is a completed entity; its various geographical positions exist prior to the motion of a ship. This is the meaning of the statement that a ship successively *occupies* different positions or that it moves along an already existing track. Similarly, a body moving in the Euclidean three-dimensional space of classical physics successively *occupies* various positions. In this respect no static non-Euclidean space differs essentially from its Euclidean counterpart; and it is with this notion in the back of our minds that we are inclined to speak of a body moving *in* non-Euclidean space. Again various positions of its future path pre-exist and, so to speak, *await* its occupation by a moving body. The same idea of space as a pre-existing container of both matter and motion underlies both Euclidean and static non-Euclidean models.

But motion *in* space would be physically possible only if a separation of space from time were possible, or—what is the same—if simultaneity in an absolute sense were possible. For Euclidean and static non-Euclidean spaces agree in being classes of juxtaposed, i.e., *simultaneously existing points;* they differ by their metric, but their independence of time is their common feature, provided that their curvature is constant through time; it is of secondary importance whether it is zero, positive, or negative or whether it is everywhere the same or different at different places. (A two-dimensional model could represent static non-Euclidean space by surface of variable curvature, such as an ellipsoid or a paraboloid or even a spherical surface with local motionless humps.)

But relativistic space *cannot* be separated from time. According to the special theory there is no absolute simultaneity, that is, no absolute juxtaposition. Moreover, the space constant of the relativistic theory of gravitation varies not only locally, but with time as well. It is thus basically incorrect to claim, as some popular or semipopular expositions do, that the pre-existing non-Euclidean structure of space *enforces* bodies to move in the way that a system of channels constrains streams of water to run in certain directions. The objectionable character of such imaginative interpretations was well exposed by Bertrand Russell, whose exceptional ability to expound systematically the classical conceptual framework in his earlier works did not prevent him from being receptive to the recent revolutionary changes in physics:

> The old geometry assumed a static space, which it could do because space and time were supposed to be separable. It is natural to think of motion as following a path in space which is there *before and after the motion:* a tram moves *along pre-existing tram-lines.* This view of motion, however, is no longer tenable. A moving point is a series of positions in space-time; a later moving point cannot pursue the "same" course, since its time-coordinate is different, which means that, in another equally legitimate system of coordinates, its space-coordinates also will be different. We think of a tram as performing the same journey every day, because we think of the earth as fixed; but from the sun's point of view, the tram never repeats a former journey. "We cannot step twice into the same river," as Heraclitus says. [Italics added.] [29]

This passage stands in healthy contrast to Russell's former view that "to realize the unimportance of time is the gate of wisdom"; it stands in equally healthy contrast to his youthful defense of Newton.[30] No matter how paradoxical Russell's words may appear, they follow as a logical consequence, once the distinction between the passive and rigid geometrical container and its changing physical content is denied. On this distinction between matter and space the timelessness of space is based; once this distinction is removed, there is no basis for retaining the concept of static container. Thus, instead of matter being resorbed into space, it would be more accurate to speak of space being fused with its changing and dynamic physical content. This is what Eddington had in mind when he stressed that "besides the geometrization of mechanics there has been a mechanization of geometry" or when Reichenbach warned that it is misleading to speak about a geometrization of gravitation.[31]

Yet the idea of a timeless container, in which all matter is located and in which all motions take place, has such deep roots in the very structure of human imagination that it is almost impossible to get rid of it. As soon as we begin to chart the motion of any body, we begin to plot the future positions of which its future path will consist; we forget that these future positions *in virtue of their very futurity* are nothing actually existing; we transform their implicit and, so to speak, potential existence, their *tendency* to happen, into something *already existing;* but because at the same time, succession is a real fact perceived in the concrete form of "not yet" feeling, we spontaneously adopt a compromise solution: we claim that, although the future *positions* of the moving body exist *now,* they still are *not yet* occupied. Thus the distinction between motion and its spatial container is made; while succession is assigned to motion, it is completely excluded from space.

This distinction is implicitly present on a very low mental level, even on the sensory level of high animals: a hunting animal, e.g., the wolf in Jack London's *The Call of the Wild,* which crosses a river peninsula to make a shorter route in catching a rabbit, actually *sees* the future unoccupied position of its victim because it is formed by apparently unchanging physical features—for instance, a certain group of bushes, a bend of the river, and the like. Visual perception generally enables us to *see* the goal or targets of our present activity, whether of walking or shooting. It requires a Whiteheadian sophistication to realize that a situation perceived from a certain spatial distance and that which we effectively attain by our present activity are *two distinct events in time* which only our inadequate language, based on the Newtonian idea of motionless and eventless space, fuses into the spurious identity of "one and the same location."

Thus the very nature of our visual perception leads not only to a detailed anticipation of future events but even to the idea of pre-existing positions in space *waiting* for these events. The biological success of this psychological process obscures for us the ontological inadequacy to which Russell called attention in the passage just quoted. How stubborn this tendency is to believe in a processless container is evidenced by the fact that even now physicists continue to speak about motion of bodies *in* non-Euclidean space, or that the dynamized three-dimensional space of Riemann is placed by some relativists into a flat four-dimensional space which supposedly contains it in the same way as Euclidean space contains curved surfaces.

It is clear that the transformation of the concept of space is very radical. It affects traditional concepts of matter and motion as well. We have seen that even such a constitutive feature of spatiality as the relation of juxtaposition loses its physical meaning. But before exploring fully the *positive* meaning of the fusion of space with time, it is imperative to see the important modifications which the classical concept of time underwent by being integrated relativistically with space.

NOTES FOR CHAPTER XI

1. H. Minkowski, "Space and Time," translation of an address delivered at the 80th Assembly of German Natural Scientists and Physicians at Cologne, September 21, 1908. In Lorentz et al., *The Principles of Relativity*, pp. 75-91.
2. E. Meyerson, *La Déduction relativiste*, pp. 98-101; H. Weyl, *Was ist Materie?* (Berlin, 1924), pp. 82, 87.
3. E. Cunningham, *The Principle of Relativity* (Cambridge, 1914), p. 191.
4. *Ibid.*, p. 213.
5. L. Silberstein, *The Theory of Relativity* (London, 1914), p. 134;

Kurt Gödel, "A Remark about the Relationship between Relativity Theory and Idealistic Philosophy"; A. Einstein, "Remarks to the Essays Appearing in This Collective Volume." Both in *Albert Einstein, Philosopher-Scientist*, ed. by P. A. Schilpp (Evanston, 1949), pp. 560, 687-688.

6. H. Weyl, *op. cit.*, p. 87; E. Cassirer, *Zum Einstein'schen Relativitätstheorie* (Berlin, 1921), p. 119.

7. P. Langevin, "L'aspect général de la théorie de la relativité," *Bulletin scientifique des étudiants de Paris*, No. 2 (1922), p. 6; *Bulletin de la Société française de philosophie*, 6 avril 1922, p. 112; E. Meyerson, *op. cit.*, p. 102-110; A. Einstein, "A propos de la déduction relativiste de M.E. Meyerson," *Revue philosophique*, Vol. CV (1928), p. 165.

8. H. Weyl, *Space-Time-Matter*, tr. by H. L. Brosse (London, 1922), p. 283.

9. A. E. Eddington, *Space, Time, Gravitation* (Cambridge, 1920), pp. 51-52; P. W. Bridgman, *The Logic of Modern Physics* (New York, Macmillan, 1948), p. 74; G. N. Lewis, *The Anatomy of Science* (Yale University Press, 1926), p. 81; A. N. Whitehead, *The Concept of Nature*, Chap. III, especially pp. 53-54; also p. 178; H. Bergson, *Durée et simultanéité* (2d ed., Paris, 1923), in particular Chap. VI; H. Reichenbach, *Die Philosophie der Raum-Zeit-Lehre*, p. 134 (concerning the static misinterpretation of the "world" of Minkowski). Eddington's view was misunderstood by Meyerson; the passage quoted by him (*La Déduction relativiste*, p. 100) represents the static view which Eddington, as the context indicates, *rejects*. See also Eddington, *The Nature of the Physical World* (Cambridge, 1928), pp. 50-52, 55-58.

10. Concerning this problem in Descartes' philosophy, see Jean Wahl, *Du rôle de l'idée de l'instant dans la philosophie de Descartes*, 2d ed. (Paris, 1953), pp. 18-19. For the notion of instantaneous substances in the Arabian atomism of Mutakallimun, see K. Lasswitz, *Geschichte der Atomistik von Mittelalter bis Newton*, Vol. I, pp. 141-146.

11. C. Hartshorne, "Contingency and the New Era in Metaphysics," *Journal of Philosophy*, Vol. XXIX (1932), p. 429.

12. H. Bergson, *Creative Evolution*, p. 45.

13. K. Gödel, *loc. cit.*, p. 557.

14. B. Spinoza, *Ethica*, II, prop. 44, corol. II: "[res] quaeque propterea *absque ulla temporis relatione*, sed sub quadam aeternitatis specie debent concipi." (Italics added.)

15. Cf. my article "The Doctrine of Necessity Re-examined," *The Review of Metaphysics*, Vol. V, No. 1 (Sept. 1951), especially pp. 27-30, where I tried to show that Kant's attempt to eliminate succession from the noumenal realm cannot be regarded as successful.

16. P. Langevin, "Le temps, l'espace et la causalité dans la physique moderne," *Bulletin de la Société française de philosophie*, Séance du 19 octobre 1911, p. 37.

17. The expression used by Whitehead in *An Enquiry Concerning the Principles of Natural Knowledge*, 2d ed. (Cambridge University Press, 1925), p. 31.

18. That this follows immediately from the invariance of Minkowski's "world interval" was already shown by Langevin in 1911 (*loc. cit.,* pp. 25-26).

19. Cf. Chapter III, above, Note, 23.

20. A. d'Abro, *Bergson ou Einstein?* (Paris, 1927), pp. 304-305.

21. H. Bergson, *Matière et mémoire* (Paris, 1896), p. 232.

22. B. Russell, *An Essay on the Foundations of Geometry*, p. 17.

23. Eddington, *The Nature of the Physical World*, p. 156.

24. E. Borel, *L'Espace et le temps* (Paris, 1923), p. 204.

25. *La Déduction relativiste*, p. 135.

26. E. Meyerson, *ibid.*, p. 135; H. Bergson, *Durée et simultanéité*, p. 241.

27. A. E. Eddington, *The Expanding Universe* (Cambridge University Press, 1933).

28. J. Jeans, *The New Background of Science* (New York, Macmillan, 1933), pp. 109-110.

29. B. Russell, *The Analysis of Matter* (New York, Dover, 1954), pp. 61-62.

30. B. Russell, *Our Knowledge of the External World*, p. 167; *The Principles of Mathematics*, pp. 492-93.

31. A. E. Eddington, *The Nature of the Physical World*, p. 137; H. Reichenbach, *Die Philosophie der Raum-Zeit-Lehre*, p. 294: "*nicht die Gravitationslehre wird zur Geometrie, sondern die Geometrie wird zu einem Ausdruck des Gravitationsfeldes.*" (Reichenbach's italics.)

XII · THE MODIFICATION OF THE CONCEPT OF TIME

RECAPITULATION

THERE is no need to repeat what has already been said about the relativization of simultaneity. We have seen that absolute simultaneity *simply does not exist;* there are no instantaneous cuts across spatiotemporal becoming which would contain all "truly simultaneous" events. But contrary to the widespread impression, this elimination of absolute simultaneity affects the classical concept of space more profoundly than that of time. As the terms "space" and "the totality of simultaneous events" are synonymous, the denial of one implies the denial of the other and vice versa. In other words, the static space of Euclid and Newton does not exist: the negation of absolute simultaneity means an elimination of absolute juxtaposition. On the other hand, *succession of causally related events* remains a topological invariant, being absolute for *all* observers; only the succession of causally unrelated events is relativized, but such succession, like absolute simultaneity, does not have any operational meaning. This follows immediately from the limit character of the velocity of causal actions.

But a more detailed analysis perhaps will not be out of place here; it may shed additional light on the results already obtained.

When the finite velocity of light was discovered, it became clear that the simultaneity of distant events can never be perceived, but only *inferred*. Classical physics, however, retained the concept of simultaneity because it believed that inference must lead to identical results, that observers located in different regions of space and moving with different velocities must eventually agree about the simultaneity or nonsimultaneity of distant events. Two events are simultaneous when they are perceived at the same time by motionless observers stationed at the same distance from both events.

Today it is evident that such a definition is circular. The concept of absolute simultaneity, which has to be defined, occurs *twice* in the definiens: first in the assumption that an observer is at rest in respect to absolute space, second in the very concept of distance. We have seen that space is merely another word for the *class of absolutely simultaneous events;* similarly, the word "distance" designates a one-dimensional series of *coexisting,* i.e., *simultaneously existing*, points. No wonder that a classical physicist was able to find in his conclusions what had been silently assumed in his premises. Observers who either are not stationed at the same distance from both events or are moving with a certain velocity in respect to absolute space will, according to him, still agree with the privileged observer about the simultaneity of distant events; although they will *perceive* events which are truly simultaneous as successive and those which are truly successive as simultaneous, they will still be able to differentiate this spurious perceived simultaneity from that which they will *infer*, and which will be the same as that of the motionless equidistant observer. This process of inference, by which a spurious simultaneity was differentiated from an objective one, was based on the classical theorem of addition of velocities, which was unhesitatingly applied to the velocity of the electromagnetic vibrations. But the principle of constant velocity of light removes the basis on which this inference is based.

This means that the simultaneity of distant events is not only never perceived, but not even unambiguously *inferred;* if we persist in inferring it, we obtain different results in different frames of reference. As no frame of reference has a privileged character in relativistic physics, none of the corresponding observers has any right to claim that his own simultaneity is the only true one. All divergent claims of various observers associated with different inertial systems are equally valid.

It would be more correct, however, to say that all these divergent claims are *equally wrong* if we have to avoid a semantic obscurity which, unfortunately, is present in many expositions of the relativity theory. For relativists continue to speak about the simultaneity of distant events, although such simultaneity is a mere conceptual entity, created by definition, intrinsically unobservable, and, when computed, different in different systems. It is questionable whether the continued use of such a ghostly and fictitious term is fruitful or even meaningful. It appears to be an effect of sheer semantic inertia, a simple concession made to our traditional and outdated linguistic habits.

There have been numerous instances of similar semantic inertia in the past; the history of science abounds in them. For instance, when oxygen and nitrogen were discovered, they were called "dephlogisticated air" and "phlogisticated air" respectively. Thus the discoveries which in truth were the last *coups de grâce* to the phlogiston theory were at first expressed in the terms of the very theory which they undermined![1] We do not seem to be in a basically different position today when we continue to speak about the simultaneity of distant events within the framework of the relativity theory. It is not sufficient to join the adjective "relative" to the noun "simultaneity"; the noun itself should be dropped because of its thoroughly misleading connotations. Instead of the "relativization" of simultaneity we should speak about its *elimination*. A. A. Robb was one of a few relativists who consistently insisted on this point: according to him *"there is no identity of instants at different places at all."* [1a] The persistence of our linguistic habits merely reflects the obstinacy of the underlying mental habits; we are all unconsciously Newtonians even when we profess to be relativists, and the classical idea of world-wide instants, containing simultaneous spatially separated events, still haunts the subconscious even of relativistic physicists;

though verbally rejected, it manifests itself, like a Freudian symbol, in a certain conservatism of language.

The same reason which makes it impossible to speak meaningfully of the simultaneity of distant events makes the concept of the succession of causally unrelated events equally meaningless. Such succession is never directly perceived, but only inferred; but as it may, by an appropriate change of a system of reference, be converted into an inferred simultaneity, everything which has been said about the unreality of the latter applies *mutatis mutandis* to it.

This, however, is not true of the succession of causally connected events. Such succession is directly perceivable only in the events constituting the world line of an observer himself; it is inferred for spatially distant events which constitute world lines different from our own. But there is one important difference in contrast to the cases just mentioned. The succession of causally related events, unlike that of causally unrelated events, and unlike simultaneity, is a *topological invariant;* it remains a succession for *every conceivable observer.* This was one of the reasons why we claimed that the relativistic synthesis of space and time cannot be characterized as a spatialization of time: while juxtaposition is completely relativized (or, better, eliminated), causal succession retains its absolute character.

THE MEANING OF THE DILATATION OF TIME IN THE SPECIAL THEORY

Even the metrical relativization of time has certain limits which in popular and semipopular expositions are not sufficiently stressed. It is true that the length of temporal intervals varies according to the frame of reference; all durations associated with the systems moving in respect to mine will appear to me as lengthened: this is the famous "dilatation of time" expressed by the formula

$$t' = \frac{t}{\sqrt{1 - \dfrac{v^2}{c^2}}}$$

where t' is a time associated with system S' moving with the velocity v with respect to the system S having a time t.

Two facts should be emphasized very strongly. First, the fact that the temporal intervals appear *always lengthened* and *never contracted* has several important consequences. One of them is that the *proper time of an observer* represents the minimum interval; two events separated by a certain interval of proper time within its own system can in no system whatever appear separated by a *shorter* interval; at best they may appear to succeed each other after the *same* interval if, by chance, they are observed from a system S' *at rest* in respect to the home system S.

If the temporal interval thus never can become shorter in any system, it is evident that it *never can shrink to zero*. This has been already stated in different words: the succession of causally related events can never by any change of the system be transformed into simultaneity. But if the temporal distance can never be reduced to zero, *a fortiori* it cannot change its sign; this has already been expressed by saying that the order of causally related events can never appear reversed in any system of reference.

The absolute irreversibility of the world lines is one of the results of the relativity theory by which the status of time was certainly not weakened.

It may be objected that though the apparent length of temporal intervals has a definite lower limit, it has no upper limit. Theoretically, a temporal interval may appear infinitely dilated if the velocity of the other observer reaches the critical value of the velocity of light. But this precisely can never happen to any observer, because no matter can ever reach the velocity of the electromagnetic vibrations. Besides, other considerations based on the quantum theory which will be mentioned later indicate that not only is the critical velocity of light unattainable, but that, very probably, even the asymptotic approach to this value has a certain limit. There is therefore no ground for the fear that there are certain systems in which the flight of time may appear suspended.

Another point which should be equally stressed is that in the special theory of relativity the dilatation of time as well as the contraction of lengths does not have the naive ontological significance which it possessed in the original Lorentz hypothesis. As proposed originally by Lorentz and FitzGerald, the modifications of the temporal and spatial intervals in the moving systems of reference were genuinely *real* because their motion was *real* in the absolute sense, being a displacement with respect to absolute space; thus the dilatation of time and contraction of geometrical intervals measured, so to speak, the physical difference between the state of absolute rest and that of absolute motion. Both modifications were regarded as the real causes of which the *appearance* of the constancy of light was an effect.

In the special theory of relativity the very opposite is true: the constancy of the luminous velocity is regarded as the true physical cause of the *apparent* dilatation of time and *apparent* contraction of distance. This follows immediately from their *reciprocal* character. While in the original Lorentz-FitzGerald theory the temporal intervals were *actually* dilated in the moving systems and remain unaffected in the stationary ones (both terms "moving" and "stationary" having then an absolute significance), in the special theory there is a perfect *reciprocity of appearances*. To an observer in the system *S* the duration of physical processes in the system *S'* appears to be lengthened, but an observer in *S'* will claim the same thing about the system *S*. This reciprocity was conspicuously missing in the absolutist theory of Lorentz for the simple reason that there was then no absolute equivalence of all inertial systems; one of them which had the privilege of being motionless in respect to absolute space had also the privilege of being associated with the true Newtonian time, flowing evenly and with constant rapidity.

With the elimination of absolute space and absolute motion any reason for retaining the privileged frame of reference disappears and, consequently, the perfect equivalence of all inertial systems is assured. The reciprocity of appearances is a logical consequence of such an equivalence, which is the very essence of the special theory. About this point there is no disagreement possible among those who understand the special theory. Thus Max Born, in answering some opponents of the special theory who claimed that the dilatation of time and contraction of lengths, being physically *uncaused*, contradict the principle of causality, says:

> Thus the contraction is only a consequence of our way of regarding things and is not a change of physical reality. Hence it does not come within the scope of the conception of cause and effect.[2]

Similarly Jean Becquerel concluded:

> In brief, the contraction results simply from the different ways in which two observers define simultaneity and from the fact that the shape of a moving body can only be defined as the locus of the simultaneous positions of the different points of the body.[3]

The same reasoning applies to the dilatation of time as it follows immediately from Lorentz's transformation formulae. From this point of view the dilatation of time is comparable to *the effect of perspective* by which the apparent size of spatially distant events is seemingly reduced. Henri Bergson in his critical work about the relativity theory repeatedly used this happy analogy for illustrating the *apparent* character of the modification of spatial and temporal intervals. One passage is worth quoting in full:

> As a painter I have to represent two figures, John and James, the former beside me, the other two or three hundred meters from me. I shall draw the first life size and I shall reduce the other to the size of a dwarf. A fellow painter standing near James, if he also wants to paint the two of them, will do just the opposite; he will make John very small and James of normal height. Furthermore, we shall both be right. But granting that we are both correct, has one the right to conclude that John and James have neither normal height nor dwarf-like stature, or both of them at once, or whichever you

like? Evidently not. . . . When I am beside John, measuring him whenever I like and painting him life size, I am giving him his real dimensions; when I represent James as a dwarf, I only express the impossibility of touching him—even, if I may say so, the degree of this impossibility; the *degree of impossibility* is precisely what we call distance, and it is the distance which perspective takes into account. Likewise, within the system where I am, and which I make motionless by imagining it as my own system of reference, I measure directly a time which is mine and that of my system. But by the very act of making my system motionless I have set in motion others, and in divers ways. They have acquired different velocities. The greater their velocities, the more they contrast with my own motionlessness. It is this greater or lesser distance between the values of their velocity and the zero-value of my velocity which I am expressing in my mathematical representations of the other systems by assigning them more of less slow times, all of them slower than mine just as I am expressing the distance between James and me by reducing James's height. The plurality of times which I obtain in this way does not exclude the unity of real time; on the contrary, it presupposes it. In the same way the apparent reduction of James's height on different canvases representing his body at different distances indicates that the real James retains the same height.[4]

In this passage Bergson is really insisting on the *equality of proper or local times.* What we call "lengthened" or "dilated" durations are in truth nothing but "proper times" observed from different frames of reference. The alleged dilatation of time is thus an *effect of perspective,* so to speak, although the perspective in question is the *perspective of velocity* rather than that of spatial distance. The "local time," that is, the time interval between two events within its frame of reference, remains unaffected; it appears to be lengthened only to an external observer, that is, to an observer moving with a certain velocity with respect to the events observed.

It is true that some physicists insist that the distinction between "appearance" and "reality" in the special theory of relativity is not justified and that the minimum-time interval or "proper time" is in no sense more real than the plurality of dilated times. This is the view, for instance, of Max Born.[5] But would this not stand in a strange contradiction to his statement quoted above, in which he insisted that the dilatation of time is not real in the physical ontological sense? If the dilatation of time is *not* real, how can it otherwise be characterized? Is not the term "apparent" the only adequate one in contrast to the term "real" which Born rejects? A similar inconsistent and vacillating attitude may be found in A. d'Abro. On the one hand, he uses nearly the same metaphor as Bergson in characterizing the apparent modification of time intervals. While Bergson compares it to the optical effect of the perspective, D'Abro compares it to the apparent modification of the optical image in a concave mirror.[6] On the other hand, D'Abro claims that to ask which duration of the whole class of durations perceived from different frames of reference is real is as meaningless as to ask which color of an object is real:

> As for wondering which of these durations is real we might as well wonder what the real color of an opal is. From one point of view it may be yellow, but red if we move to the left and green or blue if we move to the right.[7]

Underlying these vacillating attitudes of Born and D'Abro is the belief that the distinction between "real" and "apparent" is contrary to the spirit of the relativity theory. For, according to them, if we attribute the character of "reality" to the proper time of a phenomenon, while regarding the dilated times as apparent or less real, we are returning to the prerelativistic concept of the privileged system. To illustrate this by a concrete example: if we claim that the proper time or "local time" of the atomic vibration is its *true* time, do we not *ipso facto* single out one system, i.e., the system which is at rest in respect to the atom, as more privileged than any other? And do we not thus unwittingly accept one of the basic postulates of prerelativistic dynamics?

But this conclusion is completely unwarranted. Even a relativist does not doubt that *every observer is at rest with respect to himself* without necessarily identifying his own immobility in respect to himself with the absolute motionlessness of the Newtonian space. This unique relation of "being motionless with respect to himself," which is nothing but a physical expression of the law of contradiction, was correctly recognized by Bergson *as one absolutist element* in the relativity theory; from this, the privileged character of the "proper duration" follows naturally.

This may also be shown by a closer analysis of D'Abro's claim according to which the question which duration is real is as meaningless as the question which color of an object is real. What is a color of an object? Nothing but a certain wave pattern of reflected radiation, a pattern which, as D'Abro points out correctly, is different in different directions and changes when an observer is moving. But it is evident that this wave pattern surrounding the object is by definition *external* to the object itself; not only does it reside *outside* the object, but it owes its very existence to factors independent of the object— the incident light, the transparency of the surrounding medium, and others. This was the reason why already by Lucretius it was clearly seen that color cannot be a constitutive property of any object.[8] But it is not correct to claim that the status of proper duration or local time is about as subjective as that of the secondary qualities; on the contrary, it belongs to *the very nature* of the physical process which constitutes the object itself. The proper duration of any physical process must be therefore regarded as the *causal nucleus* of all other "dilated" durations; or, even more concisely, the proper durations *appear* to be lengthened in other frames of reference than their own by the effect of the "perspective of velocity."[9]

But although Bergson's view was basically correct, it was obscured by some other assertions which cannot be upheld as long as the relativity theory is accepted. For instance, his iden-

tification of "apparent" and "unobservable" is completely unwarranted. He claimed that the relativistic dilatation of time
as well as the contraction of lengths is unobservable in principle and will never be verified empirically. Both these assertions were false: the dilatation of time is not only observable,
but has already been verified.

Bergson arrived at his wrong conclusion by the following
spurious reasoning: every observer perceives only his own local
time, in which no lengthening of duration takes place. By means
of Lorentz's formulae he computes that his own duration must
appear lengthened to any other observer moving with respect
to him with a certain velocity. But as soon as the first observer
really entered the system of any other one, this dilatation would
disappear, although he would judge again that it must take place
in his original system. Thus, Bergson claims, the relativistic
effects of dilatation of time and contraction of lengths do not
really occur; they are only "phantasmatic" in the sense that
they are always "attributed" to an external observer, never
actually perceived or registered by a real observer.[10] They are,
in Bergson's words, mere "illusions of mental optics," of the
fact that a real observer is mentally identifying himself with
an observer in a different system and *imagines* experiencing his
observations; but these observations are merely imaginary and
disappear as soon as the first observer enters a different system.

Underlying Bergson's reasoning is the assumption that no
observer can experience any other duration than the proper
duration of his own system. This is not correct; for, were it
true, nothing going on outside of any system would be perceivable. By the same logic the relativistic increase of mass would
be unverifiable; for an observer would perceive only the masses
which are associated with his own system, that is, the masses
relatively at rest with respect to himself; these masses remain
constant. Thus the experiments of Kauffmann and Guye, which
were performed long before Bergson wrote his book about
relativity, and which confirmed the relativistic increase of mass,
would have been impossible. Moreover, even the phenomenon
of magnetism would be, on the basis of Bergson's logic, imper-

ceivable because the magnetic field manifests itself only to observers moving relatively to the electric charges; for an observer associated with the moving electric charge there is no magnetic field.

But the relativistic dilatation of time is not only verifiable in principle; it has already been verified. The first verification was indirect: the confirmation of the relativistic formula for the addition of velocities. This formula follows from Lorentz's equations, which include also the formula for transformation of the time coordinate, of which the formula for the dilatation of time is a mere consequence. The relativistic theorem for the addition of velocities was confirmed by measuring the velocity of light in moving water; the measurements were performed by Fizeau long before the advent of relativity and were interpreted in the terms of the aether theory as a "partial drag of aether by the moving bodies"; but while this interpretation was possible only on the basis of complex and artificial assumptions about the nature of aether and its relation to ponderable matter, the experimental results follow smoothly as simple mathematical consequence from the special theory of relativity.[11]

A more direct verification of the dilatation of time has come in recent years: in 1941 it was found that the rate of distintegration of mesons measured by an observer motionless with respect to the earth is slower than expected and that the rate of slowing down depends on the relative velocity of mesons according to the relativistic formula.[12]

THE MEANING OF THE DILATATION OF TIME IN THE GENERAL THEORY

But Bergson was mistaken in one more respect: he wrongly believed that the lengthening of time in the *general theory of relativity* has the same apparent (referential) character as that in the special theory. This erroneous belief was based on his assumption that in gravitational fields as in inertial systems there is a perfect reciprocity of appearances; in other words, that the dilatation does not affect the proper durations of any systems and that it is, as in the special theory, an effect of "the perspective of velocity." [13] This, however, was a mistake due to the failure to realize that, according to the general theory of relativity, the course of time itself is lengthened by the action of the gravitational field or, what is the same, by the curvature of space-time.

This effect is empirically verifiable, at least in principle, as it should manifest itself in a red shift of spectral lines in gravitational fields of great intensity. Such a red shift would indicate the slowing down of atomic clocks in gravitational fields; its undisputable verification is extremely difficult because, if it exists, it is partially or completely obscured by the Doppler effect resulting from the relative motion of the earth and the observed luminous source, as well as from the motion of the incandescent vapors in the atmosphere of the stars observed. Nevertheless, the red shift is sufficiently distinct in the spectrum of the companion of Sirius to be regarded as a reliable confirmation of the general theory. [14]

It is evident from what has been just said that the dilatation of time in gravitation fields is of a different kind than in the special theory; while in the latter it was merely a quasi-perspective distortion resulting from the relative motion of two inertial systems and perfectly reciprocal in both systems, in the former it is an actual modification of the proper time itself. It is clear that there is no reciprocity in the general theory of relativity. Although an observer in a weaker gravitational field, as, for instance, of the earth, will perceive the red shift in the spectrum of the companion of Sirius, the converse is not true; the reciprocity of appearances would take place only if an observer and object observed were located in gravitational fields of equal intensity.

It is clear that the error of Bergson, who in this respect was followed by A. O. Lovejoy, [15] was due to the fact that he applied the principle of complete reciprocity of appearances, which holds in the special theory, to the general theory as well; he thus overlooked that in the latter the two frames of reference considered are *not* equivalent. The last statement may sound paradoxical as long as we do not realize that the term "theory of relativity" is not appropriate in all respects and, considered abstractly, may become definitely misleading.

The nature of the misunderstanding of the dilatation of time in the general theory may be best illustrated by analyzing the famous paradox of the time-retarding journey. The paradox became known in the form given to it by Paul Langevin as early as 1911 under the name of the *voyage au boulet*.[16] It may be briefly summarized as follows. Suppose that an observer is placed inside a projectile or a space ship which moves with a velocity approaching the velocity of light away from the earth; suppose that the velocity is only by 1/20,000 lower than the velocity of light; suppose that this motion continues for one year and that at this moment the direction of the motion is reversed and the space ship observer starts moving back to the earth. The total duration of the round trip will thus be two years *for the observer in the projectile*. Within the framework of classical physics it was self-evident that an observer on the earth would live through the same interval of time as an observer in a space ship; in other words, that he would be two years older than he was when the space traveler left the earth. According to Paul Langevin, *it will not be so;* the interval of two years, lived by a traveler, will correspond to the interval of *two centuries* on the earth and will certainly surpass the life span of any person who witnessed the departure of the traveler. In other words, the time interval of the space traveler will *actually be dilated* in comparison with the time interval of earthly observers.

Langevin used another less spectacular illustration of the dilatation of time. If we suppose that one of two specimens of radioactive substances leaves the surface of the earth with a velocity not far below the velocity of light, and if we suppose that after traveling one year it returns to the specimen which was left on the earth, it will be found that the rate of radioactive disintegration proceeded much more slowly in the traveling specimen than in that which remained on the earth. The radio-active clock traveling through space would be considerably slowed down with respect to the terrestrial clock. If the speed of the flying specimen with respect to the earth were the same as in the first illustration, the radioactive chronometer returning to the earth would be 198 years behind the disintegration of its terrestrial counterpart.

Langevin's *Gedankenexperiment* [thought experiment] was criticized by both Bergson and Lovejoy on the grounds that it is incompatible with the special theory of relativity. For the basic idea of the special theory is that of the dynamical and optical equivalence of all inertial systems; from this the complete reciprocity of appearances—contraction of lengths, dilatation of time intervals, increase of masses—follows. Let us state this once more. All these effects are doubtless *observable*, but observable only for an outside observer. They are products of the *perspective of velocity*, without being real modifications within the systems themselves. It is clear that within each inertial system inertial rest-mass remains by definition constant because each observer cannot move with respect to himself; for the same reason, within each system the proper times remain the same. On the other hand, in Langevin's *Gedankenexperiment* there is no such symmetry of appearances; only the proper time of the traveler in a projectile is modified, not that of the earthly observer; thus after his return the traveler would find that he was only two years older while finding that the earthly observer was long dead, since two centuries would have elapsed from the time of their farewell party.

Now is this compatible with the principle of relativity? Why, asked Bergson in 1923, should it not be the other way around? Why should not the earthly observer be only two years older after the return of the projectile from the two-centuries-long round trip? It is sufficient to assume that the traveling observer is at rest and the earth is moving away from it with the same velocity, but in the opposite direction. According to the special theory no system is privileged; thus this assumption is perfectly legitimate. The mistake underlying Langevin's *Gedankenexperiment* is, according to Bergson and Lovejoy, an unconscious assumption that the system of the earthly observer is a privileged one. Nothing is in sharper conflict with the special theory than such unconscious geocentrism; it would mean an unconscious return to Lorentz because, were this view true, the dilatation of time would be a *real* effect, produced by the absolute motion of the projectile in space. What is even worse, it would be an unconscious return to Aristotle and Ptolemy by unwittingly endowing the earth with the property of being the privileged frame of reference.

Bergson's objection is very serious and cannot be dismissed lightly; his criticism, as Lovejoy pointed out, was certainly not answered by D'Abro, whose attitude, besides being ill-tempered and not always fair, was far from consistent, and who, as we have seen, in certain passages defends the very view of Bergson which in other passages he violently rejects.[17] As long as we remain on the ground of the special theory of relativity, the objections of Bergson and Lovejoy retain their full force. But both Bergson and Lovejoy overlooked one argument which they might have used. The whole idea of the time-retarding journey is impossible within the framework of the special theory, which deals only with inertial systems and not with the phenomena of acceleration. Yet in Langevin's *Gedankenexperiment* an enormous acceleration is introduced at the very moment when the traveling projectile reverses its path and begins its return trip. According to the principle of equivalence, the phenomena of acceleration are dynamically equivalent to the effects of the gravitational field; in other words, the whole problem of a cosmical round trip lies within the purview of the general theory.

This was recognized by Einstein as early as in 1918 and only a few years later by Thirring, Becquerel, and Whitehead and finally by Reichenbach.[18] If we realize that a powerful acceleration which results in reversing the velocity of the projectile is equivalent to the action of a gravitational field of considerable intensity and if we bear in mind that gravitational fields effectively produce a dilatation of time, then the reciprocity of the two systems, of the earthly observer and the cosmic traveler, disappear and the criticism of Bergson and Lovejoy is no longer justified. Thus we may conclude that, although Bergson and Lovejoy were entirely correct in pointing out that the idea of a time-retarding journey is incompatible with the special principle of relativity, they overlooked its meaningfulness within the general theory in which the reciprocity of two systems disappears. Then the dilatation of time, instead of being a perspective-like distortion as it is in the special theory, acquires the character of a genuine modification of proper time itself in *one* system only, that is, without its symmetrical counterpart in another system.

What was valid and invalid in criticism of Bergson's and Lovejoy's kind was lucidly stated by Whitehead in the symposium on the problem of simultaneity in 1923:

> Accordingly the traveller in the meteorite, from the earth to the star and back, is "always at the center of the universe, co-ordinating it from an unchanging position"; also the chronologer on the earth is "always at the center of the universe, co-ordinating it from an unchanged position." Why should the chronologer reckon two hundred years to the traveller's two years? Why should it not be the other way round? Apparently it is not a matter of chance; for we are all quite certain that it is the man who travels to the star who will go slow in his reckoning. Yet the traveller has an equal right to say that the earth suddenly started with great velocity on a voyage in space, and suddenly stopped and came back, *and that, curiously enough, just as the earth stopped at its furthest distance, a star came up to him and then retreated.* [Italics added.]
>
> My own explanation is that there is a universe, of which both the traveller and the chronologer have diverse experiences dominated by the diverse histories of their bodies as elements in that universe. *The real diversity of relations of their bodies to the universe is the cause of their discordance in time-reckoning.* [Italics added.] [19]

It is thus evident that the critics of Langevin's *Gedankenexperiment* overlooked one important fact: that instead of *two bodies*, the earth and the projectile, we have here a more complex situation of *two systems:* one is the projectile itself moving relatively in respect to the second system, which is the earth *and the great stellar masses of the universe.* Only if the earth and the projectile were the only two bodies in the universe, would the reciprocity of effects be restored. It is true that even in this case there would be an asymmetry of dynamical effects at the moment in which the projectile is reversing its velocity and begins to return to the earth; the effects produced by the gravitational field of the earth would naturally be considerably smaller than those produced by the gravitational field of the "fixed" stars, but they still would be incomparably larger than those produced by the gravitational effect of the projectile itself. Thus the true reciprocity would be restored only if both the earth and the projectile, besides being the only bodies of the universe, were at the same time of approximately equal size. In any other circumstances the appearances are *not* reciprocal and the effective slowing of the proper time of one system in respect to the other takes place.

IN WHAT SENSE TIME REMAINS UNIVERSAL

But although Bergson was wrong on some important details of interpretation (which, it is fair to say, were not clear even to some professional physicists and to some of his opponents) his claim that the relativity theory not only does not remove, but even substantiates, the reality of universal time, remains essentially correct. Paradoxical as it may sound, a close and rigorous analysis of the paradox of the time-retarding journey will show this convincingly.

But first it is necessary to get rid of the semantic confusion arising from the use of inappropriate and misleading terms. Precisely such terms are "time retardation" and "time lengthening." Both of these terms are tinged by visual and geometrical associations. We speak of retardation of one body when it moves with a smaller velocity and is "left behind" by a faster-moving body. Similarly, when one geometrical interval is lengthened with respect to another one, then their extremities cannot coincide; one will be "ahead" of the other. Nothing of this sort is happening in Langevin's thought experiment. By definition both observers not only are living the same moment of time at the instant of their separation, but they find each other in *the same moment of time* after they are reunited; otherwise it would be meaningless to speak about their reunion or meeting. What else does this mean except that the two intervals of time, that of the traveler and that of the earthly observer, *being obviously bounded by the same successive moments, are necessarily contemporary?* In other words, the intervals express two complementary aspects of *one and the same stretch of universal duration* which underlies them both, although it is measured differently in each of them. It is evident that the stretch of duration separating the two events and common to the two systems is *not* affected either by the relative motion of the systems or by the dynamic effects of acceleration. What is affected is the *time units*, whose dilatation by the effect of gravitation accounts for different reckoning of time by the two systems. But the topological relation of succession between the two events, that is, between the moment of separation and the moment of reunion, remains unaffected; for both events lie on world lines which, as we already know, are *irreversible* no matter what frame of reference is chosen.

This topological constancy of the causal succession undoubtedly led Whitehead to differentiate the universal "creative advance of nature" from the discordant time series which are its various complementary manifestations:

> The difficulty as to discordant time-systems is partly solved by distinguishing between what I call the creative advance of nature, which is not properly serial at all, and any one time-series. We habitually muddle together this creative advance, which we experience as the perpetual transition of nature into novelty, with the single time-series which we naturally employ for measurement. The various time-series each measure some aspect of the creative advance, and the whole

bundle of them express all the properties of this advance which are measurable.[20]

Two philosophers, who in other respects agreed very little, found themselves in an agreement with Whitehead on this point. Six years before Whitehead wrote the passage just quoted, Bertrand Russell wrote:

> But the principle of relativity has given prominence to the conception of "local time," and somewhat diminished men's confidence in the one even-flowing stream of time. Without dogmatising as to the ultimate outcome of the principle of relativity, however, we may safely say, I think, that it does not destroy the possibility of correlating different local times, and does not therefore have such far-reaching philosophical consequences as is sometimes supposed. In fact, in spite of difficulties as to measurement, the one all-embracing time still, I think, underlies all that physics has to say about motion.[21]

Similarly Bergson in his *Durée et simultaneité*:

> Not only do the multiple times of the relativity theory not destroy the unity of real time, but they even imply and uphold it . . . Without this unique and experienced duration, without this time common to all mathematical times, what would it mean to say that they are contemporary, that they are contained in the same interval? What else could such an affirmation mean? [22]

Bergson's only error was that this unity of time immanent to all frames of reference ("ce Temps unique, intérieur à chaque système") should be understood in a *metrical* sense; hence his defense of absolute simultaneity which is hardly compatible not only with the spirit, but even with the letter, of his own philosophy.[23] Whitehead was clearer in this respect when he insisted on the nonmetrical properties of the universal temporal passage. In this sense, according to him, time extends *beyond* nature. We may agree with the last statement only if we restrict the term "nature" to quantitatively determinable entities and relations; but Whitehead himself in the later period of his thought, when he accepted an "organic philosophy of nature," hardly would have accepted a similar restriction.

There are some qualitative or topological relations which are indispensable; such is the *relation of contemporaneity* without which a simple assertion of the existence of discordant temporal series (as illustrated by the paradox of the time-retarding journey) cannot even be made. The recognition of the universal cosmic duration is precisely nothing but a recognition that such a relation of contemporaneity between metrically discordant temporal series effectively exists. There is nothing supernatural or irrational about this assertion; on the contrary, it is an indispensable part of coherent relativistic language.

The suspicion of "irrationalism" arises naturally out of the fact that there seems to be a close relation between this universal temporal passage and our private, subjectively experienced passage of time, embodied in what William James called the stream of consciousness. Thus Whitehead concludes his discussion:

> So far as sense-awareness is concerned there is a passage of mind which is distinguishable from the passage of nature though closely allied with it. We may speculate, if we like, that this alliance of mind with the passage of nature arises from their both sharing in some ultimate character of passage which dominates all being.[24]

A similar view was expressed before Whitehead by Bergson when he claimed that the universal cosmic becoming is in its innermost essence something qualitative, that is, comparable to the stream of consciousness, which also defies all attempts to order it serially in the strict arithmetical sense.[25] And, under the impact of Bergson, James in the last phase of his philosophy generalized his originally purely psychological notion of "stream of thought" into the "everlasting coming of concrete novelty into being" on the cosmic scale.[26]

We are still too much conditioned by the tradition of classical physics not to feel at first a shock of distrust when we hear similar expressions. Classical physics was characterized by its attempt to eliminate qualities and everything tinged by subjectivity from the scheme of the universe which it tried to construct. But we know that it was curiously inconsistent in making an exception for some sensory qualities of touch and sight which were regarded as objectively real. Temporality, probably because of its suspicious connection with the stream of our private experience was, as we have seen, only reluctantly accepted as physically real, and not infrequently, under the double impact of Kant and Laplace, there was a tendency to dismiss its objective character entirely.

On the other hand, even such a serious and sober thinker as Helmholtz, did not hesitate to say that the general temporal character is the *only* feature which is shared both by the transsubjective nature and our private experience;[27] in all other instances there is a radical dissimilarity betwen our sensations and the corresponding physical events which cause them. Certainly, nobody would accuse Helmholtz of any kind of mysticism; yet, his statement is hardly different from the quoted statements of James, Bergson, and Whitehead. In what sense temporal passage is, to use the classical terminology, a "primary quality of nature" or even perhaps *the* primary quality of nature will be dealt with in the concluding part of this book.

The structure of psychological temporal passage, when properly analyzed, sheds an additional light on some paradoxes of the theory of relativity. What appears to be so baffling in the paradox of the time-retarding journey is precisely the fact that two very uneven temporal intervals, like two years and two centuries, are allegedly *contemporary*. How can two *uneven* temporal intervals be temporally coextensive? The paradoxical feeling disappears when we realize that in concretely experienced psychological passage the number of successive phases is not indicative of its objective duration. In other words, one and the same duration may be experienced by different persons in different rhythms. The interval experienced by a dreaming person may subjectively be very long, since it is made of shorter moments of the "specious present"; nevertheless this interval remains *contemporary* with the subjectively much shorter interval of a person awake, with the normal span of his "specious present."

Note the analogy with the relativistic paradox. Public physical time, which is differently experienced and *counted* by two different persons in virtue of their different specious presents, has a function analogous to the interval of the universal cosmic becoming which is *measured* differently by an earthly observer and a space traveler. In the same way as the time measured by clocks is unaffected by the variability of the subjective measuring units, i.e., of the specious present, the universal passage of nature remains unaffected by the relativistic variability of metric units. After his awakening a dreamer will find himself *at the same moment* of the public time as a person who was awake, just as after his return a space-traveler will find himself *at the same moment of cosmic time* as an earthly observer. The analogy has its limitations, but these limitations will only bring into full focus the true meaning of the universal passage of nature and its difference from Newtonian time.

It may first be objected that we can hardly claim that the different subjective experiences of temporal intervals are measuring operations at all. It is true that they are not measurements in any precise sense; on the other hand, it can hardly be denied that, no matter how hazy and imprecise these various unconscious judgments concerning the length of the temporal intervals are, they are *rudiments* of the future operations by which we measure time. The span of our psychological present is used spontaneously and unconsciously as a measuring standard unit of the interval of psychological time, and the variability of this unit accounts for differences of temporal experiences and for the so-called time illusions in dreams and related psychological states. In physical measurements of time the measuring process is *essentially* the same, although it takes place consciously and in a refined way; the measuring standard unit is deliberately *chosen* and identified with the experienced duration of a certain physical process such as the rotation of the earth or its multiples or fractions; different "values" of time will depend on our *choice* for the standard units. It is true that the resulting differences do not have the experienced immediacy and vividness of the temporal illusions in dreams; but this is due to the fact that the variability of the specious present is *imposed* on us without our will by the objective modification of the rate of our mental processes, while various standard units of physical time are *freely chosen* and have no bearing on our *perception* of time. But both the relativity of time *computed* and the relativity of time *experienced* are, in the last analysis, due to the variability of the measuring unit, whether its change is imposed on us or freely chosen.

Whether measured by psychological or physiological changes of different rates or by physical motions of different speeds, the time of classical physics was assumed to be *one* in order to assure the *synchronous* or *contemporaneous* character of all these different changes and motions. In this point and in this point only the universal cosmic becoming underlying the relativistic discordant temporal series is comparable to the classical time which, according to Newton, underlies various relative times measured by concrete physical changes. As Paul Weiss stated with superb clarity and conciseness:

> We must acknowledge that time is universal to account for the temporal co-presence of diverse beings and for the fact that the entities of a co-present world move into the future together, despite the diversity of their rates of change.[28]

But here the similarity between Newtonian time and Whitehead's "passage of nature" ends. Although they are both absolute, they are so in different senses. According to Newton, time is independent of concrete motions and changes occurring within it; it is by its own nature homogeneous and flows at a constant rate no matter how different the speeds are of particular motions of physical bodies. It would flow at a constant rate even if the whole material universe should completely disappear; and according to Newton, it flowed so even before the creation of the world. This separation of time from its own content is the basis of its homogeneity, as we tried to show in the first part. Such a separation cannot be maintained any longer in the light of the relativity theory. Matter was merged with space while space was fused with time. This means that we have to correct Meyerson's expression by saying that matter *is resorbed into time-space* instead of into space only. The traditional distinction between time and concrete physical processes must be seen to be as artificial as that between *space* and its *material content*. Time itself, like space, in virtue of its merging with the heterogeneous and dynamic content, loses its character of homogeneity and uniformity. The relativity of time measurements and their dependence on the different rhythms of time in different gravitational fields follow as a natural consequence. There is no unique serial temporal series in nature; time does not flow at an even rate.

Yet, in spite of their metrical diversity, the discordant temporal series remain *contemporary* with each other and this nonmetrical, topological *relation of contemporaneity* is thus the very essence of relativistic time-space. In this sense, relativistic time, though metrically not uniform, still remains topologically *one*. The relation of "being contemporary" replaces the traditional relation of spatial simultaneous juxtaposition and thus becomes a clue to the new meaning of time and space in their synthesis into the unity of relativistic time-space.

NOTES FOR CHAPTER XII

1. Cf. E. Meyerson, *De l'explication dans les sciences*, II, Appendix 2, pp. 386-403 ("La résistance à la théorie de Lavoisier"); S. E. Toulmin, "Crucial Experiments: Priestley and Lavoisier," *The Journal of the History of Ideas*, Vol. XVIII (1957), pp. 205-220; *The Overthrow of the Phlogiston Theory*, ed. by J. B. Conant in Harvard Case Histories in Experimental Science (Harvard Univiversity Press, Cambridge, 1956).
1a. A. A. Robb, *The Absolute Relations of Time and Space* (Cambridge University Press, 1921), p. 12.
2. Max Born, *Die Relativitätstheorie Einsteins und ihre physikalische Grundlagen* (Berlin, 1921), p. 189.

3. Jean Becquerel, *Le Principe de relativité et la théorie de la gravitation* (Paris, 1922), p. 45. The *apparent* character of the dilatation of time in the special theory is stressed by J. L. Synge, *Relativity: The Special Theory* (New York, Interscience Publishing Company, 1956), pp. 119-120; also by R. Dugas, *A History of Mechanics*, tr. by J. R. Maddox (Central Book Co., New York, 1955), pp. 495 f.
4. Bergson, *Durée et simultanéité*, pp. 100-102.
5. M. Born, *op. cit.*, p. 189-90.
6. H. Bergson, *loc. cit.*; A. d'Abro, *Bergson ou Einstein?*, p. 75.
7. A. d'Abro, *Bergson ou Einstein?*, p. 214.
8. Lucretius, *De rerum natura*, II, vv. 730-841.
9. This was correctly stressed by De Witt Parker, *Experience and Substance* (University of Michigan Press, 1941), p. 171.
10. H. Bergson, *op. cit.*, pp. 158-170.
11. A. d'Abro, *op. cit.*, pp. 117-118.
12. E. T. Whittaker, *A History of the Theories of Aether and Electricity*, II, p. 44.
13. H. Bergson, *op. cit.*, Appendix II, pp. 259-265.
14. A. E. Eddington, *Stars and Atoms* (Yale University Press, 1927), pp. 48-53, 122-123; E. T. Whittaker, *From Euclid to Eddington*, pp. 124-125.
15. A. O. Lovejoy, "The Paradox of the Time-Retarding Journey," *The Philosophical Review*, Vol. 40 (1931), pp. 48-68, 152-167.
16. P. Langevin, "L'Evolution de l'espace et du temps," *Revue de Métaphysique et de Morale*, Vol. XIX (1911), pp. 465-466.
17. Lovejoy, *loc. cit.*, pp. 165-167. See also my article "La théorie bergsonienne de la matière et la physique moderne," *Revue philosophique,* 78e année (1953), especially p. 41-44.
18. A. Einstein, "Dialog über Einwände gegen die Relativitätstheorie," *Naturwissenschaften*, Vol. VI (1918), pp. 697-702; H. Thirring, *Naturwissenschaften*, Vol. IX (1921), p. 209; A. N. Whitehead, "The Problem of Simultaneity" in *Aristotelian Society*, Suppl. Vol. III (1923), pp. 34-41; H. Reichenbach, *Die Philosophie der Raum-Zeit-Lehre*, pp. 222-225; J. Becquerel, *Le Principe de relativité et la théorie de la gravitation* (Paris, 1922), p. 240.
19. A. N. Whitehead, *loc. cit.*, pp. 34-35.
20. A. N. Whitehead, *The Concept of Nature*, p. 178.
21. B. Russell, *Our Knowledge of the External World*, pp. 103-104.
22. Bergson, *op. cit.*, p. 172.
23. Bergson, *op. cit.*, pp. 99, 112; Zawirski, *L'Evolution de la notion du temps* (Cracovie, 1935), pp. 305-306.
24. Whitehead, *The Concept of Nature*, pp. 66, 69.
25. Bergson, *Creative Evolution*, pp. 12-13.
26. W. James, *Some Problems of Philosophy*, (New York, Longmans, Green and Co., 1940), p. 149.
27. H. Helmholtz, *Handbuch der physiologischen Optik* (Leipzig, 1867), p. 445.
28. P. Weiss, *Reality* (Princeton, 1938), p. 230.

XIII · THE DYNAMIC STRUCTURE
OF TIME-SPACE

THE PROBLEM OF THE CONTEMPORARY WORLD
AND THE NEW MEANING OF SPATIALITY

WE ARE reaching the stage of our discussion when we can determine more positively the meaning of the relativistic synthesis of space and time. We have already stated the reasons why it is erroneous to regard this synthesis as a spatialization of time. We have also tried to justify the claim that the idea of static space, stretching instantaneously across the four-dimensional world history, is excluded by the relativity theory. But we have also warned against a glib assumption that the fusion of space and time may be unqualifiedly characterized as a *temporalization of space*. We have proposed the term "dynamization" instead of "temporalization." We now have to justify this correction more explicitly.

After having acquainted ourselves with the meaning of the relativity theory and especially with its rejection of both absolute simultaneity and instantaneous space, we are inevitably confronted with certain questions: What then really has become of these intuitive notions? Is it possible to get along without them? Does not a relativist use implicitly or even explicitly the term "distance"? And even when we claimed that there are no instantaneous spatial links in the world because they were replaced by dynamic successive causal links, did we not also use the term "distance" in saying that the duration of causal links increases with the distance?

Such a criticism is undoubtedly valid, but in a sense different from that which the opponents of relativity suppose. We have already pointed out that physical interactions on the scale of the human organism are practically instantaneous and are thus in this respect undistinguishable from the timeless network of purely geometrical relations which constitute classical space. But for the realm of greater velocities and greater "distances" (*sit venia verbo*), the intuitive notion of distance becomes thoroughly inadequate and should be replaced by a more carefully defined concept; certainly even the usage of the word "distance" is questionable. Several representatives of the so-called *causal theory of time* (A. A. Robb, R. Carnap, H. Mehlberg, H. Reichenbach, A. Markov)[1] made a bold step when they attempted to reverse the usual procedure and, instead of defining causal action in terms of space, defined spatial distance in terms of time. As Carnap says:

> It is wrong to say that when two bodies are spatially near each other, the physical interactions (*Wirkungslinien*) are of short duration; on the contrary, we have to say that when the physical interaction between two bodies is of short duration, their distance is small.[2]

Carnap's attempt to derive the topological properties of space from those of time was repeated in a more systematic manner by Hans Reichenbach in his *Philosophie der Raum-Zeit-Lehre* in 1928, while A. Markov a few years later went one step further and tried to derive even the metrical properties of time from the fundamental relation of succession. More recently the causal interpretation of distance was given by E. T. Whittaker: "When the astronomer asserts that the distance of the Andromeda nebula is a million light-years, he is stating a relation between the world-point occupied by ourselves and the world-point occupied by the Andromeda nebula at the instant when the light left it which arrives here now."[3] Thus what we call a distance is no longer the relation between "here-now" and "there-now," but between "here-now" and "there-then." This is what Whitehead had in mind when he wrote in 1919 that "spatial relations must stretch across time." [4]

The quotation from Whittaker will bring into focus another objection, which is really another form of the previous one: "But where is the Andromeda nebula *now?*" It would not be fair to answer this question by saying that the nebula perhaps does not exist any longer; or, that if it exists, it has been profoundly modified by a million years of evolution. For the question will emerge obtrusively in the following form: "No matter what the present causal successor of the Andromeda nebula is, whether it is a condensed star or a cosmic dust, it is certain that its present existence does not depend on its future causal impact on the earthly observer. Although its present light will affect future earthly observers—provided there are any left —a million years from now, it must be leaving the nebula, or whatever has become of it, *now.*"

The valid part of this statement is its insistence on the *causal independence* of physical entities which, according to conventional expression, are separated in space; the wrong part is precisely the word "now." For this relation of independence is not symbolized by an instantaneous geometrical connection spreading through the whole universe. There are, as Eddington used to say, no "world-instants"; or in the words of A. A. Robb, "an instant cannot be in two places at once." [5] *My present instant is here and nowhere else.* This does not mean that the existence of "there," or as Eddington called it, "elsewhere," is denied; what is denied is only its alleged instantaneous correlation with "here-now." "Now" is inseparable from "here"; the original connotation of the word "present" is both spatial and temporal. The Latin *prae-esse* means to be *nearby*, in the immediate neighborhood, i.e., *here.* "There" in respect to "here" is always *in the past* or (potentially) *in the future.* My present "now-here" is causally affected by the "past-there" and will causally affect the "future-there."

But what lies between this "past-there" and the "future-

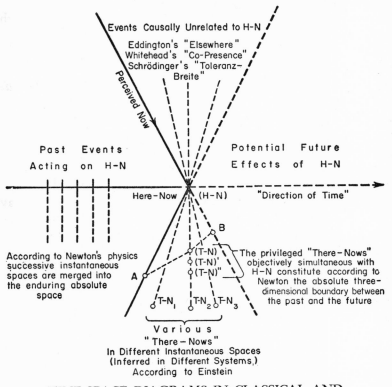

Events Causally Unrelated to H-N

Eddington's "Elsewhere"
Whitehead's "Co-Presence"
Schrödinger's "Toleranz-
Breite"

Perceived Now

Past   Events
Acting   on   H-N

Potential   Future
Effects   of   H-N

Here–Now   (H–N)   "Direction of Time"

B

According to Newton's physics
successive instantaneous
spaces are merged into
the enduring absolute
space

(T-N)
(T-N)'
(T-N)"

A

T-N₁   T-N₂   T-N₃

The privileged "There–Nows"
objectively simultaneous with
H–N constitute according to
Newton the absolute three-
dimensional boundary between
the past and the future

Various
" There – Nows "
In Different Instantaneous Spaces
(Inferred in Different Systems,)
According to Einstein

TIME-SPACE DIAGRAMS IN CLASSICAL AND MODERN PHYSICS

The main difference between classical and relativistic space-time is that in the former it was possible to have instantaneous three-dimensional cuts (instantaneous spaces) identical in all frames of reference while in the latter it is not. In relativistic space-time, absolute simultaneity was replaced by the wedge-shaped zone of the events causally independent of (H-N). But the elimination of absolute simultaneity of distant events does not destroy the reality of temporal relations. Although it is impossible to claim that (H-N) is objectively simultaneous with (T-N), (T-N)′ and (T-N)″, the event (H-N) is *preceded* by the event A and *followed* by the event B in *all* frames of reference. Moreover, the world-line A—(H-N)—B is in *all* systems of reference *contemporary* with the world-line A—(T-N)—B. Thus the simultaneity of instants (co-instantaneity) has been replaced by the "contemporaneity of fluxes" or "contemporary intervals."

there"? The answer of the relativity theory is clear: *all events causally independent of my "here-now" and of which my "here-now" is independent.* There is, as Paul Weiss has said, "the contemporary world"; but "contemporary" does not mean "co-instantaneous." [6] The contemporary world is the *whole stretch of time*, a series of events; this is the meaning of Whitehead's "co-presence" or Eddington's "elsewhere." On the earthly scale the interval containing all independent events is so small that it is practically instantaneous; hence our spontaneous belief in "there-now." But what is practically valid on the planetary scale ceases to be even approximately true for greater spatiotemporal links.

There is no "there-now"; there is only the relation of independence between "now-here" and the whole series of successive "nows" elsewhere. Which one of these successive "nows" is declared to be simultaneous with my "here-now" depends on the frame of reference, i.e., ultimately, on convention. Similarly, a retrospective dating of the emission of light from Andromeda which is reaching our eyes now will come out differently for different observers. Thus the simultaneity of distant events cannot be established, not even retrospectively. This can have only one meaning: such simultaneity *does not exist.*

There are only two fundamental relations in the relativistic universe: *successive causal connection* and *contemporary causal independence.* The first relation remains absolute, being a topological invariant in all frames of reference. The same is true of the second relation, that of contemporary independence. Two successive events may be joined by more than one causal link, as the analysis of Langevin's paradox showed. In the diagram below, if A is an event in which two world lines are branching off (such as the departure of a space traveler from the earth) and if B is the event in which the world lines meet again (such as the return of the same traveler), then although the two world lines I and II are associated with metrically different times, they are *contemporary* because they are both bounded by the same two successive events, the successive character of which is *absolute*, that is, independent of any frame of reference.

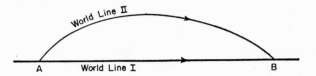

This seems to indicate that the relation of contemporaneity is thus ultimately derivable from that of causal succession; and because the latter relation has replaced that of *juxtaposition* by which the classical concept was characterized, it looks as if Carnap's claim that the topological properties of space are derivable from that of time is justified.

However, a more attentive analysis shows that this is not so. Carnap was right in what he denied; there is no objective static space separable from time. But by no logical effort can the character of *spatiality* or *extension* be derived from the concept of time defined as a one-dimensional series of instants. There was a hidden circle in Carnap's reasoning when he admitted the *multiplicity* of the world lines instead of one single world line; what else is such multiplicity than a rudiment of spatiality? Carnap virtually admitted it when he postulated *two* basic relations: that of succession and that of *coincidence*, the latter being defined as an intersection of *two* world lines.[7] It is certain that the multiplicity of the world lines is different from the multiplicity *in* time, i.e., a sheer succession. It is a *multiplicity of independent coexistents* or of *contemporary durations*. This multiplicity cannot be derived from the supposition of one single temporal series; nor can the relation of contemporaneousness be derived from it. If only a single temporal series or a single causal chain existed, then it could be contemporary only with itself; but this would be hardly anything more than a sterile tautological assertion.

Thus it is incorrect, or at least misleading, to claim that space has been simply and unqualifiedly absorbed into time. This would be true only if by time we meant not the classical concept of a one-dimensional continuum of instants (unsatisfactory, as we shall see, in the light of the quantum theory and wave mechanics, not to speak of some more basic epistemological objections), but Bergson's notion of *extensive becoming*, which is more or less synonymous with Whitehead's creative advance of nature. Such extensive becoming, in contradistinction to mathematical purely linear time, has a certain *transversal extent* or *width;* it admits the relations of *co-presence* (Whitehead)[8] or *simultaneity of fluxes* (Bergson). But what classical physics naturally overlooked was that from the *simultaneity of fluxes* it is impossible to pass over to the *simultaneity of instants;* for, as Bergson and Whitehead repeatedly emphasized, time is not made of durationless instants nor is process made of instantaneous "states."

> Now, in real duration we never pass over from the simultaneity of two fluxes to the simultaneity of two instants, *for every duration is thick; real time has no instants.* But as soon as we have acquired the habit of converting time into space, we naturally form the idea of instant. For while duration has no instants, a line *is* bounded by its pointlike extremities. And as soon as we make a line correspond to duration, "segment of duration" must correspond to segments of a line, and an "extremity of duration" must correspond to an extremity of a line: such will be the instant—something which does not exist actually, but only virtually. *The instant is what would terminate duration if duration itself stopped flowing. But this never happens.* [Italics added.][9]

Similarly, instantaneous three-dimensional cross sections in extensive cosmic becoming are such virtual stops; they are only illusory artificial products of the "cinematographic mechanism of thought"[10] and have no genuine reality in the ever-growing world. There is a great temptation in the diagram above to divide the lens-shaped area by transversal cuts, each of which would represent a class of simultaneous events at one particular instant; it would be otiose to insist that this is impossible if the relativization of simultaneity has more than a verbal significance. We must not forget also that the lens-shaped area is merely a *static* and *two-dimensional* symbol of a four-dimensional phase of the world process; therefore, we have to be once more on guard against the fallacy of spatialization which, as Bergson has just told us, consists in applying the mathematical divisibility of geometrical entities (lines, surfaces, and volumes) to temporal processes.

We are now in a position to evaluate fully and more positively the meaning of the fusion of space and time, or what is the same thing, *the transformation of the concept of distance.* It is not enough, or at least it is not specific enough, to say that the concept of spatial distance was replaced by that of spatiotemporal distance. What we used to call "spatial distance" is now to be measured, as Carnap and Reichenbach correctly observed, by the duration of corresponding causal links. If the sun is closer to us than Neptune, it is so because the sun is only eight light-minutes away while Neptune is four light-hours. But when I vividly remember what I was doing eight minutes or four hours ago, am I not also causally influenced by a "distant event"? Why in this latter case am I inclined to say that the distance in question is *purely temporal,* i.e., that no spatial distance is involved? Obviously the temporal span of a causal link is not sufficient to characterize what classical physics called "distance in space." There is a second feature involved which, together with the first, is sufficient to differentiate between spatiotemporal distance and bare temporal distance.

This second feature is precisely *the interval of causal independence.* It is precisely the length of this interval which measures the *degree of indetermination* (Schrödinger's *Toleranzbreite*)[11] concerning the simultaneity of distant events. This interval which measures the extent of "co-presence" or "elsewhere" is sixteen minutes for the sun, eight hours for Neptune, one century for Polaris, two thousand years for the great nebula in Orion, two million years for the nebula in Andromeda. It is always *double* the duration of corresponding causal links. For events occurring at the same place or, relativistically speaking, for events of the same world line, the interval of causal independence is zero, as each such event is naturally simultaneous with itself; this is nothing but a truistic exemplification of the law of identity. As in other instances, the view of classical physics is true in the first approximation; when the duration of causal links is small, the interval of causal independence (symbolized by the four-dimensional area enclosed between two causal cones) shrinks practically to an instantaneous durationless space separating the past from the future; then we can speak of timeless, i.e., purely spatial, instantaneous distances without committing a serious mistake. But outside this limited area of approximate validity it is legitimate to speak only of *spatiotemporal*, never of *spatial* distances.

Similarly, Euclidean geometry remains valid on the earthly and even planetary scale; the corresponding deviations from it are too small to be observable or to have a practical significance. But this does not make the change in the total picture of the universe less revolutionary; the fact that there are purely temporal and spatiotemporal relations in the world, while purely spatial timeless relations do not exist, shows only another aspect of the ontological priority of time over space. For the relations of causal independence, whether it is legitimate or not to call them relations, are thoroughly different from those of classical juxtaposition of simultaneously existing points. The causal independence in relativity does not mean a static separation of no less static entities, a separation which may equally well be called a rigid connection in virtue of the immutable character of the separating void;[12] it means the coexistence—or rather *co-becoming* or *co-fluidity*—of world lines. It is precisely this multiplicity of individual world lines, interacting in time but never cohering in a timeless instantaneous way, which constitutes the dynamic basis of spatiality.

The spatial picture of time as a one-dimensional continuum of pointlike instants was inadequate in at least a double sense: (1) it obscures the essential incompleteness of temporal process, and (2) it wrongly suggests that the process, like a geometrical line, is "without width," i.e., without transversal extension. But such time is only an abstraction; *becoming is always extensive and it is always incomplete*. "Extension is derivative from process, and is required by it." [13] Relativistic space is neither the timeless space of Newton nor the Cartesian or Russellian succession of perishing instantaneous spaces, each of which is miraculously re-created at each moment. It is a reality which is not only not foreign to duration, but inseparable from it; that is the main reason why the term *time-space* is preferable to space-time.

The classical picture of time as a one-dimensional continuum of instants is very probably inadequate *in a third sense*—it suggests the mathematical continuity (infinite divisibility) of time. This leads to the problem of the applicability of the concept of infinite divisibility to the temporal processes as viewed by modern physics; and in view of the close connection of time and space it is clear at once that the whole question of spatiotemporal continuity is raised. This will be discussed in the next pages.

DOUBTS ABOUT SPATIOTEMPORAL CONTINUITY

The concept of spatiotemporal continuity seemingly remained unaffected by relativity theory. Relativistic space-time was defined as a four-dimensional *continuum* of pointlike events; there were no doubts about the *infinite divisibility* of spatiotemporal regions. The world lines of Minkowski were considered to be as continuous as the trajectories of classical physics. This was only natural: the relativity theory was by its nature a *macroscopic theory* whose main object was the macrostructure of the universe. Its most revolutionary consequences concerned astronomy and cosmology, that is, the structure of the universe in the large; the question whether the concept of spatiotemporal continuity is legitimate does not arise on the macroscopic level. The non-Euclidean character of space-time is negligible even on the planetary scale, and its curvature may be even more safely disregarded on the atomic scale.

This was at least the basic idea of Riemann: the curvature of any non-Euclidean continuum may be disregarded when its infinitesimal regions are considered.[14] In other words, if the universe as a whole is Riemannian, its parts which are of the same order of magnitude as atoms may be regarded as being Euclidean even more approximately than "the world of the middle dimensions." Volumes of atomic magnitude appear to be almost perfectly Euclidean and *ipso facto* also homogeneous and continuous; for the last two features were, as we have seen, implicit in Euclidean geometry. Thus because deviations from classical geometry are significant only on the cosmic scale, while negligible on the human scale and even more negligible when volumes of atomic and subatomic dimensions are considered, it looked plausible to treat microscopic space as having the properties of Euclidean space, including its continuity.

But we have to be on guard against hasty judgment. It is true that spatiotemporal continuity has not been directly challenged by the relativity theory; it is true that the world lines of Minkowski may be regarded as a mathematically continuous succession of durationless instants. Nevertheless, we must remember that the relativity theory denied any objective significance for the concept of the "world-wide instant." Was there not in this denial a certain implicit danger for the concept of instant in general? This may be answered by pointing out that the concept of instant loses its objective significance only when large cosmic distances are considered; it remains applicable with practically unlimited accuracy to the zone of middle dimensions, and *a fortiori* to the world of atoms and electrons.

But this answer overlooks the fact that the microphysical world is the world not only of minute distances but also of *very large velocities*, for which deviations from the classical concepts, including that of absolute simultaneity, should be most conspicuous. Indeed, spectacular confirmations of the relativity theory were found on the microcosmic scale: the increase of mass with velocity, the equivalence of mass and energy, Sommerfeld's relativistic correction for the elliptical orbits of electrons, and finally, the existence of spin as an unsuspected consequence of relativity.

Thus the assertion that the relativity theory is an *exclusively* macroscopic theory certainly needs qualification. But if strictly instantaneous, that is, durationless, cuts are inadmissible on the microscopic as well as the macroscopic level, what other significance can they retain? Since the difference between a world-wide instant and an atomlike instant seems to be merely a difference of degree, it looks as if the fictitious character of the former implied the fictitious character of the latter. The simultaneity of distant events remains relative no matter whether the events are separated by cosmic distances or atomic dimensions.

Against this it may be objected that it is still possible to speak about instants when the spatial distance is *zero*, as in the case of a single world line. Not only is each event constituting a world line simultaneous with itself (which is hardly anything more than a truism), but there is nothing in the relativity theory which would forbid one to regard a world line as mathematically continuous, i.e., as consisting of a mathematically continuous succession of durationless events. Indeed, the assumption about the pointlike character of world events is made either silently or explicitly by the majority of relativists.

But to say nothing of epistemological reasons for doubting its adequacy, the concept of world events with zero volume and zero interval of time is also suspect in the light of another important aspect of the relativity theory which has been already discussed: *the geometrization of matter*. The development of microphysics showed beyond any doubt the extreme complexity of matter and, in particular, its *atomic structure*. How can this fact be reconciled with the claim that matter is merely a local irregularity of non-Euclidean space if we insist at the same time that space on an atomic scale is even more nearly Euclidean than space of the middle dimensions?

We face the following dilemma. *Either* matter is reduced to a particular geometry of space (more accurately, time-space) and then the very existence of the grains of matter and electricity should be interpreted geometrically and it would be then impossible to uphold the Euclidean continuous character of intra-atomic space; *or* we accept Riemann's idea about the Euclidean (and therefore continuous) character of the intra-atomic space; and *then* we have to regard the existence of electrons, neutrons and other particles as irreducible to geometry, that is, as something existing *in* space, but without being identical with it. The latter alternative would mean a return to the classical idea of space as a *container* of material.

It was precisely a reluctance to return to the classical distinction of the "full" and the "void" which was the main motive inspiring various unified-field theories like those of Einstein, Weyl, Eddington, Kaluža, and Schrödinger. The earliest attempt was made by Hermann Weyl only shortly after the formulation of the general principle of relativity.[15] He fully realized that the relativistic geometrization of matter should be extended to the microcosm. If the proposition that matter is merely a local wrinkling of time-space is true, then it must be true even of the microphysical constituents of matter, i.e., of electrons; but, according to Weyl, this is possible only if we give up not only the Euclidean character of space, but also its continuity, which the space of the general relativity theory still possessed. Inspired possibly by a little known essay of Bernard Riemann,[16] Weyl regards the electron as a sort of "gap" or "hole" in the non-Euclidean continuum.

This apparently grotesque idea may be made more understandable by a two-dimensional model, just as the concept of the finite Riemannian space is made more intelligible by its two-dimensional spherical model. Imagine any curved surface, for instance, a paraboloid of rotation which contains a small opening at its vertex. A point moving on this surface could move only along the lines compatible with the nature of the surface; there would be no rectilinear motions in the Euclidean sense, although there would still be motions along the geodetic lines. Also, it is evident that no motion could penetrate the opening at the vertex of the paraboloid. It is easy to generalize this consideration to a three-dimensional curved continuum. In this case the nature of the curvature as well as that of the opening cannot be visualized, but will manifest itself by kinematic and physical effects: the non-Euclidean curvature will produce the effects of the gravitational and electromagnetic field, while the "opening," though itself outside of space, will produce the effect of the "impenetrability" of the electron. The inside of the opening will be inaccessible for any point moving in such a space, for to penetrate "there" would mean to leave space itself. This two-dimensional illustration has all the limitations already listed in Chapter XI; in particular its static character will inevitably obscure the dynamic nature of non-Euclidean time-space. But these reservations apart, it conveys graphically the geometrization of the electron and its surrounding field.

Weyl's ingenious hypothesis is interesting also in another respect: it shows how an attempt at resorbing the discontinuity of subatomic particles into the continuity of the spatiotemporal medium ends eventually in the denial of the continuity of the same medium. It is true that by extending the concept of continuum in the way in which it is done by the theory of functions, we can still claim that spatial continuity belongs even to Weyl's type of space. It is the continuity of a "multiply connected continuum" (*ein mehrfach zusammenhängendes Kontinuum*) contrasting with the "simply connected continuum" (*einfach zusammenhängendes Kontinuum*) of classical Euclidean space.

It is true that even Weyl's continuum is infinitely divisible. The existence of the "openings" does not impose any limit on its divisibility for the simple reason that "openings" are "outside" the continuum itself. It may still be called homogeneous because by definition its limits surrounding the "openings" are excluded from the continuum itself; in Weyl's words, the edges of the "holes" are physically as inaccessible as if they were infinitely distant.[17] All physical properties of what we called the "electron"—gravitational and inertial as well as electrostatic —are produced by the peculiar non-Euclidean structure of the spatiotemporal continuum *around* these physically inaccessible openings. It would then be meaningless to claim that the intra-electronic space is indivisible *because inside of the electrons there is no space at all.* [18]

In spite of this formal preservation of continuity, there is hardly any question but that the concept of continuum thus redefined means a radical departure from the visual continuity of Euclidean space, in which even subatomic and subelectronic volumes are divisible *ad infinitum;* such infinite divisibility was a simple consequence of the relativity of magnitude. In Weyl's "continuum" the first postulate of Euclid (according to which a straight line can be drawn *between any two points*) evidently does not hold. The boldness of Weyl's idea significantly con-'trasts with the attitude of Lotze, who insisted on the logical impossibility of "holes in space." (Undoubtedly, *within the Euclidean framework* Lotze was entirely right.)

The interest in Weyl's theory and any unified-field theory in general naturally declined when the attention of physicists was diverted to two theories which were successful in explaining a huge number of microphysical facts: the quantum theory and wave mechanics. Yet the impact of the both theories on the problem of the spatiotemporal continuity was not essentially different from that of Weyl: doubts about the adequacy of the concept of both spatial and temporal continuity for the microcosm were only strengthened.

At first it looked as if the classical theory of continuity of space and time had found its spectacular confirmation in the original planetary model of the atom. Nothing seemed to show more impressively the fundamental identity of microphysical and macroscopic space than the elliptical electronic orbits, ruled by the same Keplerian laws as the planetary orbits around the sun. The subatomic world looked like a miniature of the solar system; the microcosm seemingly differed from the macrocosm only by its spatial dimensions. Similarly, microphysical events were not essentially different from events on the macroscopic scale; the only difference was one of duration, and it was interesting that the ratio of microphysical temporal intervals to the temporal intervals of the macrocosm was found to be the same as the corresponding ratio of spatial intervals. This ratio was allegedly $1: 10^{22}$; this was the ratio of the radius of the electron to that of the earth, as well as the ratio of the period of a single revolution of an electron to that of the revolution of the earth around the sun. We have seen (Chapter II) that computations of this kind inspired Fournier d'Albe to reassert the Pascalian idea of the infinite chain of worlds, each containing another and each being contained within another *ad infinitum;* this seemed to be a logical consequence of the relativity of magnitude, spatial as well as temporal. Thus, in spite of the Swiftian twist of Fournier d'Albe's imagination, it appeared entirely logical not to consider the radius of the electron as an ultimate spatial unit; certainly nothing prevents us from subdividing this minute spatial interval into still more minute subintervals and so forth *ad infinitum*.

But soon the deceptive features of the analogy between the planetary system and Bohr-Rutherford's model of the atom became evident; the similarity proved to be quite superficial, if not completely misleading. In due time we shall list all the limitations of this alleged analogy, but for the present let us focus our attention on one feature of Bohr's model which considerably strengthened the doubts about the continuity of space.

The feature of Bohr's model which most conspicuously did not have any counterpart on the planetary scale was the *quantification of the electronic orbits*. Although "Bohr's postulate," as it was called, logically followed from the quantum theory, it was incompatible with classical electrodynamics, and of course it stood in a sharp and shocking contrast to the whole idea of the homogeneity of space. Why were only certain orbits "allowed" and others "forbidden"?

We instinctively and naturally ask for a sufficient reason for such a strange restriction. Even when it is shown that this restriction follows from the quantification of all physical quantities which have the same dimension as Planck's action, the same question keeps cropping up in our mind as long as the traditional concept of homogeneous space is retained. If space is homogeneous, as our visual and Euclidean imagination stubbornly requires, then it must not contain any "privileged" and "underprivileged" zones; any differentiation between "allowed" and "forbidden" regions contradicts the postulate of equivalence of all spatial points which is the essence of the principle of relativity of position. This principle, also called "the axiom of free mobility," appeared to have an a priori character to Bertrand Russell as late as at the end of the last century; yet, it is obviously violated by Bohr's restriction, which prevents electrons from moving freely in space outside the well-defined orbits. It is true that during the process of absorption of radiation an electron (still speaking in the terms of Bohr's model) "jumps" from an orbit of smaller radius to one of a larger radius, whereas during the process of emission it "jumps" in an opposite direction; but it soon became evident that a continuous spatio-temporal description of such "jumps" is impossible; there was no experimental way to determine the hypothetical positions of a jumping electron in the interval separating two orbits.

This shows a very close connection between the continuity of space and that of motion; but the continuity of motion presupposes the infinite divisibility of time. Now questions naturally arose: Are all these three continuities threatened by the quantum theory? Are there limits, imposed by nature itself, on the divisibility of space, time, and motion?

It is certainly significant that shortly after the coming of the quantum theory the possibility of the atomic structure of space and time began to be seriously considered by a number of scientists. Henri Poincaré considered the possibility of the atomic structure of time shortly before his death.[19] Several years later in 1919 A. N. Whitehead, mainly on epistemological grounds, expressed doubts about the physical existence of mathematical durationless instants, and one year later (1920) he admitted more explicitly the possibility of "quanta of time." [20] The French mathematician Emile Borel raised a similar question about space in 1923; he conceded that it might be necessary to introduce discontinuity into the very foundations of geometry.[21] Similar views were expressed by J. J. Thomson, T. Palacios, Robert Lévi, G. J. Pokrowski, H. Latzin, G. Beck, L. Schames, D. Ivanenko, V. Ambarzumian, F. March and, finally, W. Heisenberg in 1943.[22]

In the period between the two World Wars the new names "chronon" and "hodon" were invented for designating the atoms of time and space respectively. The value computed for the chronon was naturally extremely small. According to J. J. Thomson it is of the order of 10^{-21} second, while according to

R. Lévi it is 4.48×10^{-24} second. The computed magnitude of the hodon is of the same order as the radius of the classical electron: 10^{-13} cm.

For all practical purposes, and considered macroscopically, space and time are continuous: the duration of chronons is so insignificant that they may safely be equated with durationless instants; similarly, the difference between mathematical points and spatial regions of the radius of 10^{-13} cm is entirely negligible on our macroscopic scale. This, however, does not make the difference between the classical continuous space and time and its modern atomistic counterparts less radical.

PULSATIONAL TIME-SPACE

It would be premature to see in all these hypothetical attempts more than *symptoms*. As Margenau has said, the speculations about the discrete "hodon" and "chronon" on the part of physicists have been an index of the failures of their theories.[23] We have pointed out (pp. 19-20; 40-41) that both concepts—the atom of space and the atom of time—are contradictory, or at least stated in a self-contradictory language. When we claim that time consists of chronons succeeding each other, and when we claim that the duration of each individual chronon is 4.5×10^{-24} second, what do we assert except that the minimum intervals of time are bounded by two successive *instants*, one of which succeeds the other after the time interval specified? The concept of chronon seems to imply its own boundaries; and as these boundaries are instantaneous in nature, the concept of instant is surreptitiously introduced by the very theory which purports to eliminate it. A similar consideration can be applied to the atomization of space.

It is clear that we cannot get along with such a half-hearted, isolated, and *ad hoc* correction as that described above. Nothing is gained if a theory introduces in a disguised way the very concept which it overtly eliminates. In order to make our conceptual equipment more flexible and more adequate, it is necessary to undertake an extensive and systematic revision of our intellectual habits associated with the traditional ideas of space and time.

The first thing of which we have to be aware is that to speak *separately* of chronons and hodons, as if they were the atoms of space *and* the atoms of time, betrays a prerelativistic state of mind. Before relativity it seemed legitimate to treat space and time separately because their separation was one of the basic assumptions of classical physics. The impossibility of separating space from time in the special theory of relativity is the reason for giving up the concept of absolute simultaneity or, what is the same, of *purely spatial* distance. By asserting the existence of the hodon we claim that there *is* a purely spatial distance equal approximately to 10^{-13} cm; in other words, we separate space from time on the microscopic level, although it was precisely on this level that the consequences of relativity were so spectacularly confirmed.

But if we accept the fusion of space and time even on the subatomic level, then it is evident that no separation of hodon from chronon is possible; they are complementary aspects of a single elementary entity which may be called a pulsation of time-space. There is no chronon without a hodon and *vice versa*. To postulate a timeless (i.e., a chrononless) hodon would mean that instantaneous cuts of four-dimensional processes *are* possible, at least on the atomic level, that there are absolutely simultaneous events within atoms. More specifically, it would mean that there are within atoms couples of events interacting with infinite speed; for we have seen that absolutely simultaneous events would lie on a world line of any *instantaneous* physical action. All these assumptions (which are really one assumption in several forms) are contrary to the special theory of relativity and thus their plausibility is very small.

On the other hand, the assumption of hodonless or spaceless chronons does not seem to contradict directly the relativity theory, in which the existence of the infinitely tenuous world lines (that is, world lines without any spatial extent) was freely assumed. However, on closer inspection, even this assumption is incompatible, if not with the letter, then at least with the spirit, of relativity. The assumption of extensionless points, whose infinite continuous aggregates would constitute space, was merely another way of saying that space is *infinitely divisible*.

But there is no static space in the relativity theory. We have seen that the theory admits only *successive* timelike connections between events; there are no purely spacelike world lines as long as we take the relativity of simultaneity seriously. Thus the assertion of the *spatially extensionless world lines* is equivalent to the assertion *either* that there are purely spatial distances which are infinitely divisible *or* that the spatiotemporal distances themselves are infinitely divisible. As the first assertion is excluded, we have to consider only the second one. But to postulate the mathematical continuity of timelike world lines is contrary to the chronon theory. For this theory assumes that *all* timelike world lines, whether those of material particles or those of photons, are *not* divisible *ad infinitum*. We shall see how the probability of this theory is strengthened by the converging empirical evidence which necessitated the wave-mechanical theory of matter.

Thus in the light of the foregoing considerations, the assumption of the atomicity of space is superfluous because the existence of hodon is merely a certain aspect of the reality of the chronotopic (spatiotemporal) pulsations. While the chronon measures the minimum duration of events constituting a single world line, the hodon measures the minimum time necessary for the interaction of two independent world lines. Everything which had been said about the necessity of redefining spatiality can be repeated here; the only difference is that it is now being applied on the microcosmic scale. There are no instantaneous purely geometrical connections either in the macrocosm or in the microcosm; on either scale these connections should be replaced by chronogeometrical ones. On either scale the concept of spatial distance is redefined in terms of causal independence. But while the interval of independence between, for instance, the world line of the earth and that of Neptune is eight hours, it is equal to the duration of *two chronons* in the case of two microscopic "particles" when their "distance" is minimum.

For all practical purposes this tiny interval may be disregarded; in other words, the temporal link between microphysical events can be regarded as *instantaneous* and the corresponding world lines as infinitely close. The relativistic picture of the world as a four-dimensional continuum of pointlike events is *approximately* true on a macroscopic scale, but becomes seriously inadequate when microscopic relations are considered. But while the "pulsational" character of the world lines is incompatible only with what may be called "textbook relativity," it is entirely consistent with the basic assumptions of the theory.

In order to avoid a self-contradictory formulation of the pulsational character of time-space, we have to make a serious effort to get rid of all the spatial associations with which our classical concept of time is tinged. The theory of chronons, though outwardly denying the existence of instants, really assumes their existence. What does the alleged existence of chronons mean if not the assertion that two successive *instants* are separated by an interval of the order of 10^{-24} second?

But this self-contradictory statement is due to the fact that we are unconsciously trying to translate the pulsational character of world lines into visual and geometrical terms. In our imagination we represent the flux of time by an already drawn geometrical line on which we may distinguish an unlimited number of points; hence our belief in the infinite divisibility of time. The chronon theory does not basically depart from this habit of spatialization; it merely substitutes, for the zero intervals, intervals of finite length. But again these intervals are imaginatively represented by geometrical segments; and as the concept of linear segment naturally implies the existence of its pointlike boundaries, the concept of the instant, verbally eliminated, reappears in the very act by which it is denied. What is overlooked by both those who assert and those who deny the existence of chronons is that it is impossible to reconstruct any temporal process out of static geometrical elements, whether these elements are dimensionless points or segments of finite length.

At the end of Chapter XII we pointed out that the spatial picture of time is inadequate in a *triple* sense: (1) because of the essential incompleteness of time, (2) because it wrongly suggests that time, like a geometrical line, is without transversal extension and (3) because it wrongly suggests the infinite divisibility of time. The last two errors led respectively to the concepts of extensionless and infinitely divisible world lines, infinitely close to each other. To such a view the idea of chronotopic pulsation is radically opposed, but we have to be on guard not to slip back into spatializing fallacies when we try to state this theory.

It is extremely difficult to think without visual aids, especially without such subtle visual symbols as apparently color even the most abstruse concepts (like that of mathematical continuum) and of which mathematicians, untrained in introspective analysis of their own thought processes, remain unaware. Yet, a radical abandonment of visual and imaginative models in modern physics is absolutely imperative if the meaning of the present crisis in physics is not to escape us entirely. We should not mistake the stubborn resistance of old mental habits for logical cogency or "a priori necessity" of thought. The question whether any other, i.e., nonvisual, models of microphysical events and relations are possible will be considered in the concluding part of the book.

The difficulties which we encounter when we try to formulate the theory of spatiotemporal pulsations are analogous to those which faced the early formulations of the theorems of non-Euclidean geometry. As the classical language of geometry was thoroughly Euclidean, it was almost impossible to state any theorem of non-Euclidean geometry without an apparent contradiction, that is, without apparently using those Euclidean concepts whose validity was purportedly denied. Even so openminded a person as J. B. Stallo, who so remarkably anticipated the inadequacy of the classical mechanistic models, was convinced that these difficulties were insurmountable:

The radii of curvature of non-Euclidean spaces are straight radii in the old sense; for if they are not straight, they are of some definite degree of curvature, which again can be determined only by reference to another radius, and so on, either *ad infinitum*, or until we come at last to the old Euclidean straight line.[24]

At that time it was not sufficiently realized that the concept of the "radius of curvature" is merely a visual and Euclidean aid to our limited imagination and that it is possible to speak about the internal metric of non-Euclidean spaces without symbolizing them by curved two-dimensional surfaces contained within Euclidean space. We have seen how strong the tendency was, even in the minds of some interpreters of the relativity theory, to localize spherical space within a four-dimensional Euclidean container.

The difficulty which the chronon and hodon theory faces is analogous: it is extremely difficult to formulate this theory without surreptitiously reintroducing the concept of extensionless boundaries. Our language is so thoroughly molded by the intellectual habits created by infinitesimal calculus that we continue to speak of instants and points even when we are trying to deny them. Yet even some outstanding mathematicians have now begun to realize that the very concepts of point and instant may not be legitimate because the infinite divisibility of space and time, which these two concepts presuppose, may be an unwarranted extrapolation of our limited macroscopic experience. The view of Hilbert and Bernays in their *Grundlagen der Mathematik* is very significant in this respect. After considering the usual conventional solution of the first of Zeno's paradoxes by means of infinite convergent series, they make the following significant observation:

> Actually there is also a much more radical solution of this paradox. This consists in the consideration that we are by no means obliged to believe that the mathematical space-time representation of motion is physically significant for arbitrarily small space and time intervals; but rather have every basis to suppose that mathematical

model extrapolates the fact of a certain realm of experience, namely, the motions within the orders of magnitude accessible to our observation, in the sense of a simple concept construction, similarly to the way the mechanics of continua completes an extrapolation in which a continuous filling of the space with matter is assumed. . . . The situation is similar in all cases where one believes it possible to exhibit directly an infinity as given through experience or perception. . . . Closer examination then shows that an infinity is actually not given to us at all, but is first interpolated or extrapolated through an intellectual process.[25]

Similarly, more recently, Erwin Schrödinger has pointed out that the idea of *continuous range* "is something quite exorbitant, an enormous extrapolation of what is really accessible to us."[26] It was a similar doubt which more than two decades ago led Schrödinger to be skeptical about the applicability of geometry to very small regions of space, or, as we should prefer to say, of time-space.[27] As we shall see later, it is the same tendency to extrapolate that is responsible for the shocked surprise with which physicists and, even more, philosophers, reacted to Heisenberg's uncertainty principle. But it is significant that some outstanding mathematicians are now ready to adopt a more critical attitude even to such a deep-seated mental habit as that of mathematical continuity of space and time.

Hilbert and Bernays' attitude is not isolated. Karl Menger's attempt to construct a "topology without points" represents the trend in modern geometry whose possibility was anticipated by Emile Borel. Menger is clearly aware of the difficulties which he faces when he tries to replace the traditional topology of points by the "topology of lumps":

For, by a lump, we mean something with a well defined boundary. But well defined boundaries are themselves results of limiting processes rather than objects of direct observation. Thus, instead of lumps, we might use at the start something still more vague—something perhaps which has various degrees of density or at least admits a gradual transition to its complement. Such a theory might be of use for wave mechanics.[28]

The difficulty mentioned by Menger is essentially the same as that which was referred to above: the danger of introducing surreptitiously into the theory the very concepts which were regarded as unsatisfactory and were therefore to be eliminated. He apparently recommends as a remedy a return to direct experience, but this recommendation is stated in such general terms that it is easy to overlook its profound significance. I intend to return to it in the concluding section of the book.

For our present purpose it is important to retain the *negative* meaning of the chronon-hodon theories: they are symptoms of the growing realization that the concepts of extensionless points and durationless instants or—what is the same—the concepts of spatial and temporal continuity are hardly adequate tools for dealing with the microphysical reality. Wave mechanics and in particular Heisenberg's principle of uncertainty only strengthened this skepticism. The significance of the principle will be discussed more extensively later; here we shall restrict our attention to those aspects of it which have a bearing on the problem of spatiotemporal continuity.

According to Heisenberg's principle, which is also called the principle of indeterminacy, it is impossible to determine simultaneously the velocity and the position of an electron or of any other microphysical particle; the more accurate the determination of its velocity (or momentum) is, the hazier its position becomes and vice versa. In symbols,

$$\Delta p \, \Delta x \geqq h$$

where Δp means the uncertainty in the measurement of the momentum, Δx is the uncertainty in position, and h is Planck's atom of action.

A similar relation holds for all physical quantities whose products have the same dimension as Planck's constant h. An equally important uncertainty relation holds for the simultaneous determination of energy and time:

$$\Delta E \, \Delta t \geq h$$

where ΔE means the error in measuring energy and Δt is the inaccuracy in determining its moment of time. The more precise the measured value of energy, the less definite its dating becomes.

We shall see in due time the important reasons which prevent us from regarding the principle of indeterminacy as a mere technical limitation imposed on human observation by the very nature of the process by which an observer intervenes in an object observed. We shall see that its significance is far deeper and indicates the presence of real contingency in the nature of things. But if we accept this interpretation, it is evident that the impossibility of determining simultaneously the position and the velocity, or energy and time, is equivalent to the impossibility of determining the instantaneous states of the individual world lines *for the simple reason that such instantaneous states do not exist in nature*. While the relativity of simultaneity excluded the possibility of instantaneous cuts across four-dimensional becoming, Heisenberg's principle of indeterminacy in its second form forbids even such an instantaneous cut across one single world line. Its philosophical significance was stated with superb conciseness by Zigmund Zawirski in 1934:

> If the instantaneous cut of the temporal flow according to Heisenberg's formula leaves energy completely undetermined, does not this prove that the universe needs a certain time to take on precise forms?[29]

In its first form Heisenberg's principle destroys the possibility of the world lines themselves, at least as long as they are regarded in the classical relativity theory as sharply defined lines without any spatial thickness. It is not necessary to advocate the specific theories of hodon and chronon in order to question the legitimacy of the infinite divisibility of space and time; it is sufficient to draw consequences from the principle of uncertainty to see the impossibility of absolutely sharp localization and absolutely precise dating of microphysical events. It was only natural for Louis de Broglie to conclude that physics of quanta introduces, in a certain sense, "the discontinuity of becoming" and that the continuity of macroscopic time is merely an illusion resulting statistically from the enormous number of the discontinuous elementary events.[30]

It may be objected that Heisenberg's principle does not necessarily lead to the concept of the minimum spatiotemporal pulsation, although it is compatible with it. It is theoretically conceivable that while Δp is increased without limit, Δx will approach zero; similarly, for $\Delta E = \infty$, Δt would be equal to zero. Mathematically these limit cases are compatible with Heisenberg's formula: $\Delta x = 0$ would mean the possibility of precise punctual localization in space, while $\Delta t = 0$ would mean the corresponding possibility of precise dating. Thus, strictly speaking, Heisenberg's principle is mathematically compatible with the existence of pointlike positions and mathematical instants which the principle of spatiotemporal continuity requires.

For several reasons, however, this purely formal compatibility remains utterly unconvincing for a physicist. Not only is it difficult to give any meaningful physical interpretation to these limit cases, for which the indeterminacy of momentum or energy should be infinitely large, but there is also considerable physical evidence against their actual occurrence. Some facts of nuclear physics suggest the existence of a minimal spatial length of the same order as the radius of the electron, which would limit accuracy in measuring the position *independently* of the inaccuracy in measuring the corresponding momentum. The minimum possible temporal interval then would be equal to the ratio l_0/c, that is, of the minimum length l_0 and the velocity of light c. The estimated numerical values are about the same as the numerical values of chronon and hodon found by Lévi, Pokrovski, Beck, and others nearly thirty years ago.[31] If we are on guard against stating these views in prerelativistic language, they are equivalent to the theory of spatiotemporal pulsations outlined above.

Thus the inadequacy of the concept of spatiotemporal continuity seems to be for all practical purposes established. We may conclude with the words of Leon Schames, which are as valid now as they were a quarter of a century ago:

> Finally, if we compare the concept of continuity with that of atomism, it can be said that on the whole the former seems to be more in accordance with the structure of our thinking. *But the structure of our thinking and the structure of reality need not always coincide.*[32]

NOTES FOR CHAPTER XIII

1. A. A. Robb, *The Absolute Relations of Time and Space;* also *Geometry of Time and Space* (Cambridge University Press, 1936), pp. 1-25; R. Carnap, *loc. cit.* (cf. ch. X, n. 13); H. Mehlberg, "Essai sur la théorie causale du temps," *Studia philosophica* (Leopolis, 1935), pp. 120-260; H. Reichenbach, *Die Philosophie der Raum-Zeit-Lehre,* especially pp. 306-311; A. Markov, "Über die Ableitbarkeit der Weltmetrik aus der 'Früher als' Beziehung," *Physikalische Zeitschrift der Sowjetunion,* Vol. I, 3 (1932), p. 397.
2. Carnap, *op. cit.,* p. 334.
3. E. T. Whittaker, *A History of the Theories of Aether and Electricity* (London, 1953), Vol. II, p. 186.
4. Whitehead, *An Enquiry Concerning the Principles of Natural Knowledge,* p. 6.
5. A. A. Robb, *Geometry of Time and Space,* p. 15.
6. Cf. P. Weiss, "Contemporary World," *The Review of Metaphysics,* Vol. VI (1952), pp. 526-539 and my article "Relativity and the Status of Space" *ibid.,* IX (1955), especially my comment on Weiss on pp. 187, 195-197.
7. Carnap, *op. cit.,* p. 336.
8. A. N. Whitehead, *The Concept of Nature,* p. 177-78.
9. H. Bergson, *Durée et Simultanéité,* pp. 68-69.
10. H. Bergson, *Creative Evolution,* Chap. IV.
11. E. Schrödinger, "Spezielle Relativitätstheorie und Quantenmechanik," *Sitzenberichtungen der preussischen Akademie der Wissenschaften,* Phys. Math. Klasse, XII (1931), p. 3.
12. It may sound strange that classical space which was by its nature *empty,* i.e., *penetrable,* could possess the attribute of rigidity which is usually associated with the impenetrability of matter; or that the void which *separates* physical bodies could be characterized as a *connecting* agency. But let us not forget that the classical Euclidean void was a physical *container* in which individual physical bodies *coexist* together and that this container, as Newton explicitly stressed, is in its own nature rigid and unchangeable. Thus it may be said with equal accuracy that spatial distances *separate* as well as *connect*

physical bodies. Each distance remains eternally the same, no matter whether it joins (or separates) two particles or two unoccupied positions; what is changing is the *occupancy* of positions, not positions themselves. The logical connection between the simultaneity (i.e., spatial juxtaposition) and the rigidity was clearly shown by P. Langevin in the article already quoted, "L'Evolution de l'espace et du temps," p. 460. It is clear that the special theory of relativity makes the concept of rigid body as well as that of *rigid void* equally obsolete.

13. A. N. Whitehead, *An Enquiry*, p. 202.
14. B. Riemann, "Über die Hypothesen welche der Geometrie zugrunde liegen," p. 16.
15. The first German edition of Weyl's *Raum-Zeit-Materie* appeared in 1918.
16. B. Riemann, "Fragmente philosophischen Inhalts," *Gesammelte Mathematische Werke* (Leipzig, 1892), p. 529. Riemann regarded the atom as a hole into which the world-aether continuously streams. It was a theory of "perpetual destruction," i.e., the very opposite of Hoyle's theory of "continuous creation."
17. H. Weyl, *Space-Time-Matter*, p. 262; *Was ist Materie?* (Berlin, 1924), pp. 56-57.
18. H. Weyl, *Was ist Materie?*, p. 57: "im Innern dieser Säume ist kein Raum mehr."
19. H. Poincaré, *Dernières pensées* (Paris, 1913), p. 188.
20. Whitehead, *The Concept of Nature*, p. 162.
21. E. Borel, *L'Espace et le temps* (Paris, 1923), pp. 124-127.
22. J. J. Thomson, "The Intermittence of Electric Force," *Proc. Royal Soc. Edinburgh*, Vol. 46 (1925-26), p. 90; J. Palacios, "La Nature des Rayons X," *Scientia*, Vol. 38 (1925); R. Lévi, "La théorie de l'action universelle et discontinue," *Journal de Physique et de Radium*, Vol. VIII (1927), pp. 182 f.; G. J. Pokrowski, "Zur Frage nach oberen Grenzen für die Energiedichte," *Zeitschrift für Physik*, Vol. 51 (1928), pp. 730 f.; "Zur Frage nach der Struktur der Zeit," *ibid.*, p. 737; H. Latzin, "Quantentheorie und die Realität," *Naturwissenschaften*, Vol. 15 (1927), p. 161; G. Beck, "Die zeitliche Quantelung der Bewegung," *Zeitschrift für Physik*, Vol. 53 (1929), pp. 675 f.; L. Schames, "Die atomistische Auffassung von Raum und Zeit," *Zeitschrift für Physik*, Vol. 81 (1933), p. 270; V. Ambarzumian-D. Ivanenko, "Zur Frage nach Vermeidung der unendlichen Selbstrückwirkung des Elektrons," *Zeitschrift für Physik*, Vol. 64 (1930), pp. 563-68; W. Heisenberg, "Die beobachtbare Grössen in der Theorie der elementaren Teilchen," *Zeitschrift für Physik*, Vol. 120 (1942), pp. 513-538; 673-702, F. March, *Die physikalische Erkenntnis und ihre Grenzen* (Braunschweig, 1960), pp. 107-114.
23. H. Margenau, *The Nature of Physical Reality*, p. 156.
24. J. B. Stallo, *The Concepts and Theories of Modern Physics*, pp. 238-39.

25. D. Hilbert-P. Bernays, *Grundlegen der Mathematik* (Jena, 1931), pp. 15-17.

26. E. Schrödinger, *Science and Humanism* (Cambridge University Press, 1952), pp. 30-31.

27. E. Schrödinger, "Über die Unanwendbarkeit der Geometrie im Kleinen," *Naturwissenschaften*, Vol. 22 (1934), pp. 518-20.

28. K. Menger, "Topology Without Points," *Rice Inst. Pamphlet*, Vol. XXVII (Jan. 1940), No. 1, p. 107.

29. S. Zawirski, "L'Evolution de la notion du temps," *Scientia*, Vol. 28 (1934), p. 260.

30. L. de Broglie, "L'espace et le temps dans la physique quantique," *Revue de Metaphysique et de Morale*, Vol. 54 (1949), pp. 115-117.

31. W. Heisenberg, *loc. cit.*, p. 514; P. Jordan, "Zur axiomatischen Begründungen der Quantenmechanik," *Zeitschrift für Physik*, Vol. 133 (1952), pp. 21-29.

32. L. Schames, *loc. cit.*, p. 281.

XIV · THE EVOLUTION OF THE CONCEPT OF MATTER

THE INADEQUACY OF CORPUSCULAR MODELS

IT WAS practically impossible to deal with the revolutionary transformation of the concepts of space and time without indicating at the same time some concomitant and no less radical modifications to which the classical concept of matter has been subjected in recent decades. We have already indicated how the traditional distinction between kinematics and dynamics was wiped out by the general theory of relativity. The gravitational effects of matter were reduced to the effects of the local curvature of time-space, while the inertial manifestations of matter are now regarded, according to the principle of equivalence, as not basically different from those of gravitation. In other words, the inertial field is merely a gravitational field with a vanishing spatiotemporal curvature. Even the substantial nucleus of matter, designated by classical physicists as "impenetrability" or as *vis insita* by Newton, is now regarded as nothing more than a certain structural complication in the spatiotemporal medium. Whether the existence of discrete elementary particles is regarded as a singularity ("hole") within the non-Euclidean time-space or as a manifestation of the discrete (pulsational) character of time-space, the philosophical significance remains the same: the distinction between the "full" and the "void," on which the classical concept of particle was based, is now being profoundly revised.

A more systematic survey is necessary in order to show how all recently discovered facts point in the same direction and lead to the same result, which may be equally well characterized either as "geometrization of matter" or as a "dynamization" or "physicalization" of space (or rather time-space).

It was pointed out in Part I how the classical mechanistic program of corpuscular-kinetic explanation was to a large extent successfully realized on a macroscopic and even on a molecular scale. But within the dimensions approaching the size of atoms and especially of subatomic "particles," the shortcomings of the kinetic-corpuscular scheme became gradually more and more obvious. It is true that the electron theory, especially in its first phase, can be regarded as a successful culmination of the classical tendencies: the apparently inexhaustible variety in nature was reduced to differences in configuration of the same basic elements, which were the ultimate units of matter and electricity at the same time; while all infinitely variegated changes appeared to be reducible to displacements of the same homogeneous elements. There was a reasonable hope that the remaining gaps would be filled sooner or later; in particular, it was hoped that the difference between positive and negative electricity would eventually be interpreted in kinetic terms. For if the elementary positive and negative charges are merely aethereal structures or, in Lamor's words, "nuclei of beknottedness of aether," [1] then it is only natural to expect that differences in their behavior, their mutual attractions and repulsions, will eventually be deducible from the mechanics of aether and aether particles. Thus the Democritean "alphabet of Being" finally seemed to be within the reach of science.

But concrete discoveries showed more and more convincingly that the "particles" of modern physics did not exhibit the neat properties postulated by classical atomism. First, contrary to natural expectations, there was apparently no proportionality between mass and volume—one of the cherished ideas of the mechanistic scheme of nature. Nearly the whole mass of the atom is concentrated in the nucleus; the ratio of the mass of the electron to the mass of the hydrogen nucleus is 1:1834. What was even worse, not only are electrons not smaller in the corresponding ratio than protons, but, on the contrary, the revolving planet-electrons were estimated to have a radius a *thousand times larger* than that of the sunlike hydrogen nucleus! Even though this computation was later proved to be wrong,[2] it is still believed that the nuclei, in spite of possessing nearly the whole mass of the atom, have radii of the same order of magnitude as that of electrons, that is, 10^{-13} cm. All hopes of mechanistically minded physicists that the electron theory would rehabilitate the *proportionality between mass and volume* of the elementary particles, the proportionality which, as we have seen, is the cornerstone of the atomic theory, were frustrated.

The proportionality between the "quantity of matter" and "bulk," required by Newton's famous first definition, was thus challenged by microphysical experience. By accepting the different density of matter in electrons and protons, physicists were departing, whether they knew it or not, from one of the basic postulates of the atomistic-kinetic scheme of nature. Only dynamic theories of matter, like those of Boscovich and Kant, regarded differences in density as irreducible to differences in spatial distribution of equally dense elementary units.

There were other difficulties which were even more serious. A fundamental postulate of the classical atomistic view was the *constancy of the mass of the elementary units;* this was the ground for the law of the conservation of matter on the macroscopic scale. The constancy was a natural consequence of the substantiality and immutability of the atomic units—we need not repeat the reasoning expounded in Part I. But this is precisely what has *not* been found for electrons; their mass is a *function of velocity*. It increases when their velocity increases—at first very slowly, but for velocities approaching the velocity of light noticeably enough to be detected experimentally.

The corresponding formula for mass in motion

$$m = \frac{m_0}{\sqrt{1 - \frac{v^2}{c^2}}}$$

(where m_0 = mass at rest, v = velocity of body, and c = velocity of light) is a logical consequence of Einstein's new law for the composition of velocities

$$w = \frac{v_1 + v_2}{1 + \frac{v_1 v_2}{c^2}}$$

which in its turn follows naturally from Lorentz's transformation. We have already referred to this important difference between Newtonian and Einsteinian mechanics. According to Newton, any material body possessing two different velocities at the same time will have a resulting velocity equal to their vectorial sum; in the special case when their directions are equal or opposite it will be equal to their algebraic sum.

We have seen that the absence of any upper limit for increasing velocities of material bodies was merely another aspect of the physical indifference of classical space and time to physical changes taking place in it. The resistance of any body to acceleration was believed to be the same no matter whether the body was at rest or moving, and no matter how fast it was moving. This constancy of the resistance to acceleration was nothing but the *constancy of the inertial mass*, which was independent of both the position and the velocity of the body in question. In this logical connection between the homogeneity (i.e., physical passivity) of classical space-time and the rigidity and constancy of matter we have already recognized the inseparability of kinematics and dynamics *even within the classical framework*. We have already seen that, no matter how paradoxical it may sound, the structure of classical space and time was only spuriously passive, because it determined the privileged character of the inertial motion as well as the rigidity and constancy of material bodies.

Now such a constancy is denied by the special theory of

relativity, and the denial is supported by a considerable body of empirical evidence. Does this mean that the law of the conservation of matter is no longer valid? This would be a premature conclusion, and the apparently irrational character of relativistic dynamics will acquire a less shocking aspect if we bear in mind that the old Lucretian maxim *ex nihilo nihil fit* is really *not* violated in this case. This became apparent in the period immediately preceding relativity when the electromagnetic theory of matter was hailed as a legitimate successor of the old mechanical theory.

According to this theory, the "mass" of the electron was only apparent, being due exclusively to the reaction of the surrounding medium, which was then called "electromagnetic aether." When an electron is set in motion, a magnetic field in the plane perpendicular to its trajectory is created and its reaction to the motion of an electron manifests itself as an increase of mass. Thus what we used to call "matter" seemed to be of exclusively electromagnetic origin; the inertial resistance to acceleration, which Newton regarded as inherently residing *within* the particles themselves, appeared to be due to the braking effect of the surrounding electromagnetic medium.

It was also understandable that this resistance to acceleration must increase with the velocity of electrons, which cannot surpass nor even reach a certain critical velocity, that is, the velocity of light. For by this velocity all electromagnetic disturbances are propagated, including the electric field itself which surrounds an electron and is indissolubly connected with it. An electron reaching or surpassing the velocity of light would be a physical contradiction because it would break its connection with the field of which, so to speak, it is a product. Mechanical analogies illustrating this impossibility were not lacking. No structural complication of any physical medium can surpass or even reach the velocity of the elementary disturbances of the same medium. No aerial eddy, for example, can move with a greater velocity than the velocity of the molecules of air. It is evident that no aggregate can move faster than its own constituents; this holds generally for any medium, whether air or hypothetical aether.[3]

Thus it is clear that the increase of mass with velocity does not arise "out of nothing," but out of the electromagnetic energy of the aether. The mechanical analogy, mentioned above, suggests the possibility of mechanical explanation of the apparent increase of the electronic mass along the same lines as the explanation of the Lorentz-FitzGerald contraction to which we referred briefly in Chapter X. The temptation to use classical devices in order to explain relativistic effects was great indeed; three centuries of scientific tradition predisposed physicists to look for this kind of solution. Because the increase of the mass of an electron does not arise out of nothing, the principle of conservation of substance is not necessarily threatened nor is the mechanistic conception of nature with which the conservation principles, as we have seen, were regularly associated in the past. In order to save both it would be sufficient to repeat what had been done several times before: to look for some smaller and more fundamental units of nature.

It appeared difficult to condemn such attempts on a priori grounds. After the divisibility of molecules was discovered, the permanency of matter was looked for in atoms; when atoms eventually proved to be divisible, the substantiality and permanency retreated to the electrons. Now if the electrons do not possess the required constancy of their mass, why not look for some smaller and "truly"permanent particles? History seems to warn us sufficiently against being dogmatically skeptical about such attempts. One great mistake of J. B. Stallo in 1881 was to claim prematurely that the fruitfulness of mechanical explanations had already been spent; this erroneous belief led him to dismiss summarily the hypothesis according to which the molecules themselves are complex, being constituted by more elementary and truly atomic units.[4] When even the electrons had lost their constancy and substantiality, physicists began to be tired of repeating the classical procedure and resolving the electrons into more elementary and "truly ultimate" units; but at the same time it was only natural and most consonant with the classical habits to try again, even at a risk of another frustration. If electrons themselves are nothing but condensations of electromagnetic energy, is not this energy itself of *mechanical* nature, that is, a kinetic energy of aether particles?

Electrons would thus lose their substantiality, that is, constancy and individuality, as they would be nothing but relatively stable disturbances of the cosmic medium, disturbances analogous to the waves or eddies moving on the surface of an ocean. As in an ocean the true substantiality belongs not to its surface waves but to the moving and vibrating particles of water, so in aether the true constancy and individuality would belong, not to the electrons or protons, but to the aether particles of which they are constituted. The apparent increase of the electronic mass would be, in principle at least, conceivable as a result of accumulation of the aether particles in front of the moving electrons, and the upper limit for the velocity of the moving electrons would find its natural explanation in the resistance of the aethereal medium, the resistance which, according to Fournier d'Albe, tends to become infinite when the velocity of electrons approaches the velocity of light.[5] The theory of aether atoms would also save the classical proportionality between mass and volume; the difference between the mass of the electron and that of the proton would be due to the *closer packing* of the equally massive aether particles in the latter. The mechanistic hypothesis of Lenard, Wiechert, Jellinek, Oliver Lodge, and J. J. Thomson[6] were of this kind, and it has already been shown that this tradition may be traced to Kurd Lasswitz, William Thomson, and even farther back in the past, to the Cartesian physics of the seventeenth century.

But the idea of aether as a subtle material *milieu* filling space and possessing mechanical properties became gradually so discredited that the majority of physicists recognized its fruitlessness. The extreme difficulties which nineteenth-century physicists faced in trying to devise a mechanical model of aether, endowed with noncontradictory properties by which all observed phenomena could be explained, contributed largely to the growing distrust of mechanical explanations. Even before the advent of relativity, such a task was a gigantic one. A satisfactory model of aether should explain not only *all* electromagnetic phenomena (including their subclass, the phenomena of light), but also the phenomena of gravitation; after the emergence of the electron theory and discovery of relativistic effects on a microphysical scale, the task was enormously widened because a comprehensive model of aether should account for the phenomena of inertia and discrete electronic charges as well. We have already seen that underlying this search for mechanical explanation was the hope of attaining that elusive microscopic *solid particle* which, since the times of Lucretius, had fascinated imaginations of physicists and philosophers, and by its solidity and indestructibility appeared to possess the required attributes of the "ultimate element of nature."

But this alluring image steadily receded as physics advanced and penetrated deeper and deeper into the microcosm. It is hardly surprising that the frustrated physicists began to realize that the solid particle was merely a mirage of their imaginations. When even the electrons lost their alleged solidity and, as we shall see, their indestructibility and uncreatability, the whole game of searching for the "ultimate element" turned frustrating and monotonous. Although there are even now physicists who are looking hopefully toward aether as a clue to the explanation of microphysical phenomena, their number has substantially decreased since the coming of relativity. For the special theory of relativity was really a decisive blow from which the classical concept of aether never fully recovered.

Whether we regard the aethereal *milieu* as atomistic in the sense of Huygens and Lasswitz, or (less consistently) as continuous in the sense of William Thomson, or even if we resort to the more abstract concept of aether of Lorentz, one feature still is retained, its *motionlessness*. The electromagnetic aether was supposed to be *at rest*, no matter how its other properties were specified. This would mean that the optical effects of motion through such aether should be observable at least in principle; as we know, no such phenomena were observed. By the discovery of the constant velocity of light the classical mechanistic-visual model of aether was wrecked beyond repair. If we still continue to use the term "aether" then, as Einstein stressed, we should regard it as being *neither at rest nor in motion!* [7]

But why use a term with such misleading associations? For the term "aether" suggests inevitably the idea of material or quasi-material substance. What kind of "substance" is something whose properties are so thoroughly different from the ordinary matter of our daily experience, and which does not even possess the elementary kinematic properties like rest or motion? Hermann Weyl's conclusion that the role of the concept of substance in physics is over seems to be justified in the light of what happened to the supposedly ultimate and permanent substratum of all physical phenomena. [8]

THE FUSION OF MASS WITH ENERGY

Thus, instead of trying to solve the paradoxical increase of the electronic mass by classical devices which would save the validity of traditional concepts on the ultraelectronic (that is, aethereal) scale of magnitude, physicists generally followed the road of Einstein which led to the entire reformulation of the foundations of mechanics. For Einstein, the increase of the inertial mass as well as the modified law for the composition of velocities were mere consequences of the Lorentz equations, that is, of the fusion of space with time.

Even within the relativistic dynamics the axiom *ex nihilo nihil fit* is not violated, although it is free from its traditional connection with the atomistic-kinetic model of the universe. Relativistic dynamics, by generalizing the concept of mass, preserves the principle of conservation. This is done by the well-known equation $E = mc^2$, according to which every form of energy possesses a certain inertial mass and vice versa. Thus in increasing the kinetic energy of a particle, we at the same time increase its mass. The increase of mass therefore does not arise "out of nothing" but is equivalent to the fraction of inertial mass contained in the increase of kinetic energy. The extremely minute amount of this increase ($m = E/c^2$) accounts for its unobservability under ordinary circumstances and makes it observable only for large mechanical velocities as in Kaufmann's and Bucherer's experiments with beta rays or for electrons revolving fast around the nucleus in Sommerfeld's model of the atom. This means that both laws, the law of the conservation of mass and that of the conservation of energy, cease to be valid separately; but by generalizing both concepts and, so to speak, fusing them together in the sense of Einstein's equation, we create one single concept, "mass-energy," for which the principle of conservation remains valid.

It is not necessary to dwell on the amazing fruitfulness of Einstein's equation and the many applications which it found in the interpretation of physical and, in particular, microphysical phenomena. The validity of the equation is entirely general: *every* energy has its inertial mass, and vice versa. It is therefore natural to expect that light or electromagnetic energy has a certain mass and, consequently, has to exert a certain pressure and be affected by the gravitational field. Both consequences were experimentally confirmed: the first even prior to the advent of relativity by Lebedev in 1900, the second when the curvature of the light rays in the gravitational field of the sun, predicted by Einstein, was observed during the solar eclipse in 1919.

Moreover, the equation requires that *every* increase or decrease of energy involves an increase or decrease of the corresponding inertial mass. Consequently, the total mass of a material aggregate is no longer equal to the arithmetical sum of its individual corpuscular components, as was the case in classical physics. It is either decreased or increased according as the energy in the process of aggregation is released or absorbed. Thus when the formation of 1 mole of CO_2 liberates 92,400 calories, there is a loss of mass; on the other hand when 21,600 calories are absorbed in the process of formation of 1 mole of NO, the resulting mass effect is positive.

But the modifications of total mass in ordinary chemical reactions were too tiny to be observed, as is immediately evident if we divide the quantities of energy given above by the square of the velocity of light. This accounts for the fact that even the fine experiments of Landolt failed to discover any variation of mass in ordinary chemical reactions. Landolt's limits of accuracy were such that only variations involving amounts no less than the 10^{-6}th part of the total mass could be discovered. This was far below the limits of accuracy required for determining relativistic mass effects, which are of the order of 10^{-10} of the total weight.[9]

The situation is different if, instead of ordinary chemical reactions, the formations of atomic nuclei are considered. One of the most famous instances is the mass defect resulting from the formation of one alpha particle (i.e., the nucleus of a helium atom) by two protons and two neutrons. The mass of a proton is 1.00758, while the mass of a neutron is only slightly different: 1.00893. According to the classical ideas the mass of the aggregate of two protons and two neutrons should be

$$2 \times 1.00758 + 2 \times 1.00893 = 4.03302$$

whereas the mass of a helium nucleus is only 4.00280. In other words, approximately 0.030 mass units "disappeared" or, more accurately, were converted into the binding energy of the nucleus. Similar mass defects were found for other nuclei; they are greatest for the elements in the middle of the periodic table. The spectacular technological application of the energy liberated by "annihilation" of a certain fraction of mass during the process of nuclear fission is sufficiently well known not to be dwelt upon. As far as the opposite phenomenon of the "materialization" of energy is concerned, it takes place in the so-called endoergic reactions in which energy is absorbed instead of being released. In the last case there is an increase of the rest mass itself, which still remains constant in the increase of the electronic mass in motion. We shall meet even more striking phenomena of materialization and dematerialization shortly.

Meanwhile let us ponder the philosophical significance of these new discoveries, a significance which can hardly be overestimated. It is clear that matter is now no longer equivalent to *plenum* or "full space," that is, to certain well-defined regions of space filled by "material stuff" and sharply separated from the intervening void. On the contrary, mass is now very closely associated with the surrounding spatial, or rather spatiotemporal, medium, for it is present in the energetic link which joins "particles" together. Thus the distinction between "full" and "empty" loses its original Democritean or Newtonian sharpness. This distinction, already dimmed by the special theory of relativity, was entirely wiped out by the general theory of relativity.

It would be otiose to repeat what has already been stated about matter being resorbed into space, or, more accurately, into timespace. What used to be called "material substance" or "quantity of matter" has been reduced to a local deformation of space which not only lost its Euclidean character and its physical inertness ("emptiness"), but in virtue of its fusion with time deserves some more appropriate name than that which is tinged by misleading classical associations. The term "four-dimensional process" or "extensive becoming" would be far more appropriate.

But if a material particle is merely a local irregularity of the cosmic non-Euclidean medium which was formerly called "aether," it is conceivable that under certain circumstances such a deformation may disappear. Any such disappearance would be equivalent to a complete "annihilation" of matter or its "dematerialization." Oliver Lodge envisioned this possibility more than thirty years ago.[10] If the proton and the electron could be superposed or fused together, then not only would their charges be mutually neutralized, but also their masses, assuming that they are inseparable from their charges, would completely vanish. In the language of Einstein, Weyl, or Eddington, such a phenomenon would be nothing but a superposition of two oppositely oriented local curvatures of the non-Euclidean time-space; they would cancel each other like two waves of equal amplitude meeting at opposite phases, and the result would be a local disappearance of the non-Euclidean curvature. That particular region of time-space would acquire the homogeneous and undifferentiated character which characterizes what we call "void" or "absence of matter." Using Cartesian-Kelvinian language—doubtless naive, but expressive and appealing to our macroscopically conditioned imagination —we might say that the condensation or whirl-like formation which constitutes the particle itself was dissolved into the undifferentiated continuity of aether. Such a disappearance of the spatiotemporal stress would manifest itself by the rise of a wave of very high frequency whose energy would be equivalent to the internal energy of the vanished mass.

It is clear again that it would be premature to speak of the "annihilation of matter" in a literal sense, because the vanished mass is "preserved" in the inertia of the resulting electromagnetic radiation into which the pair of particles was transformed. But the indestructibility of matter is saved only because we have given up entirely its visual and intuitive properties. Certainly, the mass of a photon moving with the velocity c, which no ordinary mass can attain, which does not exist *except* in motion and disappears when it comes to rest (although, according to Einstein's equation, it is "preserved" in the quantum of energy absorbed by an atom), and which cannot be traced in a continuous fashion like the mass of the planets or of projectiles— such a mass is *toto coelo* different from the mass of solid localizable particles of Newtonian physics. In any case, Einstein's identification of mass and energy does not save the indestructibility of particles which obviously may vanish if the underlying spatiotemporal deformations, of which they are effects, disappear.

A concrete confirmation of the hypothesis of dematerialization of elementary particles came in a form slightly different from that proposed by Oliver Lodge. But in spite of differences in details the occurrence of dematerialization was established and, what is even more important, the occurrence of the converse phenonmenon, *the materialization of particles,* was demonstrated at the same time. A new elementary particle whose mass is equal to that of the electron, but whose charge is equal and positive, was discovered by Anderson in 1932.[11] When heavy nuclei were irradiated by radiation of very high frequency, pairs of oppositely charged particles appeared, and as the charge and the mass of one of them corresponded to a negative electron, the second one, whose path in the electric field was curved symmetrically in the opposite sense, had to be identified with a positive electron. Because the kinetic energy of the produced pair is incomparably smaller than the energy of the incident radiation, it is believed that the main portion of the radiation energy *was transformed into the rest mass of the two particles* and only the remaining part was converted into their kinetic energy. The law of conservation of mass-energy is obviously not violated, since the whole process is ruled by the energetic equation

$$E = 2m_0 c^2 + \tfrac{1}{2}m_0 v_1{}^2 + \tfrac{1}{2}m_0 v_2{}^2$$

where E is the energy of the incident radiation, m_0 the mass of each electron, c the velocity of light, and v_1 and v_2 the respective velocities of the particles produced. Nor is the law of the conservation of charge violated, since the electrically neutral radiation was converted into a pair of oppositely charged particles whose *total* charge is equal to zero. According to classical standards, this process is equivalent to the *materialization* of energy, that is, the *disappearance* of energy and the *creation* of matter; only by associating these two concepts, which were separate and distinct in the classical framework, into one single relativistic concept, "mass-energy," was it possible to save *formally* the conservation law. The phenomenon itself was an unexpected confirmation of Einstein's equation concerning the identity of matter and energy.

But the equation itself hardly gives any clue about the mechanism of this transformation, which defies any attempt at pictorial representation. This is hardly surprising because the equation is a consequence of Lorentz's transformation, whose various features, e.g., the constancy of the velocity of light and the rejection of absolute space, must appear shocking absurdities to all those who remain loyal to the Cartesian-Kelvinian ideal of explanation.

An inverse phenomenon, *the dematerialization of electrons*, was discovered by Thibaud and Joliot almost at the same time.[12] It was, in principle at least, a confirmation of Lodge's anticipatory guess, although in a different form. (Today we know that protons can be annihilated by being fused with the recently discovered antiprotons, and not with negative electrons as Lodge anticipated.) The extremely rare occurrence as well as the belated discovery of the positive electron was due to the fact that it cannot exist long in the presence of matter; once formed, it unites quickly with another electron of opposite charge, whereat they both *vanish* or, more accurately, their mass is entirely converted into the energy of high-frequency radiation. The lifetime of positive electrons is extremely short, being of the order of 10^{-8} second. But what is even more important is that these paradoxical phenomena are far less exceptional than was originally believed.

The development of nuclear physics in the last two decades has showed that the existence of short-lived "particles" is one of the most characteristic features of cosmic radiation. While the number of the discovered particles has increased in an almost alarming way, their behavior differs in two fundamental respects from the properties of the Newtonian and Daltonian atoms: *they are neither indestructible nor uncreatable.* According to Niels Bohr's view, which is generally accepted today, even the emission of beta radiation, which consists of negative electrons, should not be pictured in the classical sense as an ejection of the particles which *actually pre-exist within the nucleus,* but should be regarded as a process of creation, in which the particles are *created* during their ejection just as photons are created by the process of emission.[13] The idea expressed by Bialobrzeski about a quarter of a century ago that the particles within the nuclei exist in a *potential* rather than actual state was a correct philosophical anticipation of the present state of nuclear physics.[14]

But if this is so, is there any sense in applying the term "corpuscle" or "particle" to such evanescent entities, whose extremely short life time stands in almost ludicrous contrast to the constancy and eternity of the classical atoms? Do we not pour new wine into old vessels if we apply a term with such a misleading connotation to neutrons which last only half an hour, to positive electrons lasting only 10^{-8} second or to neutral π-mesons "living" not longer than 10^{-14} second? [15] Is not the term "event" much less misleading and certainly more fitting for such quasi-instantaneous entities?

The centuries of the substantialist conditioning of our minds cannot be eliminated overnight. Although the number of physicists who take the term "particle" or "corpuscle" literally is continuously decreasing, the diagrams in which particles are represented as little circles are still found in the textbooks of atomic physics. There is nothing objectionable about such visual aids as long as they are not regarded as true replicas of microphysical reality. But the temptation to regard them so is great indeed, for the simple reason that the imagination of physicists remains intrinsically realistic in spite of their positivistic declarations to the contrary. A visual picture of a little sphere with a tiny radius will always have a greater appeal to our Democritean subconscious than an apparently abstract term "event."

From the point of view adopted in this book the replacement of the term "particle" by "event" is justified not only by the obvious empirical inadequacy of the former, but also because it appears to be logically implied by our previous discussion of the concept of space and time. If space and time are fused together into the dynamic unity of time-space, which itself was fused with its concrete physical content, i.e., matter and energy; if, furthermore, there is substantial evidence for the pulsational character of time-space, the character which matter itself in virtue of its fusion with time-space must share, the assertion that what we used to call a "particle" is in truth a string of successive events will become less paradoxical. We shall see that even within their short life-span the duration of microphysical "corpuscles," instead of being an undifferentiated and homogeneous duration of Newtonian time, is differentiated into successive events.

This at least seems to be indicated by wave mechanics which, as we shall try to show, added the final touch to the ruin of the corpuscular-kinetic model of nature. But before considering this new line of facts, it is indispensable to indicate the transformation of another concept, closely correlated with the concept of corpuscular matter, that is, the *transformation of the concept of motion.*

NOTES FOR CHAPTER XIV

1. E. T. Whittaker, *A History of the Theories of Aether and Electricity*, Vol. I, pp. 287-8.
2. Indirect proportionality between radius and mass of the elementary charges follows from the formula for their electromagnetic mass: $m = 2e^2/3r$ where m is electromagnetic mass, e = elementary charge, and r its radius. Cf. J. J. Thomson, *Electricity and Matter* (Yale University Press, 1903), pp. 21, 94. As the elementary charge is the same for the electron and proton, their radii must be in inverse ratio to their electromagnetic masses, i.e., the radius of the proton should be of the order of 10^{-16} cm. It was assumed that the whole mass of both charges is of electromagnetic nature. But this result conflicted with all experimental data. No fewer than nine different experimental methods for measuring the nuclear radius lead to the conclusion that it is of the same order of magnitude as that of the electron. Cf. Robley D. Evans, *The Atomic Nucleus* (New York, McGraw-Hill, 1955), pp. 30-31.
3. Cf. P. Lenard, *Über Äther und Materie* (Heidelberg, 1911) for this kind of explanation. J. J. Thomson (*op. cit.*, pp. 22-23) used the mechanical analogy of a sphere moving through a frictionless liquid to illustrate the growing resistance of a body to acceleration.
4. J. B. Stallo, *The Concepts and Theories of Modern Physics*, p. 35.
5. Fournier d'Albe, *Two New Worlds*, p. 89. Cf. Note 3 above for a similar mechanical explanation of the upper limit of velocities as well as of the increase of mass by J. J. Thomson.
6. P. Lenard, *op. cit.*; also *Über Relativitätsprincip, Äther, Gravitation* (Leipzig, 1910); E. Wiechert, *Der Äther im Weltbild der Physik* (Berlin, 1921); Karl Jellinek, *Das Weltengeheimnis* (Stuttgart, 1921), especially p. 74; O. Lodge, *The Ether of Space* (New York, Harper, 1909); *Ether and Reality* (New York, Doran, 1925); J. J. Thomson, *op. cit.*; *The Structure of Light* (Cambridge University Press, 1925); *Beyond the Electron* (Cambridge University Press, 1928).
7. A. Einstein, *Ether and the Theory of Relativity*. An address delivered on May 5, 1920, in the University of Leyden. Tr. by G. B. Jeffery and W. Perret. In *Sidelights on Relativity* (Methuen, London, 1922).
8. H. Weyl, *Was ist Materie?* p. 18.
9. Max von Laue, "Inertia and Energy," in *Albert Einstein: Philosopher and Scientist*, edited by P. A. Schilpp (Evanston, 1949), pp. 530-32.
10. Lodge, *Ether and Reality*, pp. 143-144.

11. C. D. Anderson, *Science*, Vol. 76 (1932), p. 238.

12. "Preuve expérimentale de l'annihilation des électrons positifs," *Revue scientifique*, Vol. 73 (12 janvier 1935).

13. N. Bohr, *Quantum d'action et noyaux atomiques*, Actualités Scientifiques et industrielles, No. 807 (Paris, 1939), p. 12; R. D. Evans, *op. cit.*, p. 276-77.

14. C. Bialobrzeski, "Sur l'interprétation concrète de la mécanique quantique," *Revue de métaphysique et de morale*, 41e année (1934), p. 97.

15. Robert E. Marshak, "Elementary Particles," *Scientific American*, Vol. 191 (1952); *Meson Physics* (McGraw-Hill, New York), p. 141.

XV · THE TRANSFORMATION OF
THE CONCEPT OF MOTION

"CHANGES" SUPERSEDE "DISPLACEMENTS"

THE greater part of the content of this chapter is implicit in our previous analysis of the changes to which the concept of space and of material corpuscles were subjected. This is hardly surprising if we remember the classical definition of motion as a continuous change of the spatial coordinates of a material body (see Chap. V). The definition of motion implies the concept of the changeless subject of motion as well as that of the changeless container of motion. In other words, a moving body remains the same in the successive positions of the path through equally unchanging space. At the same time the homogeneity of space guarantees the continuity of displacement without which the identity of a particle in successive positions would be impossible.

Thus the classical concept of motion is based on the close-knit network of the following concepts:

(1) That of substantial corpuscular entities preserving their identity through time
(2) That of space, which, while it *contains* material corpuscles, remains *distinct* from them and does not participate in their motion, remaining, in Newton's words, always immovable and self-identical

262

(3) That of homogeneous time, whose function with respect to motions is comparable to the function of space with respect to bodies; it is an unchanging *receptacle* of motions, "space of motion," as Barrow said

(4) That of the spatiotemporal continuity of motion, which follows directly from the homogeneity of both space and time, and which guarantees the possibility of identifying corpuscular entities in different points of space and different instants of time

Not a single concept of the list above remains unchallenged in contemporary physics; thus it is logical to expect that the transformation of the classical concept of motion will be no less profound than that of the concepts on which it is based.

The classical notion of a moving corpuscle is based on the distinction between the "full" and the "empty," that is, between matter and space. Without this distinction the very concept of motion would be meaningless; only the fact that bits of matter are *in* certain regions of space without being identical with them makes motion intelligible; only the distinction between matter and space makes it possible for bits of matter to be *detached* from the positions which they temporarily occupy and to occupy some other positions. Yet, precisely this distinction is challenged by the general theory of relativity. We should then hardly be astonished if we find the concept of motion transformed beyond recognition; on the contrary, we should anticipate it as an inevitable consequence of the relativistic fusion of matter and space. But it is interesting to note that this implied transformation of the concept of motion is rarely stressed. What we hear abundantly about is the "relativization" of motion— merely another term for the relativization of the system of reference. But this emphasis on the relativity of the frame of reference hardly goes to the root of the matter; otherwise it would be correct to claim that Einstein was *fully* anticipated by Descartes, Leibniz, and Huygens, who all insisted on the relativity of motion. Yet, in spite of their occasional prophetic insights, it would be naive to look for even a remote foreshadowing of the relativistic fusion of space and matter in their thought. In their corpuscular-kinetic view of the universe they were not different from Gassendi and Newton.

This failure to realize the revolutionary character of the change of the concept of motion is easily understandable. Together with other concepts—space, time, matter—with which it is so closely tied, the concept of displacement is a constitutive part of the corpuscular-kinetic model of nature. After dominating scientific thought for three centuries, it has become a part of our intellectual subconscious. As a result, we fail to realize that the very terms "motion" and "displacement" are thoroughly inadequate because they are tinged with misleading classical associations. The continued use of these terms is almost comparable to a psychoanalytical symptom: it indicates the reluctance of our Newtonian subconscious to depart from traditional habits of thought. At the same time, these familiar words, which occur in the textbooks of modern and relativistic physics, naturally create in the majority of readers an erroneous impression that they are treading familiar ground. Nothing is more natural than to conclude from the familiarity of a word the familiarity of a meaning which is behind a word. Yet, some outstanding philosophers of science were clearly aware of the profound change to which the classical concept of motion was submitted and which is hidden by the continued use of familiar classical terms. As early as in 1920 Hans Reichenbach stated clearly the implication of general relativity for our view of motion:

> Space is completely filled by the field that defines its metrics; what we have hitherto called material bodies are only the condensations of this field. It makes no sense to speak of a movement of material parts as a transport of things; what takes place is a traveling process of condensation comparable to the movement of a wave in water. (The analogy is of course very rough, since it is usual to interpret the "apparent" advance of the wave in water as "real" oscillations of particles of water. In fact separate particles as bearers of the state

of the field do not exist. . . .) The concept of "an individual thing" loses any definite meaning.*[1]

With a rare explicitness Reichenbach pointed out that the crisis of the concept of *thinghood* in physics threatens equally the classical concept of motion; for what is motion without a thing which is being displaced? In 1926 P. W. Bridgman pointed out similar difficulties when the classical "thing-traveling point of view" is applied to light:

> We are familiar with only two kinds of thing travelling, a disturbance in a medium, and a ballistic thing like a projectile. But light is not like a disturbance in a medium, for otherwise we should find a different velocity when we move with respect to the medium, and no such phenomenon exists; neither is light like a projectile, because the velocity of light with respect to the observer is independent of the velocity of the source.[2]

Yet the decisive reason why neither matter nor light can be regarded as traveling entities or substances moving through space is not stated with a sufficient explicitness either by Reichenbach or by Bridgman. (Reichenbach comes closer to it, but his comparison of a material particle with a water wave is bound to be misleading in spite of his warning against taking it literally; it suggests too vividly the picture of a disturbance traveling *in* the aethereal medium *à la* Huygens or *à la* William Thomson.) This decisive reason is precisely the relativistic fusion of space and its physical content into a single dynamic entity. If, using Meyerson's expression, matter is "resorbed" into space (space-time), the distinction between the underlying

---

* Das Raum is ausgefüllt von dem Felde, das seine Metrik bestimmt; es sind nur die Verdichtungen dieses Feldes, was wir bisher als Materie betrachten. Es hat keinen Sinn, von einer Wanderung materiellen Teile als einem Transport von Dingen zu reden; was stattfindet ist ein vorschreitende Verdichtungsprozess, der aber der Wanderung der Wasserwelle verglichen werden musst. (Allerdings nur als eine grobe Analogie. Denn man pflegt sonst umgekehrt den "scheinbaren" Lauf einer Wasserwelle auf die "wirkliche" Hin- und Herbewegung der Wasserteilchen zurückzuführen. Einzelne Teilchen als Träger des Feldzustandes gibt es eben nicht. . . . Der Begriff der Einzelding verliert jede Bestimmtheit.

geometrical container and its changing physical content disappears; but this distinction was *the very basis* of the classical concept of motion. Consequently, space cannot be regarded any longer as a passive containerlike medium altogether indifferent to changes of its physical content. As the boundaries between matter and surrounding space are dimmed, motion means not only a displacement of a visible and isolated particle *in* space, but also a simultaneous displacement of the whole complex of subtle gravitational and electromagnetic links by which a "particle" is connected with the rest of the universe.

This second invisible "motion" is usually disregarded because it does not affect our senses and is unimportant for practical purposes. Even when classical physics recognized that the motion of an individual body drags after itself its whole dynamical surrounding, that is, its gravitational and electromagnetic field, it was always stressed that the underlying geometrical space, which was stretched underneath all these complex motions, remains static and indifferent to any kind of change. All the changes which occur in the dynamical surrounding of a moving body were naturally interpreted by means of mechanical and, in the last analysis, corpuscular models; Maxwell's explanation of magnetism as a collateral whirl produced in the aether by the linear displacement of the aethereal particles is a classic instance of this type of explanation.

But there is no such underlying indifferent geometrical container in the general theory of relativity; matter became a local deformation of the spatiotemporal medium. More accurately, what was called a material body is nothing but a *center of this deformation;* the deformation itself spreads out in all directions with decreasing intensity, producing thus the phenomenon of gravitational and, according to Weyl, even of electromagnetic fields. It is natural that the movement of *the center* of this deformation is accompanied by the concomitant motion of the *whole* deformation.

At this point the inadequacy of the traditional concept of motion becomes abundantly clear. It is incorrect to say that a spatiotemporal deformation is *moving in something;* such a way of speaking would imply that a spatiotemporal deformation, i.e., space-time itself, is placed in another containerlike space *with respect to which* its motion would take place. This would set us on the path of Zeno of Elea: our space is located in another space which may be located in still another space and so forth. From a strictly mathematical point of view there is nothing wrong in such a procedure: our non-Euclidean space may be located in the four-dimensional Euclidean space which in its turn may be contained within spaces of a higher number of dimensions. But from the epistemological standpoint such reification of mathematical abstractions is highly suspect, in particular if we realize that the whole procedure has been motivated by our unconscious desire to save the classical concept of motion as a *displacement of something in respect to something*.

Is there any meaning in saying that time-space or even its parts *are moving in something?* There is not the slightest shadow of empirical evidence for the existence of such imaginary hyperspace; what is given empirically is relative displacements of various spatiotemporal regions, and what is suggested by experience is the abolition of the distinction between the "full" and the "empty." But as soon as this distinction is given up, the radical transformation of the concept of motion is immediately evident. Motion is no longer a motion *in* something, but simply a motion. Moreover, as the classical concept of motion is indissolubly tied with the visual images of spatial displacement, it would be less misleading not to use this term at all and to replace it by some more general and less visual term like *change, modification, or transformation*. Thus we may say that what our perception registers as relative motions of bodies is in truth nothing but mutual displacements of the local spatiotemporal modifications. If we still postulate a spatial or hyperspatial substratum for these spatiotemporal modifications, we only show our instinctive unwillingness to give up our cherished traditional idea of space as a motionless container of all changes.

The concept of spatial displacement is inapplicable not only to material bodies but to energy as well. Bridgman stated clearly the inapplicability of the concept of spatial displacement to electromagnetic energy; but his statement has a far more general meaning as it applies to *any* transport of energy. This is understandable from the relativistic point of view, for which the distinction between matter and energy has lost its original classical sharpness. Even electromagnetic energy has its inertial and gravitational mass, as facts of radiation pressure and deflection of light in strong gravitational fields clearly show. According to the general theory, inertial and gravitational mass are merely two aspects of one and the same phenomenon, which is inseparable from certain peculiar modifications of time-space. This is the meaning of the "geometrization" of matter and its inertial and gravitational field in the general theory. Should such geometrization be applied even to the inertial and gravitational mass associated with the electromagnetic energy? The belief that this should be done was and still is the inspiring motive of all so-called "unitary field theories": to incorporate *all* energetic fields (not merely gravitation-inertial fields) into a complex dynamic manifold of time-space. Serious mathematical as well as empirical difficulties which various field theories faced in their detailed elaboration have somehow obscured the basic soundness of their underlying motive. It is difficult to see how the distinction between the "full" and the "empty," which was so radically challenged as far as the relation of matter to space is concerned, can be maintained as the basis for differentiating space from its energetic content.

Once this is understood, it will be also understood that light can be regarded neither as tiny particles, ejected from the source of light in all directions as Newton imagined, nor as transversally vibrating aether particles as Fresnel and the nineteenth-century physicists believed: in either classical theory the motion of light was pictured as a displacement of some solid stuff (no matter how minute) in a static and passive container of space which itself does not take part in any change. But separation of space from its *energetic* content is as illegitimate as that of space from matter. Thus neither masses nor light quanta can be regarded as *things traveling through space;* both matter and radiation are merely modifications of time-space, radiation being probably of a less complex type than matter; and it is utterly meaningless to speak of *motion of time-space* unless we resort to a very questionable device of embedding time-space in a hypostatized continuum of five dimensions.

It is astonishing that all essential features of the modern view concerning the relation between space, matter, and motion were prophetically anticipated by W. K. Clifford as early as in 1876 in his little-known essay "On the Space Theory of Matter." [3] His hypothesis, anticipating the general theory of relativity, was stated in four main points: (1) Small portions of space are comparable to little hills on a surface which is on the average flat; the ordinary laws of geometry are not valid in them. (2) The spatial distortions are propagated after the manner of waves. (3) This variation of the curvature of space really happens in the phenomenon of *motion*, whether ponderable or aethereal. (4) In the physical world nothing happens except this variation.

It would hardly have been possible to anticipate with a greater explicitness the revision of the distinction between the void and matter as well as the transformation of the concept of motion. In Clifford's view the phenomenon of motion is reduced to a *variation of spatial curvature*. What classical physics regarded as a displacement of some substantial quantity of matter through a static and physically inactive geometrical medium is, according to Clifford anticipating Einstein, merely a shift of a local distortion of space not with respect to some underlying geometrical container, but *with respect to other local distortions*.

Even the expression "shift of local distortion" may be misleading as it may suggest a displacement of some substantial entity through space; this would lead us back to the old idea of motion. We can never be viligant enough against creeping classical connotations! Reichenbach in the passage quoted on p. 264 stated that a shift of local distortion instead of being a transport of anything substantial through space is comparable rather to a movement of a wave in water, provided that we avoid any attempt to reduce this wave motion to the vibratory displacement of substantial aether particles. For, as Clifford clearly saw, even "aethereal motion" should be interpreted in the same way as the motion of "ponderable bodies." For this reason it is less misleading to say that, instead of local distortion being *shifted*, the space curvature in a certain region is *changed;* and this change of local curvature is what our perception registers as a displacement of a material body.

When we make an effort to depart from deeply ingrained traditional ideas, it is difficult to avoid a more detailed analysis even when such analysis may appear tedious and cumbersomely overexplicit. What is really happening according to the general theory of relativity when a physical body is changing its position? Nothing but that in one region a spatial distortion disappears or at least is reduced while it appears in the neighbouring region, which was originally more or less "flat." (It could not be entirely "flat" in virtue of the presence of the gravitational field whose curvature, in Clifford's illustration, differs only in degree from the distortion constituting the material body itself.) Thus what classical physics regarded as a movement of one body from one place to another is described in relativistic terms as an *intrinsic transformation* of both adjacent places.

Nor is this transformation confined to that region of space in which "material body" is present. Clifford's little non-Euclidean hills slope gradually into their surrounding regions; their gravitational and electrostatic fields pervade not only their neighboring regions but vastly remote reaches of the cosmic space. This was fully realized already by Faraday. Anticipating Whitehead's criticism of the "fallacy of simple location," he claimed that each atom is virtually ubiquitous because it "extends, so to speak, through the whole of the solar system, yet always retaining its center of force." [4] As mentioned above, the displacement of such an atom means a displacement *of the whole field of force* surrounding it; and because the displacement itself is now regarded as an intrinsic transformation of a certain spatiotemporal region which cannot be sharply delimited from the wider spatiotemporal context, it means that what was viewed as a displacement of a quantity of matter in space is in truth a transformation of a considerable portion of the universe.

This was anticipated by Bergson at a time when the first signs of the contemporary upheaval in physics had barely begun to appear. He wrote in 1896:

> The change is everywhere, but inward; we localize it here and there, but outwardly; and thus we constitute bodies which are both stable as to their qualities and mobile as to their positions, a mere change of place summing up in itself, to our eyes, the universal transformation.

Similarly Whitehead:

> In a certain sense, everything is everywhere at all times. For every location involves an aspect of itself in every other location. Thus every spatio-temporal standpoint mirrors the world.[5]

The term "universal transformation" should not be understood in the sense "*instantaneous* universal transformation." To say that a spatiotemporal distortion, constituting the essence of a physical particle, spreads through the whole universe is to use a metaphor which should not be taken literally. This spreading is a *time-consuming process* and may be regarded as practically instantaneous only for the surroundings on a planetary scale. Changes in the gravitational and electromagnetic fields spread with a finite velocity, and for this reason they cannot be regarded as pervading the *whole* universe. Moreover, to what extent does the concept of the totality of the universe remain meaningful after the denial of absolute simultaneity of distant events? We have seen that the term "the world at an instant" or "world-wide instant" is meaningless because it requires the existence of instantaneous geometrical connections rejected by relativistic physics. Thus, for the motion of a particle to be a *simultaneous* transformation of the whole universe would require a *rigid* connection of a center of the spatiotemporal deformation with the deformation itself; only then would an instantaneous transformation be possible. But this is plainly incompatible with both the spirit and the letter of relativistic physics.[6] In this respect Faraday's view that each atom pervades the whole solar system is more correct and more in agreement with relativity than Bergson's claim that a motion of a particle means a transformation of the *whole* universe.

But this qualification apart, Bergson's statement was essentially correct in anticipating one implication of general relativity: *the retreat of the concept of displacement before that of qualitative transformation.* Does this mean that contemporary physics returns by a roundabout way to the Aristotelian concept of motion? This is true to a certain extent, and Hermann Weyl did not fail to notice the affinity between modern field theory and the Aristotelian concept of motion.[7] Every motion, including a simple motion in space, is according to Aristotle an inward process, a qualitative transformation, *alloiōsis.* Even the motion of a freely falling body is not a mere displacement of an immutable entity, but an inward change; for a stone does not become a true stone until it reaches its natural place. Thus even a spatial displacement is an inward qualitative transformation. In the foregoing analysis of the modern concept of particle we have seen that there is nothing self-identical or immutably abiding in what we continue to call "particle" or "corpuscle"; and in the next chapter we shall try to show that the very essence of a particle is constituted by change, process, events. This may be justified also by relativistic considerations: various spatiotemporal distortions overlap and each of them is continuously subjected to the modifications which in the form of gravitational or electromagnetic waves come from distant regions of time-space.

Here, however, the similarity between the modern field theory and Aristotelian physics ends. Needless to say, there are important differences. When Weyl pointed out that the general theory of relativity represents in a certain sense a return to the Aristotelian idea of "natural place," he forgot to state specifically the limits of this analogy. It is true that relativistic space is, like the space of Aristotle, heterogeneous, its different local curvatures corresponding to qualitative differences of Aristotelian "natural places." But while the space of Aristotle is rigidly stratified, its qualitative differentiation into five concentric zones remaining always the same, time-space of general relativity is continuously changing. Not only are there no privileged frames of reference comparable to the earth or the celestial spheres in the system of Aristotle, but also the spatiotemporal region is continuously being modified by the impact of its cosmic surroundings. Thus, in spite of a certain Aristotelian coloring of modern physics, it would be preposterous to speak of any "return" either to Aristotelian physics or metaphysics. There are no simple returns in the development of science; it is true that there may be occasional regressions or relapses, but this happens only if external circumstances interfere with its unhampered development.

It may also be objected that it is incorrect to speak of a qualitative diversification of space or its qualitative transformation. The only diversity which the general theory of relativity admits is that of *quantitative differences of space constant;* similarly, every physical change is reduced to change of space-time curvature. This, however, should not deceive us. Space and time for classical physics were both homogeneous; but such homogeneity is *denied* now. It is true that the heterogeneity of space and time, admitted by modern physics, is supposedly of a quantitative kind; or at least it is expressed so—mathematical physics cannot proceed otherwise. But the differences between various regions of a gravitational field, and, in particular, the differences between the field itself and its center, are *real dynamic differences* which must be called qualitative. Classical physics recognized only *one* qualitative distinction: that between space and matter. All regions of space were qualitatively identical, that is, homogeneous; likewise, all pieces of matter were devoid of any qualitative difference. This single qualitative distinction, admitted by classical physics, is now obliterated.

Superficially, this looked like a complete triumph of a quantitative world view, as a completion of the process by which matter was geometrized; this, as we have seen, was Meyerson's, Bergson's and Cassirer's interpretation. But we have tried to point out the shortcomings of this interpretation. If matter

274 Philosophical Impact of Contemporary Physics

was geometrized, it was only because space was *dynamized* and its homogeneity denied; if matter was "resorbed" into space, it was only because space was fused with time into a single dynamic diversified whole. We may still claim that this diversification is of a "purely quantitative" kind; but to do this would mean to mistake the terms of tensor equations for real physical entities and to confuse mere *symbols* with concrete physical differentiated events. After all, as Hirn had observed already in the last century, "the world is not a mathematics,"—at least as long as we do not relapse into some sort of neo-Pythagoreanism (to which some neo-Kantians seem to be dangerously close). The question of what we mean by the word "physical quality" will be treated in Chapter XVIII of this book. Here it is enough to say that, in contrast to classical space and time, relativistic time-space is intrinsically diversified in its different parts; although these differences are expressed by mathematical symbols, they correspond to very real physical differences and changes which were absent in the classical world-picture; finally, it is *not* misleading to call these differences and changes qualitative.

The dilemma "qualitative change versus spatial displacement" may be traced to the very dawn of the Western thought. It was first represented by the opposition between Democritus and Heraclitus. Aristotle, when he opposed atomism and thereby also the concept of spatial displacement, was following Heraclitus, whom Weyl regarded correctly as the founder of the antimechanistic and antiatomistic tradition in philosophy.[8] Thus it would be more correct to speak of the *Heraclitean* rather than the Aristotelian tinge of contemporary physics. After Galileo and Newton this antimechanistic trend receded without completely disappearing. In his historical study of the concept of motion Ludwig Lange lists three possible views of motion.[9] Motion is regarded (1) as a change of position with respect to absolute space, or (2) as a change of position with respect to some material body; or (3) as an outer sign (*äussere Erfolg*) of some inward change which occurs within a moving body itself. Newton and all his followers belong to the first category; Leibniz as a physicist and Huygens to the second category; while Leibniz-metaphysician, followed in this respect by Lotze, Clifford, and Bergson, represents the third view.

Like Leibniz, modern relativists oscillate between the second and the third theory, but on the whole they are leaning toward the second theory: motion defined as a change of position with respect to some physical body. The shortcoming of this view is due to the failure to realize that in the general theory *the very individuality of physical bodies is questioned* and with it even the definiteness of a physical frame of reference. As soon as this is realized, the third view is, implicitly at least, adopted. Thus when Reichenbach deals with general gravitational fields, which in the language of Riemann's geometry are characterized by locally and temporally variable tensors, he explicitly compares them with the world of Heraclitus's everlasting flux, πάντα ῥεῖ.[10] Such is the real physical world. Stationary gravitational fields are merely ideal approximations; only the general fields are physically real. In such a world motion must be regarded, in Bergson's words, as "the transference of a state rather than of a thing."[11]

The substitution of the concept of change for that of displacement becomes less paradoxical if we remember the fusion of space with time and also that this fusion, as we have seen, is not entirely symmetrical because, while it is entirely incorrect to regard it as a spatialization of time, it is appropriate to call it a dynamization of space. Since space itself acquires a processlike character, the fusion of matter with time-space means that change is *not* confined to the change of position only, but affects equally the two entities which classical physics regarded as changeless: the geometrical container of motion and the material vehicle of motion. In Chapter XIV we considered the last point, but rather in its negative form: we tried to show how new "particles" of modern physics cannot be regarded as substantial entities. We are now going to approach the same topic more positively in order to show to what extent matter acquires the character of dynamic process and how the classical particles have been replaced by strings of successive events.

EVENTS REPLACE PARTICLES

In his excellent summary of the principles underlying classical physics, J. B. Stallo pointed out that mass and motion were regarded as mutually inconvertible.[12] This was the reason why mass was regarded as constant, that is, independent of its velocity; the elementary particles, whether they were at rest or in motion and no matter how fast they moved, remained always identical in their mass, volume, and shape. This was also the basis of the *essentially passive* character of classical matter; no motion could ever spring from matter itself, while conversely, matter remained eternally impervious to any quantity of motion attached to it. We have seen that the most serious objection against the Boscovich-Kant theory was precisely that it assumed motion as springing mysteriously from the very nature of pointlike masses.

The so-called "dynamic characteristics" of classical matter were due exclusively to the fact that the *masses were endowed with motion;* all dynamic effects were thus traceable not to masses as such, but to *masses already in motion.* This was the very essence of all kinetic explanations. But in all instances, the relation of matter to motion remained a purely external one. Although any quantity of matter could be associated with any amount of motion, no conversion of one into another was thought to be possible. Thus the law of the conservation of matter and the law of the conservation of momentum remained *two distinct laws;* the total quantity of matter, whether of one single particle or of a whole aggregate of particles, remained entirely unaffected by any change in velocity attached to it. This was the reason why it was possible to speak only of the *motion of matter*, never of motion *in* matter. The second expression would have sounded irrational and senseless: it would imply the variability of material substance itself. Thus, in the classical picture, motion, though invariably associated with matter, retained its distinctness from it. The formation of the concept of momentum (as a product of mass and velocity) obscured but did not eliminate this distinctness; the amount of mass itself never affected its own velocity except indirectly, i.e., by modifying forces acting upon it; and the change of velocity never modified the mass of a moving body.

The special theory of relativity ended this separation: mass became a function of velocity. It remains very approximately constant only when the corresponding motion is relatively slow; but for velocities which are not negligible compared with the velocity of light its constancy disappears. This is one of the aspects of the relativistic identification of mass and energy: every form of energy, including the energy of motion, has its mass effect and must therefore modify the total inertial mass. Thus the law of the conservation of mass and the law of the conservation of energy are fused into a more comprehensive law in which mass-energy is constant. The increase of mass is not *creatio ex nihilo*, because the corresponding increment in mass pre-existed, so to speak, in an amount of kinetic energy added to a particle from outside.

Although this fusion of the two originally independent laws into a single law makes the paradox of variable mass intellectually more palatable, it is bound to obscure its tremendous revolutionary significance. For there is no question but that Einstein's formula for the dependence of mass on velocity does away with another basic classical distinction: that *between matter and motion* or, if we believe that some philosophical distinctions are an unconscious outgrowth of distinctions made originally on the physical level, the distinction between *substance and change*, or *being and becoming*.

This became even more conspicuous in the development of wave mechanics. If any hopes remained of retaining the classical concept of an immutable particle, to which motion can be attached, so to speak, externally like a horse to a vehicle, the further development of the quantum theory dashed them utterly. The phase of the quantum theory known as wave mechanics synthesized in an original manner the ideas of Planck and those of Einstein. The classical quantum theory asserted the atomicity of *action*, that is, of the product of energy and time. Contrary to the frequently heard popular version, the quantum theory has *not* asserted the atomicity of energy, except in a very special sense. It is true that for energy at any given frequency there can exist only whole multiples of the minimum quantum hf ($h =$ Planck's constant of action, $f =$ frequency): $2hf$, $3hf$, . . . , nhf. But as the frequency itself was assumed to vary continuously, there were no universal "atoms of energy" of equal magnitude in the same sense as we have the atoms of electricity.

If we insist on speaking of the atomic structure of energy, we have to bear in mind that the alleged atomism of energy may be compared to the "qualitative atomism" of Dalton in the last century: just as each chemical element is composed of its own atoms, so to each particular frequency of radiation there correspond specific "atoms of radiation." On the other hand, one thing always remains constant in the microphysical energetic reactions: the product of energy and the corresponding interval of time. This product is always equal to the universal Planck's constant h. It is one of a few quantities which remain invariant in different inertial systems, and its presence is responsible for nearly all paradoxical aspects of microphysical events.

Originally, the constant h was believed to belong only to the realm of radiation; but gradually the quantization in the sense explained above was extended even to the mechanical energy of microphysical particles. Besides Bohr's historically famous quantization of the electronic orbits, it is important not to overlook the unexpected triumphs of the quantum theory in the area in which the corpuscular-kinetic view of classical physics seemed to be established beyond any doubt: the kinetic theory of matter. Thus some discrepancies concerning the specific heat of certain gases were explained by Einstein (whose contributions to the quantum theory were obscured by the fame of his own relativity theory) by the assumption that the mechanical energy of vibrating molecules can vary only *discontinuously*.[13] Similarly, the absence of rotation of the molecules of monoatomic gases was explained as another consequence of the quantum theory: the energy of the translatory motion of the gaseous molecules is *too small* to communicate the minimum amount of energy necessary for their rotations.[14] This unexpected universal validity of Planck's equation for the mechanical energy of microphysical particles was the first indication of the haziness of the boundary between matter and radiation.

Furthermore, according to the special theory of relativity, the concept of energy is considerably wider than it used to be in classical physics. Every material particle, even when by an appropriate choice of frame of reference it is made completely devoid of kinetic energy, still possesses some "internal energy," which had no counterpart in classical physics. It is true that in a vague and qualitative form Leibniz and Spencer came close to this energetization of matter when they insisted that even so-called "impenetrability" (Leibniz's ἀντιτυπία) is of a dynamic nature. But neither of them suspected its tremendous amount, determined by the product of the mass and the square of the velocity of light. Also neither of them could even remotely suspect the revolutionary implications of the relativistic energetization of matter. Like Planck's equation $E = hf$, Einstein's equation $E = mc^2$ has been found universally valid in all areas of physics. But if all energy is quantized, the quantization must equally apply even to the *internal energy* associated with the inertial mass of a particle. This is precisely what is obtained by combining the two equations into one which is a basic equation of wave mechanics:

$$mc^2 = hf$$

This leads to the paradoxical result that *all* energy, including the "internal energy" of mass must have a vibratory character. Thus the frequency of vibrations associated with the inertial mass of the electron is 1.24×10^{20} per second, while for heavier protons the duration of a single associated vibration is of the order 10^{-23} second, fairly close to the hypothetical value of the chronon.

To sum up: while Planck assigned a corpuscular character to radiation, which had previously been conceived in purely undulatory terms, Louis de Broglie attributed a vibratory character to matter, which, until his time, had always been regarded as made of particles. (In this context it is of secondary importance whether these particles were endowed with a certain minute bulk as in classical and modern atomism or whether they were regarded as material points without spatial dimensions.)

The possibility of interpreting these "material waves" (*Materiewellen, ondes matérielles*) in a concrete sense, that is, as disturbances taking place within a material medium, is as limited as that of interpreting the "light corpuscles" or "photons" in the sense of the old emission theory of Newton. We again witness the fact that there are no simple returns in the development of science. Attempts to interpret the undulatory character of matter in a mechanical and pictorial sense are hardly anything more than psychological symptoms indicating the tenacity of our inherited mental habits. For this reason no attempt will be made here to describe in detail this last failure of the mechanically conceived aether in physics; a brief and concise summary will be sufficient.

Yet, it was only natural that when wave mechanics appeared there was a great temptation to interpret the hypothetical waves associated with material particles in a concrete and almost visual sense. It appeared entirely logical to agree with Arthur Compton that if there are waves, there must be *waves of something*.[15] The question what this mysterious *something* is was entirely analogous to the question faced by physicists of the nineteenth century when they were curious about the substratum of luminous and electromagnetic vibrations. Even if we forget for a moment all the difficulties inherent in the classical idea of aether, it is clear that the application of a similar idea to wave mechanics faces even greater difficulties. From the fundamental relations of De Broglie it follows first that the velocity of the hypothetical waves should be *greater* than the velocity of light; second, that waves of various lengths should move with different velocities, the longer ones moving faster. The first requirement appeared certainly strange in the light of relativity theory while the second one contradicted the classical idea of aether as a nondispersive medium.

Both difficulties, however, were only apparent. The first was removed by an ingenious application of the classical Rayleigh principle which differentiates between the *phase velocity* and *group velocity:* an individual material particle is associated, not with an individual, but with a *whole train of waves of different frequencies* which in their superposition form a so-called *wave packet*. It was pleasant to find out that from the theory it followed that the velocity of such wave packets coincides with that of associated material particles. Mass and energy of particles is associated with wave packets, not with the individual "hyperluminous" waves which carry no mass either in the classical or relativistic sense. Thus the relativistic requirement that the luminous velocity must be the uppermost possible velocity for all masses, is not violated.

The second difficulty concerning the different speeds of the constituting hyperluminous waves looks quite serious in the light of the well-established fact that the velocity of all aethereal vibrations is constant and does not depend on their frequencies. But even this difficulty can be removed in two ways: either by assigning to the hyperluminous waves another medium, the so-called "subaether," which, unlike the classical electromagnetic aether, is a highly dispersive medium; *or* it was possible to postulate a different behavior of one and the same aether with regard to different frequencies. In other words, while aether for relatively slow vibrations behaves as a nondispersive medium, for faster vibrations it acquires the properties of a highly dispersive medium. The second way was certainly more appealing to those who respect Occam's rule; it is certainly more economical to postulate a single substratum for various vibrations than several. Moreover, the second explanation had some interesting classical analogies: the universal aether apparently changes its properties much as the properties of gas change suddenly at certain critical values of pressure and temperature. For a certain range of frequencies, spreading from the electromagnetic waves to the gamma rays, aether behaves as a completely nondispersive medium; all wave lengths travel with the same velocity. But for faster vibrations, whose superposition constitutes what we used to call "material particle," the aether acquires the properties of a supradispersive medium, analogous to some highly dispersive macroscopic substances; the corresponding vibrations are propagated with a velocity directly proportional to their frequencies. Moreover, all these vibrations are propagated with a velocity larger than the velocity of electromagnetic waves. J. J. Thomson pointed out an interesting macroscopic analogy to this phenomenon in the behavior of the Heaviside layer in the upper regions of the atmosphere, where residual rarefied gases are strongly ionized by the solar radiation. This region behaves optically like the model of aether, postulated above.[16] Such a model of the aether is in line with Stokes's famous attempt to account for some apparently contradictory properties of aether, and it bears some similarity to Fournier d'Albe and Karl Jellinek's mechanical explanation of the limit character of the velocity of light.

One feature common to all such attempts is an unlimited confidence in the fruitfulness of classical mechanical models. The case of J. J. Thomson is particularly instructive; from his prize-winning study on vortex motions[17] to one of the latest books about the structure of the electron, the continuity of his thought and loyalty to the same corpuscular-kinetic view of nature is truly impressive. The first interpretations of wave mechanics by Louis de Broglie and Erwin Schrödinger were precisely along the same lines. In 1925 Eddington summed up the original theory of Schrödinger in the following terms:

> Imagine a sub-aether whose surface is covered with ripples. The oscillations of the ripples are a million times faster than those of visible light—too fast to come within the scope of our gross experience. Individual ripples are beyond our ken; what we can appreciate is a combined effect—when by convergence and coalescence the waves conspire to create a disturbed area of extent large compared with individual ripples but small from our own Brobdingnagian point of view. Such a disturbed area is recognized as a material particle; in particular it can be an electron. The sub-aether is a dispersive

medium, that is to say, the ripples do not all travel with the same velocity; like water ripples their speed depends on their wave length or period. Those of shorter period travel faster. Moreover the speed may be modified by local conditions. This modification is a counterpart in Schrödinger's theory of a field of force in classical physics.[18]

It was necessary to give a fair hearing to this theory before pointing out its intrinsic as well as empirical difficulties. It is evident that a theory of this kind is a new edition of the classical hydrodynamical model of aether whose roots may be traced to the Cartesian physics of the seventeenth century. It has two conspicuous features of the Cartesian-Kelvinian thought: (1) the explanation of every action at a distance by means of a hypothetical material medium and (2) the explanation of material particles as local disturbances of the same medium. But it is clear that any return to the idea of a material or quasi-material medium would bring back all the enormous difficulties which mechanical theories faced in the past; in particular, it would imply a return to the concept of an absolute system of reference and thereby all outdated concepts of Newtonian dynamics. It would mean a revival of the discredited effort to picture the subatomic world in pictorial terms borrowed from the zone of the middle dimensions. The probability of such retrogression is certainly small and simple epistemological considerations speak against it.

But there were more immediate difficulties present. As early as 1929 Louis de Broglie, the discoverer of wave mechanics, who was first strongly attracted by a hydrodynamical model similar to that described above,[19] made a list of these difficulties.[20] First, the wave packets have a tendency to spread in space; if the electrons were constituted by such wave packets, they would not be stable. When we remember the extremely short life span of some recently discovered "particles," this feature will not appear surprising; the "dematerialization" of positive electrons, for instance, means, in terms of the fluid theory of matter, nothing but a dissolution of a local disturbance into the undifferentiated continuity of the aethereal medium. Such facts apparently substantiate the claim of the fluid theories that "particles" are merely misnomers for local disturbances of aether.

On the other hand, it is then difficult to explain the relative stability of some particles, in particular of negative electrons. In this respect, Schrödinger's original theory faces the same difficulty with which the classical fluid theories were confronted: to explain the apparent stability of physical corpuscles. The stability of a well-defined disturbed region always appeared within the framework of fluid theories as a sort of happy accident.

But there was another and even more serious difficulty which appeared, paradoxically enough, with the experimental confirmation of wave mechanics. The experiments made first by Davisson and Germer, and shortly afterwards by G. P. Thomson, a son of J. J. Thomson, established beyond doubt that a beam of electrons passing through a thin layer of crystal lattice gives rise to the same diffraction patterns as the X rays. The undulatory character of matter was thus established; but at the same time the peculiar character of De Broglie's waves was clearly shown. As their most disquieting peculiarity, they seemingly excluded any intuitive interpretation. If an electron were really constituted by a wave packet, then its existence would be dissolved in the process of diffraction, as the action of a crystal lattice would precisely effect a separation of its constituting frequencies. This, however, has not been observed. For what is the physical significance of the dark diffraction rings which the exposed photographic plate showed? They evidently represent *the rings of maxima* formed by all the spots blackened by the impact of impinging electrons; while the rings of minima indicate their absence. This clearly shows that what is being diffracted is not a lone electron, but a *whole beam*. An incident De Broglie wave does not represent an individual electron, but a *statistical aggregate of particles;* it is not a concrete physical process in any usual sense, taking place in a material or semi-material medium of aether or subaether, but a "wave of probability," a periodic function, indicating the probability of an occurrence of a particle at a certain place. The electrons in passing through thin films of matter are dispersed along the directions of maximum probability, and their total impact gives rise to the dark rings of maxima on a photographic plate. This statistical interpretation of De Broglie's waves, first proposed by Max Born and W. Heisenberg[21] was gradually accepted by most, though by no means all, physicists, and has become in the last quarter century an almost orthodox interpretation.

Thus there is cumulative evidence that microphysical entities do not have properties even remotely similar to those of macroscopic bodies. What are still being called "particles" or "corpuscles" by contemporary physicists do not have corpuscular properties at all. Microphysical "corpuscles" have neither impenetrability nor constancy—not even the persistence through time of classical atoms. The lifetime of some particles is exceedingly brief, an almost instantaneous flash; certainly, it is unbecoming to call such evanescent entities by a name which suggests the indestructibility and eternity of Lucretian atoms. At the end of the Chapter XIV I proposed to replace the term "particles" by that of "events." In the light of wave mechanics this proposal is even more justified. For, as we have seen, wave mechanics associated a kind of a periodical process with "material corpuscles." At first there was a hope of interpreting the associated vibrations as vibrations of some hypothetical material or quasi-material medium. Because this medium would in the last analysis consist of particles,[22] it would be possible to recover the concept of permanent corpuscular entity, enduring through time, on a finer microphysical, "subaethereal" level. But these hopes were not fulfilled; the "waves of probability" replaced the "waves of subaether."

The associated vibrations are *not vibrations of something;* they are inherent in material entities themselves; or, better, the material "particle-events" are *constituted* by them. This is the meaning of Gaston Bachelard's statement:

From criticism delivered by wave mechanics, it follows that the particle has no more reality than the composition that manifests it. *There are temporal events at the very foundation of its existence.* [Italics added.][23]

Bachelard fully realizes that this fusion of *thing* and *movement* is psychologically extremely difficult to achieve because it stands in such a sharp opposition to their classical separation.[24] In his *Science and the Modern World*, A. N. Whitehead proposed to remove this paradoxical feature of the quantum theory by denying the mathematical continuity of time. He briefly referred to the possibility of the existence of "quanta of time" as early as in 1920, in his *Concept of Nature;* he was already moving in this direction in his *Principles of Natural Knowledge*, where he questioned the traditional view according to which time is composed of durationless instants.[25] In this respect Whitehead was not the first; the possibility that the quantum theory may impose on us the idea of the atomicity of time was considered by Henri Poincaré in his posthumously edited *Dernières pensées*. In the very same year—1913—René Berthelot was deeply shocked by Bergson's denial of the mathematically continuous time of classical physics.[26] This view was expounded by Bergson in his *Matter and Memory* as early as 1896, that is, prior to the appearance of the quantum theory, and at the time when the very first signs of the present transformation of physics had barely begun to appear.

We have considered the converging evidence for the inadequacy of both the concepts of spatial and temporal continuity in Chapter VI; we have seen how an increasing number of physicists was led by this inadequacy to postulate *minimum length* and *minimum duration*. But I tried to point out that to speak about the separate existence of "hodons" and "chronons" betrays the prerelativistic habit of thought; the two notions should be united into a single concept of *spatiotemporal pulsation*. Its "spacelike" component is the hodon, while its "timelike" component is the chronon. They are inseparable; while the indivisibility of chronons excludes the infinite divisibility of temporal intervals, the finite value of the hodon expresses the fact that the world lines are not infinitely thin, but possess *transversal thickness*, even though this thickness cannot be considered in its instantaneous cross section. Using relativistic language, we may say that the proper times of electrons are constituted by the succession of chronons, provided we do not forget the relativistic inseparability of chronons from hodons; then it would be, philosophically at least, more accurate to say that what we used to call "particle" or "corpuscle" is constituted by the succession of chronotopic (spatiotemporal) pulsations. This naturally follows from the relativistic fusion of matter and time-space; if we once admit the pulsational structure of time-space, then matter itself must share it.

A material particle thus loses its character of a substantial entity, existing *in* space and enduring *through* time; it becomes a local and often only a temporary modification of the spatio-temporal medium which we used to call "aether" and whose spurious continuity hides its pulsational character. Whitehead was guided by a correct insight when he proposed to replace the traditional term "aether" by "aether of events" in order to convey more adequately the absence of its infinite divisibility and its processlike character.[27]

NOTES FOR CHAPTER XV

1. H. Reichenbach, *Relativitätstheorie und Erkenntnis Apriori* (Braun-schweig, 1920), p. 98.
2. P. W. Bridgman, *The Logic of Modern Physics*, p. 164; also p. 100-01.
3. *Proceedings of Cambridge Philosophical Society*, II (1876), pp. 157-58.
4. Cf. Chapter VII, above, Note 9.
5. H. Bergson, *Matière et mémoire*, p. 233; A. N. Whitehead, *Science and the Modern World*, p. 133.
6. P. Langevin, *Bulletin de la Société française de philosophie*, séance de 19 octobre 1911, p. 23-24.
7. H. Weyl, *Was ist Materie?*, pp. 43-44.
8. Weyl, *ibid*. According to Weyl the antiatomistic tradition is characterized by the following names: Heraclitus—Anaxagoras—Archytas—Plato.

9. L. Lange, "Die geschichtliche Entwicklung des Bewegungsbegriffs," *Philos. Studien*, III (1886), p. 340.
10. H. Reichenbach, *Die Philosophie der Raum-Zeit-Lehre*, p. 302.
11. H. Bergson, *op. cit.*, p. 225.
12. J. B. Stallo, *The Concepts and Theories of Modern Physics*, pp. 27, 66.
13. W. Pauli, "Einstein's Contributions to Quantum Theory" in *Albert Einstein: Philosopher and Scientist*, pp. 149-158, especially 153-156; Max Born, "Einstein's Statistical Theories," the same volume, pp. 163-177, especially p. 169; Jean Perrin, *Les Atomes*, 2d ed. (Paris, 1927), pp. 100-105.
14. J. Perrin, *op. cit.*, pp. 105-107.
15. *Electrons et photons. Rapports et discussions*. Institute International de Physique Solvay (Paris, 1928), pp. 86-87.
16. J. J. Thomson, *Beyond the Electron*, pp. 14-21.
17. J. J. Thomson, *A Treatise on the Motion of Vortex Rings* (Cambridge University Press, 1883).
18. A. E. Eddington, *The Nature of the Physical World*, p. 211.
19. Louis de Broglie, *Physique et microphysique* (Paris, 1947), Chap. VIII, "Souvenirs personnels sur les débuts de la mécanique ondulatoire"), pp. 181-190.
20. Louis de Broglie, "Déterminisme et la causalité dans la physique contemporaine," *Revue de métaphysique et de morale*, Vol. XXXVIII (1929), pp. 437-40.
21. M. Born, and W. Heisenberg, "La mécanique des quanta" in *Electrons et Photons*, pp. 143-181, in particular pp. 164-165.
22. Cf. Chapter VII, above, under the heading "The Fluid Theories of Matter." Like Huygens, Philip Lenard and Karl Jellinek insisted on the corpuscular character of aether.
23. G. Bachelard, *Le Nouvel esprit scientifique*, 4th ed. (Paris, 1946), p. 85.
24. *Ibid.*, p. 140.
25. Whitehead, *Science and the Modern World*, pp. 53-54; *An Enquiry*, pp. 2-8; *The Concept of Nature*, pp. 56-57, 162.
26. R. Berthelot, *Un romantisme utilitaire*, Vol. II (Paris, 1913), p. 222.
27. Whitehead, *The Concept of Nature*, p. 78.

XVI · THE END OF THE LAPLACIAN ILLUSION

CHAPTER XV has shed new light on the impossibility of sharp localization of microphysical "particles." According to the prevailing interpretation of wave mechanics, no electron, strictly speaking, exists *at* a given point; there is only a certain probability of finding it there. This probability is the only "thing" which is accessible to measurement. The principle of uncertainty, formulated by Heisenberg,[1] forbids a simultaneous knowledge of the position and velocity of any elementary particle. There is no place here for the explanation of this now well-known principle, whose exposition may be found in any elementary textbook of modern atomic physics. Suffice it to say that any increase of accuracy in the measurement of position is accompanied by a growing haziness in the measured value of velocity and vice versa. This follows immediately from the relation

$$\Delta p \cdot \Delta x \geqq h \qquad \text{(see Chapter XIII)}$$

The haziness in our knowledge of a present state inevitably entails a limitation of our knowledge of future states. Because the present state of any particle is given by the correlation of the precise values of its position and momentum, it is obvious that its future positions and velocities can be predicted only with a certain probability, never with classical Laplacian certainty. We have only to remember that in the classical Laplacian model of the universe "the world at a given instant" was definable as a huge instantaneous configuration of elementary particles, each possessing besides its definite mass also a sharply defined position and velocity; a "state of the world" thus defined virtually contained all past and future configurations and velocities because any event in world history was in principle deducible from any sharply defined cosmic state. According to the principle of uncertainty both the concept of precise position and that of sharply defined velocity lose their meanings; consequently, the concept of the "state of the world at an instant" loses its definiteness too. This concept has already been thoroughly discredited by the relativistic criticism of the simultaneity of distant events; Heisenberg's principle brought merely a final *coup de grâce*.

Not only does this principle exclude the possibility of a precise localization in space, but in its second formulation

$$\Delta E \cdot \Delta t \geqq h \qquad \text{(see Chapter XIII)}$$

it ruins the possibility of a sharp *localization in time;* for any particle localizable at a mathematical instant would be literally without any definite value of energy. Thus the concept of energy at a definite instant has lost its legitimacy in the same degree as that of definite position associated with definite velocity.

After all that has been said about the crisis of classical concepts of particle and motion and about the inadequacy of the concepts of instantaneous position and instantaneous velocity, it is only natural to expect that the traditional concept of *rotary motion* will be modified in an equally profound and revolutionary way. After all, the concept of rotary motion is merely a special case of the concept of motion in general and the transformation of the latter entails inevitably the transformation of the former. This is brought into full focus by the third and the fourth forms of the principle of indeterminacy.

In the third form of the principle the conjugated variables are angular momentum A and angular position γ; the products of the corresponding uncertainties must then be

$$\Delta A \cdot \Delta \gamma \geqq h$$

The complete absence of uncertainty about angular momentum would leave the angular position of an electron on its orbit completely undetermined; a result which is hardly surprising in view of what had been already said about the meaninglessness of its precise localization. From the point of view of wave mechanics, which regards orbital electrons as "standing waves" this is only natural; an electron is, so to speak, "omnipresent" all along its orbit. As the maximum uncertainty of the angular position is correlated with the precise value of the angular momentum, and as the former cannot be larger than 360°, that is, 2π, it follows that the value of the latter must be $h/(2\pi)$; for only then $(2\pi h)/(2\pi) = h$. From this, as F. A. Lindemann pointed out more than a quarter of a century ago,[2] Bohr's condition for the first quantum orbit follows immediately.

The term "orbit" is thus completely misleading. Can we speak at least of its *radius* or, using the undulatory language, of the distance of the electronic "standing wave" from the nucleus? The classical formula for the radii of quantum orbits of the hydrogen atom

$$r = \frac{h^2 n^2}{4\pi^2 m_e e^2}$$

seemingly indicates that we can. For in the expression above, all symbols apparently stand for well-defined quantities: $h =$ Planck's constant, $n =$ quantum number, $m_e =$ the mass of electron, $e =$ its charge. But F. A. Lindemann pointed out that the conjugated coordinate to the square of the charge is the reciprocal velocity $\frac{1}{v}$, in other words, the time taken to pass through a unit distance. "The more accurately we can state the velocity, the more accurately we know the charge. Conversely, inaccuracy in our knowledge of the velocity can be interpreted as inaccuracy in our knowledge of the charge."[3] As the first form of Heisenberg's principle excludes the accuracy in our knowledge of the velocity, the accurate determination of charge is equally excluded; this in turn would bring an inaccuracy into our knowledge of the radius as well. This follows also from the second form of Heisenberg's principle in which the conjugated variables are energy and time.

In the fourth form of the principle of indeterminacy the conjugated variables are the moment of inertia I and the angular velocity ω:

$$\Delta I \cdot \Delta \omega \geqq h$$

Now, if we adhere to the strictly corpuscular image of the electron, the precise value of its momentum of inertia will leave its angular velocity completely undetermined. This conclusion is inevitable as long as the quantities which enter into the formula for the moment of inertia of the electron, i.e., its mass and radius, are regarded as sharply defined values. Thus the very insistence on corpuscular representation leads to a contradiction; the electronic sphere would have a definite radius, definite size, definite mass—but no angular velocity, not even a zero velocity! (For even zero velocity represents a definite value.) This means that we have to be on guard against accepting the alluring image of the electron as a rotating charged sphere, the image which the term "spin" inevitably brings to mind. This image is incompatible not only with the indeterminacy principle, but with the relativity theory as well: for a point on the circumference of the alleged electronic sphere should rotate with a speed 300 times faster than that of light! [3a]

Forms three and four of the principle of indeterminacy are less frequently referred to than the first two. Even textbooks of atomic physics not infrequently fail to treat them explicitly, while in philosophical discussions hardly any mention of them is ever made.[4] Yet, their significance must not be underestimated. They definitely destroy two alluring classical images which survive in microphysics: that of a *rotating solid* and that of a *well-defined continuous orbit* on which a planet-electron, rotating on its axis, revolves around a nucleus. At the beginning of this century physicists and laymen marveled at the "unity of nature in space," especially at the striking similarity between our solar system and the microsystems of planets-electrons. Part I showed how appealing this analogy between macrocosm and microcosm was, how it dominated the imagination of Pascal, Leibniz, and Huygens in the seventeenth century, and how it re-emerged at the beginning of this century in the Gulliverian speculations of Fournier d'Albe and others. The name of A. Righi's book, published in 1921, *Comets and Electrons*, was certainly significant.[5]

We have already pointed out how fallacious the analogy between the atom and our solar system was; the analysis of the last two forms of the uncertainty principle only confirms our earlier conclusion.

The indeterminacy principle sheds an unexpected light on Nernst's discovery, which had been made prior to the rise of wave mechanics: that microphysical particles retain some energy even at absolute zero temperature. Translated into the classical terminology, this means that the particles in question are *still vibrating and rotating* even when, according to the kinetic theory of matter, they should be completely at rest. From the classical point of view, according to which the concept of material body is logically separable from its motion, this discovery was difficult to understand; no reason can be given for the impossibility of completely stationary particles. Not only is there nothing contradictory in conceiving a body without motion, but even according to the principle of relativity *any* moving body can be made stationary by an appropriate choice of the frame of reference. (There is here another limitation of the relativity theory which is due to its macroscopic character: only on *the macroscopic level* is it possible to eliminate any motion by an appropriate choice of the system of reference; similarly only on *the macroscopic level* is it possible to speak very approximately about the continuity of time-space and the infinitely thin world lines.)

But so-called "zero energy" will appear less paradoxical if we bear in mind the results of our discussion in Chapter XV concerning the radical transformation of the concept of motion.

If motion cannot be separated from a "thing moved" and vice versa, then the existence of the so-called "zero energy" is merely another striking confirmation of the inseparability of two concepts which are fused into a single dynamic notion. Needless to say, this synthesis is, psychologically speaking, an extremely difficult operation; all our classical mental habits revolt against it. In the words of Gaston Bachelard:

> Underlying this physical synthesis is a metaphysical synthesis of "thing" and "motion." It corresponds to a synthetic judgment extremely difficult to formulate, since it is vehemently opposed to the analytic habits of ordinary experience, which unhesitatingly divides phenomena into two realms—static phenomena (things) and dynamic phenomena (motions). We must restore to the phenomenon all its linkages and get rid of our notion of *rest*. In microphysics it is absurd to assume matter at rest, since it exists for us only as energy and sends us no message except by radiation.[6]

The psychological difficulties are lessened if we realize that the traditional distinction between matter and motion owes its spurious convincingness to its sensory origin, to the conditioning of our mind by the "zone of the middle dimensions." Outside this zone the distinction loses even its approximate validity. Once we realize this, we shall be in a better position to understand that "zero energy," like wave-mechanical vibrations, is not, properly speaking, a kinetic energy in the traditional macroscopic sense at all. It is not comparable to Brownian motion because it has nothing in common with the thermal vibrations. As Lindemann emphasized, it is only another aspect of the inseparability of the geometrical and dynamic coordinates which is the very essence of the principle of indeterminacy.[7] According to Bachelard's expression, it is "primary mobility, preceding, so to speak, the thermal mobility" (*"mobilité première, anté-cédente à la mobilité thermique"*).[8] Such a statement sounds completely unintelligible and even meaningless within the classical corpuscular-kinetic framework; but in view of what has been said in Chapter XV about the concept of *change* replacing that of displacement, and the concept of *event* replacing that of particle, it loses its paradoxical character, even though its positive meaning does not possess the same deceptive Cartesian clarity as the classical concepts. We shall return to its positive meaning at the end of this chapter.

From what has been said it is clear that physicists hardly exaggerate when they speak of the *crisis of determinism* in contemporary physics. Yet, in the language of those physicists who insist on the inadequacy of classical determinism there are certain features which inevitably produce misunderstandings and confusions, and which eventually weaken their own basic claim. When these physicists speak about the "uncertain position" of the electron or about its "uncertain velocity"; or when they speak about the "probability of the occurrence of an electron" at a given position; or when they speak about the "impossibility of determining simultaneously both the position and momentum of a particle," then not only laymen, but even philosophers or philosophically minded physicists are almost inevitably misled. They are naturally inclined to understand the terms "uncertainty" and "probability" in their usual subjective sense. In such a sense the indeterminacy of the microphysical events is of purely subjective origin, being nothing but the human uncertainty resulting from our technical incapacity to find all determining circumstances of an observed phenomenon. Such an indeterminacy of the velocity and position of microphysical particles would exist in our own knowledge only and not in the nature of things; the microphysical reality *in itself* (Kant would say *an sich*) would be strictly determined, while all haziness, all uncertainty, all indeterminacy would be a result of the intervention of a physicist who by his act of observation modifies the conditions of the observed phenomenon. This view was clearly stated a few years after the formulation of Heisenberg's principle by the French philosopher Léon Brunschwicg:

> It remains to understand that this [Heisenberg's principle] by no means implies the breakup of determinism;

it merely means that at the present stage of our experimental technique we cannot be satisfied any longer with a simple-minded and dogmatic form of determinism which is interested in reality without being interested in knowledge. . . . The uncertainty relations merely mean that *the determinism of the observed phenomenon* is in itself nothing but an abstraction because it is inseparable from *the determinism by which the act of observation is ruled.*[9] [Italics in the text.]

According to this interpretation the whole situation, to which the instruments of an observer belong as much as does the observed phenomenon itself, is subject to the same rigorous determinism as that of classical physics. If it were so, then the statistical probability of microphysical events would be of the same kind as the statistical laws in the classical kinetic theory of gases. When this theory was proposed in the second half of the last century, nobody doubted that the individual gas molecules move according to the strict laws of Newtonian mechanics, even though in experimentation and calculation physicists were able to deal only with huge molecular aggregates. For the Laplacian mind, which, as we have seen, was merely a picturesque expression for the objective and impersonal order of nature and which would not be bound to laborious experimental and observational procedures, no uncertainty, no indeterminacy would exist; the velocities and positions of the microparticles as well as the values of their energy and their temporal dates would appear in all their definiteness—unequivocal and sharp, though tremendously complex and humanly inaccessible. In this view nature itself has no "fuzzy edge"; all fuzziness, all ambiguity, all indefiniteness resides, not in the nature of things, but in the mind of an observer. Microphysical indeterminacy is due to the disturbing influence of observation; but the compound determinism of the observed phenomenon and the process of observation remains intact.

Thus instead of being threatened by Heisenberg's relations of uncertainty, classical determinism would *explain* their existence. Herbert Spencer, were he alive, would certainly be pleased by such an attitude; for he certainly would regard the existence of the uncertainty relations as another exemplification of his cherished "law of persistence of force," to wit, the law of the conservation of energy applied to the process of observation itself. For if the quantity of energy remains always and rigorously constant, not even its tiniest fraction can ever disappear and therefore its influence cannot be disregarded. But precisely such tiny fractions of energy are present in the form of photons which in the gamma-ray microscope "disturb" the object observed. The conventional explanation of the indeterminacy by the Compton effect has a more Spencerian ring than the authors of the textbooks of physics realize. Even Heisenberg himself, as Karl R. Popper wittily observed, "tries to give a causal explanation why causal explanations are impossible." [10]

Contemporary physicists generally do not share this deterministic view. With a few exceptions, to which, paradoxically enough, both Einstein and Planck belonged, physicists today reject the assumption of the hidden strictly determined processes which would underlie the apparent contingency of the observed phenomena. In their view, the observed statistical laws of macrophysics are not mere surface phenomena, ultimately reducible to classical causal models; on the contrary, the statistical laws are regarded as ultimate and irreducible features constituting the objective physical reality. This attitude is largely due to the positivism prevailing among contemporary physicists, who insist on a consistent elimination of *all* unobservable factors. Einstein explicitly acknowledged his intellectual debt to Hume and Mach; his rejection of the absolute frame of reference was motivated by repeated failures to detect its existence by means of mechanical, optical, or electromagnetic experiments. There is no question but that a similar positivistic motive is conspicuously present in the minds of the physicists dealing with the problem of determinism in quantum mechanics: they consider the empirically unattainable determinism as useless as the hypothetical aether which escapes all means of empirical detection.

It is interesting, however, to see Einstein hesitating to apply

Occam's razor to classical determinism, although he had previously boldly used this razor in eliminating the empirically unverifiable motionless aether. This merely shows that a pure and undiluted positivism in an extremely rare phenomenon; as we shall see, Einstein's reluctance to depart from determinism was due to certain unconscious or semiconscious metaphysical predilections. This explains why Einstein, who was a fairly consistent phenomenalist in his theory of relativity, was much less so in his attitude to quantum phenomena, although at present classical determinism is as unverifiable as absolute space or absolute motion.

It is even more instructive to observe those physicists who, adhering more consistently than Einstein to the rule of parsimony, regard as futile all hopes to explain the uncertainty relations by hidden unobservable causal models. Yet, in spite of all positivistic and agnostic declarations to the contrary, their imagination in most cases remains incurably realistic and they naturally retain an urge to *imagine* in some way the allegedly unobservable background of phenomena. When Heisenberg, for instance, begins the explanation of his principle by his famous *Gedankenexperiment* [experiment in thought], in which a microparticle is "illuminated" by the high-frequency radiation by which its momentum is modified,[11] does this mean that, contrary to his own conscious convictions, he still visually imagines the elementary particles as individual corpuscular entities basically similar to macroscopic bodies of our daily experience? It is probable that Heisenberg and all philosophically minded physicists would claim that, if any imaginative visual content is present in their mind when they use the words "particle" or "corpuscle," it is an irrelevant and accessory psychological phenomenon accompanying the abstract thought which is expressible in precise mathematical symbolism. They would insist that it is the thought which really counts; the concomitant images are completely irrelevant.

I think that this is a serious mistake which stems from an unfortunate separation of psychology and epistemology. It is simply not true that what we conceive abstractly is always independent of the concomitant unconscious or semiconscious imaginative content. A detailed analysis would show that often the convincing power of abstract ideas has its roots in the semiconscious imaginative fringes surrounding them. Instances of this kind have already been mentioned in Part I; let us recall briefly one of them—the classical concept of spatiotemporal continuity. Underlying this concept is our subjective incapacity to stop *imagining* smaller subintervals within any interval of space and time, no matter how minute it may be. It is impossible to separate epistemology from psychology for the simple reason that no sharp boundary separates "reason" from "imagination."

Even those who persistently insist on the independence of their epistemology from psychological factors do accept, either knowingly or unwittingly, a certain theory of mind, that is, a certain *psychology* convenient for their purposes. But they seem to be less aware that this psychology is rather outdated now, since it is based on the artificial separation of "clear" and "pure" thought from the allegedly "confused" sensory content. This division of mind into independent faculties is one of the main characteristics of seventeenth- and eighteenth-century rationalism and it is very definitely present in the Kantian separation of *Sinnlichkeit* and *Vernunft*. But already Locke and Leibniz had begun to question the existence of the sharp boundaries allegedly separating reason and imagination: Locke in moving the the boundary up in order to include reason in sensory perception and its derivatives, Leibniz in moving the boundary down in order to transform sensory perception into a rudimentary form of reason. It is not necessary to commit oneself to a particular epistemology in order to realize that neglected imaginative elements not only accompany but also tinge and influence even the apparently abstract operations of thought, sometimes in a decisive way. Epistemology, and the epistemology of modern physics in particular, would profit enormously from a sort of "psychoanalysis of knowledge" in Gaston Bachelard's sense[12] which would unmask the inhibiting influence of our Euclidean and Newtonian subconscious in the minds of those physicists who sincerely believe themselves to be entirely free from them.

Such subconscious or semiconscious visualization is certainly responsible for why a picture of an individual particle spontaneously emerges in our mind as soon as we pronounce a word like "electron," "proton," "meson," etc. From such an image it is impossible to separate its constitutive properties—its position at a certain time and its motion or lack of motion within a certain frame of reference. The very concept of particle consists of the association of its position, its mass, and its motion; or, more technically, of its position and momentum. In truth, these two features—position and momentum—are the only residuum which abstract dynamics retained from the original crude and sensory image of Lucretius and Gassendi. As Louis de Broglie observed not very long ago,[13] in speaking of microscopic particles we have the tendency to imagine very tiny grains of sand; naturally, we are aware of the inadequacy of such imagery, and following the ancient atomistic tradition, we eliminate from such a picture all sensory characteristics, all "secondary qualities," until eventually nothing but the basic geometric and mechanical properties remain. When finally the concept of corpuscle is reduced to the conjunction of its position and momentum, we have reached *the farthest limit* we can go; one more step will inevitably lead to the elimination of the concept itself.

Psychologically as well as logically it is entirely impossible to divorce the concept of velocity or that of position from the concept of particle without destroying the concept of particle itself. Within a certain frame of reference a particle can have only *one* definite position and *one* definite velocity; a particle without any definite velocity or without definite momentum, a so-called "unsharp particle" ("la particule imprécise") is nothing but a pseudo-idea, a mere combination of words, a sheer *flatus vocis*. But this pseudo-idea is a result of the compromise between the positivistic maxim, which excludes all unobservables, and our almost irresistible tendency to visualize. The same thing is true of the concept of "probability of occurrence of a particle at certain place." Again in this wording the visualizing tendencies of imagination, which manifest themselves in the usage of such terms as "place," "occurrence," "particle," clash with the abstract positivistic principle which demands the exclusion of all unobservables.

From this *impasse* there seem to be only two ways out: either to yield to the natural proclivity of our imagination—needless to say the imagination already purified in the sense of classical physics—and admit that microphysical particles have a precise location in space and are endowed with a well-defined quantity of motion; or to press the revision of our concepts to its logical conclusion and give up the idea of individual particles entirely, like all other sensory or pseudo-sensory notions which physics borrowed from the world of macroscopic experience. The first way would imply the rehabilitation of the classical determinism which would extend to all microphysical events; then the alleged "uncertainties" or "indeterminacies" would be devoid of any objective significance, being merely gaps, perhaps even temporary gaps, in our knowledge. Logically there is hardly any middle ground between these two solutions. It is epistemologically intolerable, at least in the long run, to retain a Newtonian and Democritean subconscious which is entirely incompatible with our conscious convictions and verbal utterances. Yet, this uncertain oscillation between subconscious Newtonianism and its conscious rejection seems to be a characteristic attitude on the part of a great number of physicists today, in particular those who insist on the irreducibility of the statistical laws to some hidden causal micromechanisms.

This is merely another way of saying that the second way is psychologically incomparably *more difficult* than the first one. Classical determinism was, as we have seen, regularly associated with the corpuscular-kinetic models of reality; if we reject determinism and still speak about corpuscles, we evidently use an inadequate language. Hence such monstrosities as a particle without any definite position or velocity. Nearly a quarter of a century ago a dissatisfaction with this situation was clearly stated by Schrödinger:

> The quantum mechanics of today commits the error of maintaining concepts of the classical mechanics of points —energy, impulse, place, etc.—at the cost of denying to

a system *in a precisely determined state* any definite values for these magnitudes. This shows how inadequate these concepts are. *The concepts themselves must be given up, not their sharp definability.* Attempts are made to avoid the monstrosities of ill-defined concepts by carrying out hundreds of mental experiments to show clearly that the magnitudes in question under the circumstances cannot in principle be accurately measured. [Italics added.] [14]

Not only the concept of corpuscle, but even *the more general concept of precise spatiotemporal location* becomes inadequate (Chapter XIII). Indeed the whole conceptual framework of classical physics is thoroughly incompatible with the claim that the contingency of microphysical events is of an objective nature, instead of being merely a result of our technical limitations or of the disturbing effect by which an observed phenomenon is modified in the very act of observation. But this constitutes a very serious handicap for those who defend this claim, that is, for those who do not share the view of Léon Brunschwicg, quoted above, nor the hopes of Albert Einstein and, more recently, of Louis de Broglie, David Bohm, and Jean Pierre Vigier, according to which the uncertainty relations will be eventually reducible to a causal model, basically not different from the causal models of classical physics.[15]

The defenders of the deterministic interpretation have the tremendous advantage of having the ready-made language with the corresponding conceptual framework strengthened by three centuries of scientific tradition and twenty-five centuries of philosophical tradition; for, let us not forget, philosophical determinism is twenty-five centuries old. It would be unfair, of course, to claim that the deterministic interpretations lack the refinement and complexity of their rivals; but, as we shall see, in their basic features and by their basic motives, they are, often consciously, a return to the past. For this reason the way of deterministic interpretation will, for a certain time at least, appear more attractive and more natural, while the opposite interpretation strikes us as adventurous and baffling. This is hardly surprising; physical indeterminists have neither an adequate language nor a corresponding conceptual framework at their disposal; whenever they try to express their views, they naturally become entangled in artificial mental experiments which are necessarily misleading because they involve macroscopic experimental arrangements and the use of the *corpuscular* (i.e., macroscopic) language, utterly unsuitable for the description of microphysical events.

But in spite of this attractiveness, the deterministic interpretation cannot be trusted now. Before summing up the important epistemological reasons which make a rehabilitation of classical determinism extremely improbable, we have first to consider the weight of physical facts pointing toward the same conclusion.

In the first place, the true significance of the uncertainty principle was and still is being obscured by the considerations in which the role of observation is unduly stressed. Not only a layman, but even a philosopher interested in physics, not infrequently even an average physicist himself, as long as he is not sufficiently acquainted with the logical structure of wave mechanics, has the impression that the microphysical uncertainty is nothing but the *uncertainty of measurement* resulting from the intervention of an observer and his observing instruments. The usual textbook presentation of Heisenberg's principle leads almost inevitably to such a view.

Too much insistence on the act of observation and the presence of the observer brought a misleading note of epistemological idealism into discussions revolving around the principle of indeterminacy. This note was welcomed with an almost equal satisfaction, although for very different philosophical reasons, by idealistically oriented physicists and by neopositivists. This will become less paradoxical if we remember that neopositivists, in particular in Germany and Austria, have never lost their Kantian tinge, especially in their epistemology; the dividing line between positivists and Neo-Kantians is sometimes quite dim, and from phenomenalism to idealism is just one step. After all, the ancestors of contemporary idealists and positivists— Berkeley and Hume—were, in their epistemology at least, not so far apart. An analogous attitude was adopted by the same two groups toward the theory of relativity. The words of Alfred North Whitehead criticizing this attitude may be applied *mutatis mutandis* to present neopositivistic and idealistic interpretations of the principle of indeterminacy:

> There has been a tendency to give an extreme subjectivist interpretation to this new doctrine. I mean that the relativity of space and time has been constructed as though it were dependent on the choice of the observer. It is perfectly legitimate to bring in the observer, if he facilitates explanations. But it is the observer's body that we want, and not his mind. Even this body is only useful as an example of a very familiar form of apparatus. On the whole, it is better to concentrate attention on Michelson's interferometer, and to leave Michelson's body and Michelson's mind out of the picture.[16]

This passage may be almost *verbatim* repeated, if we replace Michelson by Heisenberg and if we substitute "Heisenberg's gamma-ray microscope" for "Michelson's interferometer," and "indeterminacy" for "relativity of space and time." We can go further and say that even the presence of the instrument, whether Michelson's interferometer or Heisenberg's gamma-ray microscope, serves in either case to exhibit some particular effects of the objective features of nature, whether relativistic binding of space and time or microphysical indeterminacy.

This is not intended to discount the correctness of Heisenberg's *Gedankenexperiment;* its only shortcoming is to confine our attention to a special case only. For the influence of the physical apparatus on the observed phenomenon is only a *special instance of physical interaction in general whose character is everywhere and always dominated by Planck's constant h;* the uncertainty principle, that is, the impossibility of punctual localization in space and time, follows logically and inescapably from the indivisibility of the atoms of action. Planck's atom of action is a universal constant, independent of any observer and relativistically invariant; hardly anybody claims that its appearance in empirical data is brought up by an intervention of the observer. If we regard action as a fundamental physical reality, then, on closer reflection, it will become obvious that the reality of sharply localized corpuscles, endowed with precise instantaneous values of momentum and energy, must be denied. We have seen that such a conclusion was reached by Schrödinger in 1934; it was, implicitly at least, formulated by Eddington a few years earlier:

> The suggestion is that an association of exact position with exact momentum can never be discovered by us *because there is no such thing* in *Nature*. [Italics in the original.] [17]

But we have seen that the association of position with momentum is practically the only remnant which survived in abstract dynamics from the original sensory and crude notion of corpuscle. If even this last remnant is questioned, is there anything at all which is left of the concept of corpuscle? A more recent statement of Philip Frank cogently criticizes the intrusion of corpuscular notions into various expositions of the principle of indeterminacy:

> Very frequently, in popular presentations which are occasionally written by scientists, the laws governing the atomic objects are formulated in a misleading way. Some authors have said that according to the contemporary laws of motion for atomic particles the position and velocity of a particle cannot be measured at the same instant. If we measure the coordinate (position), we "destroy" the possibility of measuring the momentum, and *vice versa*. This formulation is misleading because it gives the impression that before the measurement there was a "particle" that possessed both "position" and "velocity," and that the "measurement of its position" destroyed the possibility of "measuring its momentum." As a matter of fact, the atomic object itself cannot be described by the terms "position" or "veloc-

ity." Obviously, what does not "exist" cannot be "destroyed." [18]

Since the assumption that an atomic object behaves like a "real particle" is incompatible with the observable facts of atomic physics, neither position nor momentum is possessed by the object; *they cannot be measured because they do not exist.* For the same reason, the possibility of measuring them cannot be destroyed because it has never existed. [Italics added.] [19]

The only objectionable term in the passage quoted is "atomic object." The term "object" has subtle corpuscular overtones which may be misleading, if not for Frank himself, at least for his readers. The term "atomic event" is free of such misleading associations; we refer to what has been stated in Chapter XV. The extent of the contemporary crisis in physics cannot be fully grasped if we do not realize that the very concept of *substance* or *thinghood* has become questionable. The term "object" misleadingly suggests the permanence of a certain thing—more specifically, a constant conjunction of observable properties. But we already know that the alleged microphysical "objects" are not permanent; furthermore, *not even within a single instant* can they be characterized as conjunctions of positon and velocity. The atomic structure of action, in which very probably the pulsational character of time-space manifests itself, makes it impossible. Once more: for microphysical indeterminacy we do not have the disturbing effect of observation to blame, but Planck's constant of action itself.

It is always possible to hope that future physical discoveries will disprove the atomicity of action, that it will be shown that the indivisibility of action is spurious and is due exclusively to present limitations of our technique of observation. Has it not already happened several times in the history of science that what was regarded as a definite and ultimate limit of nature has been eventually shown to be only a *temporary* limit reached by our investigation? For instance, has not the allegedly indivisible atom of Dalton eventually been divided into its component parts? Can we be absolutely sure that no fractions of action smaller than h exist in nature?

Such an attitude, though theoretically permissible, can hardly be called fruitful, and it is extremely implausible that the expectations which it arouses will ever be fulfilled. To say nothing of the epistemological reasons which will be discussed later, the evidence for atomicity of action is both qualitatively and quantitatively incomparably more convincing than the limited empirical evidence of the last century for the alleged indivisibility of Dalton's atom. It is hardly probable that the mass of evidence accumulated by this time—frequently along independent and divergent lines of investigation—against the further divisibility of action is either a coincidence or a result of our present technical limitations. Moreover, the majority of those who hope to explain the indeterminacy principle as a result of our experimental and observational limitations do not deny the existence of the constant h. Apparently they do not realize their inconsistency. To recognize the existence of h and to deny objective indeterminacy is as little consistent as to recognize Newton's law and to deny the validity of Kepler's laws, which are its mathematical consequences.

THE CONTINGENCY OF MICROPHYSICAL EVENTS

A short glance at *radioactive disintegration*, that important group of microphysical phenomena, will show that (1) indeterminacy relations are independent of the interaction between the observed fact and the observer and (2) it is extremely doubtful whether they will ever be reduced to some classical corpuscular-kinetic model. The most paradoxical feature of natural radioactive decay is not that it is entirely independent of external conditions like temperature or chemical binding, although it is true that this feature appeared, at the time of the discovery, very surprising. It definitely indicated that radioactive transformation instead of being an ordinary chemical process, in which the atoms of various elements preserve their identity, is an *intra-*

atomic change in which the very constitution of atoms is changed. No matter how astonishing this discovery was after nearly a century of firm belief in the immutability of the chemical atom, it was comparatively easy to imagine a mechanism of the radioactive transformation without basically departing from the classical habits of thought. All that was necessary was to postulate that atoms, instead of being simple and undifferentiated units, are themselves complex; this, as we have seen, was already anticipated by Robert Boyle.[20] Then it is understandable that when one or more constituent parts are ejected from the interior of the atom, its physical and chemical properties will be modified. Even the mechanism of disintegration was easily conceivable, at least in principle; the fact that radioactive explosions occur spontaneously in the heaviest elements, that is, in the elements whose nuclei have a very large number of constituent parts, seemingly suggests that the ejection of alpha particles as well as of beta electrons is *caused* by *apparently random* fluctuations of the internal kinetic energy of other constituent particles.

In this sense the radioactive emission would not be different in principle from the process of evaporation, in which, even under a relatively low temperature, a few individual molecules escape from the main body of liquid. Indeed Isaac Newton did not imagine the mechanism of luminous emission in any radically different way; according to him, the violent agitation of aether particles ejects the corpuscles of light from the inside of material bodies.[21] In this way the correlation between heat and light was qualitatively explained; for Newton, following in this respect his fellow countryman Francis Bacon, regarded heat as motion of minute particles.

But the truly baffling feature of the radioactive phenomena was the discovery that the nuclear alpha particles are emitted from the nucleus *even when they do not have a sufficient velocity to climb over the surrounding potential barrier*. According to the laws of classical mechanics no particle can penetrate a zone in which the difference between its total energy and its potential energy would be negative. The potential barrier surrounding the nucleus represents such a "forbidden zone," where

$$E - V < 0$$

($E =$ the total energy, $V =$ potential energy of a particle). Within the classical framework this was merely a truistic statement that the kinetic energy of any particle can never become negative as this would imply the absurd consequence that its velocity would become imaginary! Yet, what was a sheer physical impossibility for classical physics is regarded only as an *exceedingly small probability* by wave mechanics. No matter how minute these probabilities are, they are realized in the radioactive emissions described above. The inadequacy of classical mechanics could not have been more clearly demonstrated. On the other hand, wave mechanics not only explains facts inconceivable within the classical framework, but leads to correct quantitative derivations of various decay constants which were previously accepted as bare empirical data.

The concept of impossibility and of causal necessity were closely correlated in classical thought, physical as well as philosophical; indeed they were complementary aspects of one and the same ontological claim. According to this claim, whatever happens *must* happen and whatever does not happen *cannot* happen; there is no middle ground between impossibility and necessity and, consequently, possibility or contingency is a mere symptom of human ignorance as Spinoza and Democritus had already stressed.[22] The substitution of the concept of small probability for that of impossibility implied the concomitant substitution of the concept of large probability for causal necessity. These two correlated substitutions measure the departure of wave mechanics from the rigid necessitarianism of classical thought. The concept of objective possibility, so resolutely rejected by classical determinism, re-emerges in contemporary physics in the form of objective probability.[23]

This is especially striking in the concrete case of the radioactive emission of alpha particles. Not only is it *possible* for a particle with insufficient kinetic energy to pass through the potential wall, but also it is *not necessary* for a particle with sufficient kinetic energy to surmount the same barrier. According to classical mechanics the particles of the first kind were *necessarily* reflected from the potential wall while the particles of the second type *necessarily* surmounted it. It is not so in wave mechanics: particles of both kinds *may be either* reflected *or transmitted* by the nuclear potential wall, although the corresponding probabilities are not equal. From this point of view radioactive explosions are regarded as *contingent events* whose irreducible chance character manifests the basic indeterminacy of microphysical occurrences.

This follows also from the way in which Heisenberg's principle of indeterminacy is applied to this particular group of phenomena. While in classical physics the surmounting or crossing of the potential barrier was a manifest absurdity, Heisenberg's principle, applied here, provides us with a certain explanatory insight, even though the paradox, for the reasons which will be stated later, does not entirely disappear. Both forms of the uncertainty principle lead to a plausible explanation of what is called the "tunnel effect." Using the first form of the principle

$$\Delta p \cdot \Delta x \geqq h$$

we see that if the uncertainty concerning the momentum is sufficiently small, the uncertainty about the position of a particle is so large that it can be located on either side of the potential wall. It can be shown that such a case occurs when the width of the potential barrier is of the same order as De Broglie wave length. But if the particle is present on the outer side of the barrier, then, according to physicists, "we should have to regard it as having successfully passed through the barrier." [24] If we apply the second form of Heisenberg's principle

$$\Delta E \cdot \Delta t \geqq h$$

then, for a sufficiently small amount of time, the uncertainty of the energy is so large that there is a finite probability that the energy E of the particle can exceed the height of the potential wall.

From either presentation it can be seen clearly that the uncertainty principle does not depend in any way on the accuracy of measurement.[25] There is no intervention of an observer in the case of radioactive explosions which occur spontaneously and independently of any extranuclear factors. The function of the human observer here is passive; it is reduced to counting particles in a certain interval of time and measuring their energy *after* their emergence from the nucleus. It is true that even this apparently passive role means an intervention in the observed physical process; thus the counting of the emitted particles is impossible without using a spinthariscope or Geiger counter, and to these observational procedures everything which Heisenberg stated in his original formulation of the principle applies. But this intervention does obviously occur *after* the event, that is, *after* the radioactive explosion has taken place. Thus the uncertainty of the radioactive disintegrations is independent of the limitations of human experimental technique; the term "indeterminacy" or "contingency" is far more appropriate and much less misleading than "uncertainty."

The phenomena of radioactivity are not the only ones which support this objectivistic interpretation of the principle of indeterminacy. The facts of radiation belong to the same category. In the terms of Bohr's model the emission of photons occurs when an electron returns from an outer orbit to an inner one; then the energy of the emitted light-quantum is equal to the difference of energy between the higher energy level and the ground-state level. Bearing in mind the inadequacy of the corpuscular model of the atom, it is more appropriate to say that the emission of light quanta occurs when the atom returns from its "excited" (i.e., energetically richer) state to its "ground" (i.e., normal) state. It is thus evident that the presence of an "excited" state is a necessary condition for the emission of light; an atom must first absorb some excess energy in order to radiate it in the form of a photon. But this absorption of energy is *not* the *cause* of the subsequent emission, though it is a required *condition* for it; a spontaneous return of the atom into its normal state with a concomitant emission of radiation has no less a statistical character than a radioactive explosion. (This analogy between luminous emission and radioactive disintegration was noticed, interestingly enough, by Einstein himself, who nevertheless remained an adversary of microphysical indeterminism.)[26]

Neither Bohr's model nor the later wave-mechanical model provides for the causal explanation of "quantum jumps" which correspond to the emission of radiation. In the days of Bohr's model physicists used to say that an electron "spontaneously" returns to its lower orbit, without specifying the cause for it. Although the total energetic balance sheet was in satisfactory agreement with the principle of conservation of energy, *the mechanism of the emission* remained entirely unclear. Wave mechanics merely brought into focus the undetermined and statistical character of luminous emission as well as of radioactive explosions. As early as in 1929 Pascual Jordan[27] spoke of the "radioactive character" of the luminous emission when he pointed out that the existence of so-called "metastable states" established the undetermined character of the emission of light. For in metastable states an atom *persists* in its excited state much longer than in most cases; while in most cases the life of excited atoms is not longer than 10^{-8} second, in the metastable states it may last 10^{-2} second or even 1 second. There seems to be no immediate necessity for the return of an excited atom to its ground level, or, if the corpuscular language of Bohr's original model is used, for the return of an electron to its original inner orbit. The analogy between the various lifetimes of radioactive nuclei and the different lifetimes of "excited atoms" is quite conspicuous, and Jordan's suspicion about the "radioactive character" of luminous emission is quite justified.

On the other hand, opponents of microphysical indeterminism can always claim that the last word has not yet been spoken and that the possibility of a deterministic explanation still persists. In the case of radioactive explosions it seems to be especially plausible to believe in the existence of hidden causes which time and again bring about the ejection of alpha particles from the nuclei. As already stated, the very fact that spontaneous radioactivity occurs only in the very complex nuclei of heavy atoms seems to justify the belief that each particular emission is caused by a momentary fluctuation of the internal kinetic energy of the constituent parts. Thus the so-called "tunnel effect" would not be, properly speaking, a tunnel effect at all; a particle would not cross the "forbidden zone" with insufficient kinetic energy, but it would *climb* over it, having, by a happy coincidence, a sufficient amount of energy for doing so. The terms used by contemporary nuclear physicists—like "heating of the nucleus" or "evaporation of nucleons from the nucleus"—are pregnant with classical kinetic and, consequently, deterministic associations. This is the basis of all hopes of locating on the subquantum level the "hidden variables" determining the quantum phenomena. From this point of view the "random fluctuations" of the energy of alpha particles, which lead either to their emission or their reflection on the potential wall, are only *apparently* random; they are analogous to the apparent irregularities of Brownian motion. As a contemporary opponent of microphysical indeterminism says:

> Hitherto in physics (as in other fields) when one had met with an irregular statistical fluctuation in the behavior of the individual members of an aggregate, one assumed that these irregular fluctuations also had causes, which were however as yet unknown, but which might in time be discovered. Thus in the case of the Brownian motion, the postulate was made that the visible irregular motions of spore particles originated in a deeper but as yet invisible level of atomic motion. Hence, *all* the factors determining the irregular changes in the Brownian motion were not assumed to exist at the level of the Brownian motion itself, but rather, most of them were assumed to exist at the level of atomic motions. Therefore, if we study the level of Brownian motion itself, we can expect to treat, in general, only the statistical regularities, but for a study of the precise details of the motion, this level will not be complete. Similarly, one might suppose that in its present state of development, the quantum theory is also not complete enough

to treat all the precise details of the motions of individual electron, light-quanta, etc. To treat such details, we should have to go to some as yet unknown deeper level, which has the same relationship to the atomic level as the atomic level has to that of Brownian motion.[28]

What increases the plausibility of this approach is, apart from the general philosophical attitude which is unconsciously or semiconsciously present, the peculiar language of even those who support the indeterministic interpretation. We have seen that the terms "corpuscle," "energy," "velocity," and "positions" abound in texts concerning the applications of the principle of indeterminacy to radioactive phenomena, although in virtue of the same principle these terms lose their meaning. Thus we can find the following passage in one textbook of nuclear physics:

> *A particle cannot be localized more closely than its de Broglie wave length divided by 2π.* In the present case, if the barrier width a is comparable with or less than $\lambda/2\pi$, we cannot say whether a particle whose momentum is $p = h/\lambda$ is found on the right side of the barrier or on the left side. But if the particle is found on the right side of the barrier we should have to regard it as having successfully passed through the barrier.[29]

Contrary to the intention of the author, the impression of this passage is misleading in several ways. The words "we cannot say . . ." convey the impression that the uncertainty in the question is merely subjective; while the final sentence presupposes (*a*) that the particles pre-existed in the nucleus and (*b*) that it moved along a continuous trajectory through the "forbidden zone."

Assumption (*a*) is questionable. As Schrödinger observed, no particle can be observed more than once;[30] what we actually observe is two different *events* which we connect by the image of a corpuscle persisting through time. But this, as Lindemann observed, is "a mere concession to our habits, not to say infirmities." [31] It will be needless to repeat what has already been said about the nonpermanency and the eventlike character of microphysical "particles." In the particular case of radioactive emission, the particles *inside* the nucleus cannot be observed in principle without breaking the nucleus apart; its existence inside of the nucleus is only *assumed* in order to satisfy our substantialistic mode of thinking. Moreover, in the case of the emission of beta electrons, it can be *proved* that it is impossible to assume their pre-existence within the nucleus.[32] According to Niels Bohr, beta particles are *created* in the process of emission, just as photons are created in the act of their own emission. Although the pre-existence of alpha particles in the nucleus cannot be as cogently denied as that of beta electrons, it becomes extremely doubtful once we realize the general inadequacy of corpuscular models in microphysics.

Assumption (*b*) is as already shown (p. 309) plainly impossible; to postulate the spatiotemporal continuity of the trajectory through the "forbidden zone" amounts to the assertion of imaginary velocity. This does not make any sense unless we claim that we are interested only in mathematical symbolism and not in its pictorial interpretation. But this claim would mean giving up all attempts to construct any corpuscular model, and consequently also giving up the belief in the pre-existence of the particles within the nucleus. For the continuity of the trajectory guarantees, so to speak, the identity of the particle through time; we cannot have one without the other.

But opponents of microphysical indeterminism would certainly protest against such an identification of their position with the corpuscular-kinetic scheme of nature. They would probably stress the fact that in spite of the original historical association with atomism, physical determinism is a far broader concept and that its ultimate destiny is not bound up with that of the concept of corpuscle. They would probably point out that already in the last century the bonds between determinism and the corpuscular view were loosening, when field theories, which were as much deterministic as classical atomism, began to penetrate, first the domains of optics, electricity, and magnetism, and eventually the whole realm of physics.

But appearances notwithstanding, the opposition between corpuscular and field theories of matter was superficial rather than basic, and both belonged to the same classical tradition. We have seen that although the fluid theories of matter from Descartes to William Thomson apparently dissolved the contours of atoms in the universal continuity of the cosmic medium, the question whether the aether or the field itself is continuous or atomic remained open; also that by the most consistent minds the second alternative was implicitly preferred. Thus atomism reappeared on a smaller scale of magnitude as the "aether particles" replaced electrons and protons. But even when the radius of "aether particles" was reduced to zero and thus aether was made continuous in the mathematical sense of the word, the belief in the basic discontinuity of nature was rather obscured than given up. For mathematical continuity, being merely a different term for infinite divisibility, is, as such widely different thinkers as Poincaré, Bergson, Weyl, and Cassirer recognized,[33] a *disguised discontinuity;* the concept of a discrete element is retained even when its size is reduced to zero.

From this point of view we may claim that the dilemma "continuity versus atomicity" never really existed in classical physics: philosophically speaking, Descartes, Leibniz, Boscovich, Kant, and Faraday were as atomistic as Gassendi, Dalton, and Lorentz. From Pythagoras' monads and Democritus' atoms to the pointlike centers of force and the pointlike elements of field the route was long and devious; but basically it was one and the same route, which led to the view of nature as composed of mutually external units, even if these units were supposed to exist in infinite number within the smallest intervals of space and time. This concept of spatiotemporal "continuity," or if we prefer a less misleading word, of infinite divisibility of nature in space and time, is the *very basis* of classical determinism and —what is even more important—remains the basis of the neo-deterministic interpretations of contemporary microphysics.

This will become clear when we consider briefly the two most famous opponents of physical indeterminism: Albert Einstein and Louis de Broglie. The case of De Broglie is especially striking because his present deterministic position is a result of recent conversion, or rather reconversion to his original view, which he had given up twenty-five years before. Einstein, on the other hand, maintained his attitude of distrust toward contemporary physical contingentism consistently through all his life. The view of reality that both Einstein and De Broglie prefer belongs to the *Cartesian tradition* in physics and philosophy of science. L. de Broglie himself concedes it explicitly and sees the most promising feature of his theory in a return to Cartesian clarity (*clarté cartésienne*).[34] Let us recall briefly the most important features of the Cartesian tradition in physics and philosophy of science as it may be traced from Descartes to William Thomson. It is characterized by the persistent tendency to eliminate or at least to blur any sharp distinction between material bodies and the space which surrounds them. According to Descartes, matter, being identical with space, must share with space its mathematical continuity; for this reason there can be no atoms. On the other hand, space, being identified with matter, must share with matter its impenetrability; for this reason the void is impossible. This led Descartes and his followers to regard what we call "material particles" as mere complications of the all-pervading aethereal liquid. Needless to repeat what has already been said in the first part of the book and to list all the difficulties which such an ambitious enterprise faced. Let us only recall that the basic difficulty of reconciling the existence of the plenum with that of motion was never overcome by either Descartes or his followers. They were forced to concede explicitly or in a disguised way (cf. Chapter VII) the existence of the void, in an unintentional agreement with the rival atomic hypothesis.[35]

The basic reason why Descartes and his school could not succeed in their enterprise is now clear: they knew only the Euclidean form of space, which is by its own nature homogeneous and rigid, and for this reason cannot be fused with its physical content which is diversified and changing. In this respect Einstein was in a more favorable position because he had more flexible intellectual tools at his disposal. His non-Euclidean continuum, which possesses curvature different in different places and changing from one instant to another, simulates so well the properties of the diversified and changing physical content that it cannot be differentiated from it. In this sense the general theory of relativity may be regarded as a continuation of the Cartesian tendency to fuse space and physical reality into a single entity. To be sure, Einstein's general theory of relativity is Cartesian only in a very special sense; for not only are the Euclidean character of space and its homogeneity given up, but space is fused with time; thus it is more correct to speak of the *physicalization* or *dynamization* of space than of the geometrization of matter and time.[36]

There is, however, another feature of Einstein's general theory of relativity which is more distinctly Cartesian and therefore more distinctly traditional. This is the assumption of the mathematical continuity of space, time, and matter. From this follows another typically Cartesian assertion: that the spatiotemporal continuum in virtue of its infinite divisibility cannot contain any real individualities, any *indivisibilia*, in the etymological sense of the word. Einstein was too cautious to deny the existence of physical particles. He condemned Ernst Mach for opposition to atomism.[37] But from the times of his general theory of relativity he was inclined to interpret the existence of the particles as mere structural complications arising within the continuity of space-time. In other words, he regarded "particles" as mere anomalies of the continuous physical field. It is the latter which is the basic reality; its apparent discontinuity is explainable in terms of its continuous structure. This basic conviction accounts for Einstein's persistent search for the theory of the unitary field in which all the various manifestations of physical reality, including gravitation and electromagnetism, would be incorporated. It also accounts for his unshakable hope that rigorous determinism of the classical type will be eventually restored in microphysics. For if the discontinuity of quantum phenomena is only an appearance derivable from the continuous structure of the unitary field, then microphysical indeterminism is only apparent too because the main argument in its favor—the indivisibility of action—falls to the ground.

In other and more technical words, according to Einstein the whole of physical reality, including the corpuscles, should be described by the partial differential equations of the unitary field. The solutions of these equations should be free of singularities which would correspond to the *existence of the sources* within the field. Such sources would mean a disguised return to the duality corpuscles-field which Einstein resolutely rejects. The existence of the sources would mean the introduction of factors which are foreign to the structure of the field and the completeness of the description would be in danger.

The salient features of Einstein's view will stand out if we compare it with the view of Hermann Weyl. According to Einstein:

> Matter which we perceive is merely nothing but a great concentration of energy in very small regions. We may therefore regard matter as being constituted by the regions of space in which the field is extremely intense. . . . There is no place in this new kind of physics both for the field and matter *for the field is the only reality*.[38]

From this point of view, the electron represents that region of the electromagnetic field where the field intensity is incomparably higher than in its surroundings; but according to Einstein, the same field equations (though certainly more complex ones than the classical equations of Maxwell) hold *inside* the electron as well.

According to Weyl, who in this respect was probably inspired by Riemann,[39] the electrons are constituted by the *gaps* in the spatiotemporal field. For this reason it is meaningless to speak about regions *inside* the electron. Moreover, these gaps are the *sources* of the field, the sources from which the field is produced *according to statistical laws only*. Weyl thus restored the duality of matter and field. While the field represents the region of the continuous and strictly determined physical actions, matter represents a field-producing agency (*das Feld-erregende Agens*) essentially discontinuous and undetermined in its manifestations. In this way Weyl tried to do justice to the phenomena of quanta.[40]

Einstein's opposition to Weyl's view was based on a strict adherence to the idea of the all-embracing unitary field free of discontinuities as well as of singularities, all of whose changes are describable by means of partial differential equations. This is another illustration of how strict determinism and the concept of spatiotemporal continuity are practically inseparable.

The deep affinity between Einstein's theory of unitary field and various theories which try to restore determinism in microphysics by introducing "hidden parameters" is unmistakable, though it will probably appear more clearly to a future historian of scientific ideas. Even today it is not difficult to see that various "theories of hidden parameters" are species of unitary field theories, with which they share two basic assumptions: determinism and spatiotemporal continuity. In De Broglie's original interpretation of wave mechanics, particles were regarded as regions of the continuous undulatory field in which the amplitude was considerably higher than in the surrounding regions. It is significant that in 1927 Einstein encouraged De Broglie to persist in his search for a deterministic interpretation in spite of De Broglie's first unsuccessful attempt in this direction.[41]

But at that time Louis de Broglie did not follow the advice. For twenty-five years he adopted the indeterminist view of Heisenberg, Born, Bohr, and the majority of physicists. Even in recent years he still regarded his conversion to indeterminism as "final." [42] One of the reasons for his disagreement with Einstein was his correct realization that the general theory of relativity is a macroscopic theory and cannot deal adequately with the basic discontinuity of the quantum phenomena which can be disregarded on the macroscopic scale.[43] But when in 1951 David Bohm resumed De Broglie's original efforts to construct a hydrodynamical model of wave mechanics and when slightly later Jean Pierre Vigier called De Broglie's attention to the analogy between his original hypothesis in 1927 and the general theory of relativity, the situation changed radically and the time for the second conversion came.[44]

This second conversion of De Broglie was rather a reconversion to his original determinism of 1927, and philosophical motives played in it a far greater part than experimental facts. De Broglie's nostalgia for Cartesian clarity has just been mentioned. It is hardly surprising that he also returns to the idea of precise location of corpuscles and to the view that the uncertainty relations represent a *mere surface aspect* of physical reality. The corpuscles are for him, as for Einstein, *products of the field*, and their motions are in his theory guided by the undulatory field as unequivocally as the movements of "particles" (viz., local anomalies of the field) are determined in the general theory. From this point of view, the atomicity of action and the indeterminacy which it implies, instead of being an ultimate feature of reality, must be, so to speak, an *epiphenomenon* produced by hidden mechanisms whose nature does not differ basically from the mechanisms of classical physics. To believe otherwise would mean to sacrifice the two most cherished dogmas of classical thought—spatiotemporal continuity and determinism.[45]

It is loyalty to these two dogmas which makes the opposition to microphysical indeterminism so suspect. It is difficult not to see the analogy between the "theory of hidden parameters" and the *ad hoc* hypotheses which were postulated in order to explain in a classical way the negative result of Michelson's experiment; the reluctance to give up the concept of absolute space was as strong then as is now the reluctance to give up strict determinism.[46] The resistance to indeterminism of any kind is especially strengthened by the wrong assumption that *any* departure from classical determinism, no matter how slight, means the end of the possibility of *any* rational description of the world and, consequently, a suicide of reason.

We shall return to this point shortly; for the present, let us bear in mind the conclusion of our previous discussion which was only strengthened by our analysis of Einstein's and De Broglie's views: the concept of spatiotemporal continuity is *the very basis* of classical determinism and any threat to this basis is a threat to determinism itself. C. S. Peirce recognized this shortly before the beginning of the contemporary crisis of physics when he wrote:

> For the essence of the necessitarian position is that certain continuous quantities have certain exact values. Now, how can observation determine the value of such a quantity with a probable error absolutely *nil?* [47]

Today we would rephrase the last question in the following way: How can observation determine such quantities if *no sharp values* in nature exist and if the whole concept of infinite divisibility of space and time is an unwarranted extrapolation of our limited macroscopic experience?

THE INADEQUACY OF THE QUANTITATIVE VIEW OF NATURE

To speak on the microphysical level of the precise values of energy is as meaningless as to speak of well-defined positions and velocities of alleged particles. This follows from the second form of Heisenberg's principle of indeterminacy (see p. 290). But if this is so, is it still meaningful to speak of the law of the conservation of energy on the microphysical level? Evidently not. As Louis de Broglie observed as early as 1929,[48] the only way to consider energy constant is to assign it a well-defined value; the constancy of energy means always *the constancy of a certain quantity* of energy. Yet, it is precisely this quantity which, according to the second form of Heisenberg's principle, remains ill defined, i.e., retains a fuzzy edge which, though negligible on the macroscopic level, cannot be disregarded on the level of microphysical processes. The existence of this fuzzy edge prevents us from claiming absolute validity for the law of the conservation of energy, even if the traditional concept of energy is amended in the relativistic sense.

This negative consequence of the principle of indeterminacy is rarely stated explicitly. Usually *the very opposite claim* is made, viz., that the validity of the conservation laws has been verified even on the microphysical level.[49] In this respect, textbooks of atomic physics are more Spencerian in their spirit than their authors are aware of. The misunderstanding is due to our continued usage of the term "energy," even though this concept is devoid of intelligible meaning on the scale of individual subatomic events. Here is another instance of an illegitimate extrapolation of macroscopic concepts to the microcosm, or if we prefer a psychological point of view, another instance of our semantic and mental inertia which prevents us from getting rid of traditional concepts. The concept of energy is one of many traditional concepts whose realm of application does not extend below the lower limits of the zone of the middle dimensions. In Lindemann's words:

> We maintain that energy is just as much a statistical concept as temperature. It has no meaning unless averaged over a finite time, any more than temperature has a meaning unless averaged over a considerable number. In the same way that fluctuations of energy would be called fluctuations of temperature, if one attached any meaning to this term in relation to a single particle, one could refer to the fluctuations of energy in a single particle not affected by any external force. Over the time t the mean value of deviation would be h/t.[50]

In other words: to speak of a definite quantity of energy within a single subatomic occurrence is as little meaningful as to speak of the definite temperature of a single molecule of gas.

The passage quoted is interesting in one more respect; although it rejects unambiguously the adequacy of the concept of energy on the microscopic (or rather, *microchronic*) scale, at the same time it exhibits the extreme difficulty of stating this rejection in a language free of the very term which is being rejected. If we continue to use the term "energy," then the indeterminacy principle forces us to speak about "fluctuations of energy." Then we face the following dilemma: either these "fluctuations" are *caused*, and then we are back in classical determinism; or we may say, as Lindemann indicates, that microphysical energetic quantities spontaneously,

324 Philosophical Impact of Contemporary Physics

that is, *causelessly*, fluctuate around certain mean values. The first alternative is favored by Einstein, De Broglie, Bohm, and Vigier; from their point of view the radioactive explosions are *determined events* whose mechanisms elude us merely because of their complexity. More specifically: alpha particles are able to leave the nucleus *only* because they possess in the moment of their ejection energy sufficient for climbing over the potential wall; and they have this sufficient energy *only* because their normally low energy is momentarily increased by intranuclear collisions. This is a corpuscular and deterministic model of the radioactive emission; there is no need to repeat the criticism of it which has already been given. But if we favor the second alternative, then we are espousing a contingentism of an almost miraculous type; for we concede the existence of *uncaused* fluctuations of energy.

There is, however, *the third way* which is apparently suggested by Lindemann himself when he shows his dissatisfaction with both alternatives considered above. The horns of our dilemma have two features in common: (1) they agree in assigning to microphysical energies *definite* values; in other words, they agree that the concept of energy remains meaningful on the subatomic level; (2) they agree that fluctuations of microphysical energies are *real changes*, real increases or decreases of energy, that is, real transitions from one definite value to another. They disagree on one important point: whether these fluctuations are caused or not. Determinists in their claim remain loyal to the spirit of Democritus, Newton, Laplace, and Spencer. Indeterminists, in opposing this claim but in retaining the definite values of microphysical quantities, implicitly or explicitly concede the possibility of absolute creation and destruction of energy. Their intellectual ancestors are few: in antiquity Lucretius with his idea of *clinamen*, in the modern era Renouvier with his assertion of the possibility of "absolute beginnings" in nature.

There are two obvious disadvantages of this kind of indeterminism: (1) it is *absolute*, that is, by accepting *creatio ex nihilo* it not only denies the Laplacian type of causality, but *any* kind of connection between the past and present events; (2) it rejects determinism while retaining its whole conceptual framework. This was especially obvious in the case of Lucretius, whose "spontaneous deviation" is clearly a foreign element incongruously grafted on his otherwise entirely mechanistic system. And the position of those who would accept causeless fluctuations of energy would not be essentially different from that of their Roman predecessor; not only would their indeterminism be equally absolute and therefore equally irrational, but it would remain equally incongruous with the remaining part of their conceptual framework. This incongruity would arise from their attempt to retain the traditional concept of energy whose constancy is at the same time being denied.

It is important to stress that such absolute indeterminism, paradoxical as it may sound, is as incompatible with the objectivist interpretation of the indeterminacy principle as is absolute determinism of the classical type. Absolute contingentism agrees with absolute determinism that there are well-defined quantities of energy on the microphysical level even if we are unable to measure them accurately. If, however, the concept of energy is inapplicable to the microcosm, there is no sense in speaking of its definite quantity whether we regard it as constant or as changing abruptly and causelessly from one definite value to another. If we admit the objective character of microphysical indeterminacy, then the idea of *creation* or *destruction* of energy *is as illegitimate as its constancy* for the simple reason that the very concept of *quantity of energy* loses its classical macroscopic meaning. We have stated the reasons which suggest that the concept of *quantity of any kind* loses its adequacy on the subatomic level.

What then would be that third way which Lindemann merely suggests without elaborating? Such a solution would be somehow intermediate between the intransigent classical determinism and the equally intransigent contingentism of absolute and miraculous kind. We concede that the words "somehow intermediate" are unsatisfactorily vague. But we can acquire a preliminary glimpse of their positive meaning by stating once more their negative significance. The fallacy common to the strict Laplacian determinism and its no less radical denial is *the quantitative view of reality*. The conviction that physical reality may be regarded as a constant substantial quantity persisting through time was the *leitmotiv* of classical thought, philosophical and scientific, as Emile Meyerson established in his works. In philosophy it inspired the search for the ultimate unchanging substratum underlying all apparent phenomenal changes; in science it found its expression in the formulation of *conservation laws:* first the law of the conservation of matter, and later the laws of the conservation of energy, of momentum, of charge. The affinity between various philosophical substances and various constant physical quantities, whether of matter or energy, is certainly undeniable; in the minds of certain naturalistically-minded philosophers like Spencer, Nietzsche, Ostwald, and Haeckel the concepts of philosophical substance and physical substance merged.

One of the philosophically most significant results of microphysics is that this view, which filled nineteenth-century minds with an almost religious emotion, is no longer valid; the correlated ideas of *quantity* and *constancy* fail at the microphysical scale. The fact that these ideas preserve their usefulness within the realm of middle dimensions does not diminish in any way the philosophical significance of their basic inadequacy. Today it is impossible to share the enthusiasm of Hippolyte Taine who, speaking of the law of conservation of energy, exclaimed: "The immutable ground of being has been attained; we have reached the permanent substance" [Le fond immuable de l'être est atteint; on a touché la substance permanente].[51] Today it would be equally impossible to make the law of the conservation of matter the cornerstone of philosophical thought, as materialists of all ages have done; nor would it be possible to repeat the magnificent attempt of Herbert Spencer to derive all more special laws of nature from that of constancy of energy. Today it would be impossible to speak hymnically about the universe as a "metallic quantity of force," as Nietzsche did in the last part of his posthumous *Wille zur Macht*.[52] The inapplicability of the concept of constant quantity to the basic elements *or rather events* of the physical world makes much of nineteenth-century thought as well as its twentieth-century prolongations obsolete. For the concept of *the quantitative constancy of nature* was always correlated with the concept of strict determinism, which in the second half of the last century radiated from physical sciences into all other areas.

There is no need to repeat what has been said about this correlation in the first part of this book.[53] Let us only briefly recall how the view of nature as a constant quantity of matter and motion had been expressed already by Lucretius, who regarded the indestructibility and uncreatability of being as the very basis of the order of nature. When twenty centuries later Herbert Spencer and Wilhelm Ostwald tried to derive the law of causality from the law of the constancy of energy, they were inspired by essentially the same idea. It is then hardly surprising that the contemporary crisis of physics equally affects the two closely correlated ideas: strict determinism and constancy of being.

We hear much less about the crisis of the conservation laws than about the crisis of determinism; but this merely shows that the prestige of the former is still great enough to make us overlook the consequences of the principle of indeterminacy. We hear even less about the crisis of the *concept of motion*, although its correlation with the two preceding concepts is beyond any doubt. We know that the classical definition of motion as a displacement of matter in space was introduced in order to preserve the principle of constancy of substance; for the only kind of change which does not threaten this principle is *change of position*. Since then the idea of the constant quantity of matter, which persists through time while only its spatial distribution is changing, has dominated—and apparently still dominates to a considerable extent—our thought. The historical connection of the concept of motion with that of determinism is as clear as their logical connection. Explicitly formulated determinism and the kinetic view of nature were born at the same time and, if we disregard the curious inconsistency of Epicurus and Lucretius, have remained conjoined since. Motions of particles were always regarded as *causally determined* motions. When modern dynamics formulated the causal laws governing the motion of particles in the form of conservation laws, it brought into focus only in another form the close connection between kinetism, determinism, and the principle of quantitative constancy of nature. Is it surprising that when doubts concerning determinism and the conservation laws appear, the kinetic model of nature is also in danger?

Chapter XV pointed out the definite, though still rather implicit and generally not yet recognized, tendency in modern physics to substitute *changes* for displacements and *events* for particles. In the context of the present chapter these trends appear in a new light. The obtrusive force with which determinism imposes itself on our mind is due to its close connection with the corpuscular-kinetic scheme, which confers its deceptive "Cartesian clarity" upon determinism itself, even in its abstract form. Is it then surprising that the rival indeterminist hypothesis can never be adequately expressed within the scheme which, historically as well as logically, has always been associated with determinism of the most uncompromising type? Any attempt to express any kind of contingentism in the terms of the kinetic model of nature is bound to fail; the corpuscular-kinetic scheme by its own nature resists any such attempt. If we persist, the result will be nothing but absurdities and incongruities, like "unsharply localized particles," "particles without definite momentum," "energy quantities with dim edges," "electrons freely choosing their future orbit" or "causeless fluctuations of energy." The new wine is poured into old bottles, with the usual results. Not only does indeterminism fail to fit the traditional conceptual framework, but when forced into it, it necessarily acquires the improbable form of *absolute* indeterminism. This is natural; indeterminism within a quantitative view of reality will always appear in the form of creation or destruction of a certain quantity of either matter or energy or momentum, that is, in the form of *creatio ex nihilo* or *reductio in nihilum*. But such absolute creations and annihilations are characteristic of *absolute,* that is, *miraculous* indeterminism which is incompatible with *any* kind of coherent universe.

If contingentism cannot be adequately expressed in the form of traditional kinetism, why not throw the old bottles away when the old wine is gone? Is there a chance of gaining a more positive insight into microphysical contingentism by trying to express it in the nonkinetic and noncorpuscular terms suggested in Chapter XV? Would it be possible thus to obtain a more rational form of contingentism which would not destroy all connection between the successive events without merging them artificially into the timeless Laplacian formula? This is the last question which we shall face in the next chapter.

NOTES FOR CHAPTER XVI

1. W. Heisenberg, *The Physical Principles of Quantum Theory*, tr. by Carl Eckart and Frank C. Hoyt (University of Chicago Press, 1930), Chaps. II, III.
2. F. A. Lindemann, *The Physical Significance of the Quantum Theory* (Oxford, Clarendon Press, 1932), p. 83.
3. *Ibid.*, p. 110.
3a. H. Margenau, *The Nature of Physical Reality* (McGraw-Hill, 1950), p. 313; E. Bauer, *L'Electromagnétisme hier et aujourd'hui* (Paris, 1949), p. 175.
4. Two notable exceptions are F. A. Lindemann and Gaston Bachelard, whose books are referred to below.
5. A. Righi, *Kometen und Elektronen*, deutsch von M. Ikle (Leipzig, 1921).
6. G. Bachelard, *Le Nouvel esprit scientifique*, pp. 140-41.
7. Lindemann, *op. cit.*, pp. 53, 68.
8. G. Bachelard, *L'Expérience de l'espace dans la physique contemporaine* (Paris, 1937), p. 74.
9. Léon Brunschwicg, "Science et la prise de conscience," *Scientia*, Vol. LV (1934), p. 334; also *La Physique du XXe siècle et la philosophie*, Actualités Scientifiques et Industrielles, No. 445 (Paris, 1936). The same view was adopted by H. Margenau (who has since abandoned it) in his early article "Causality and Modern Physics" in *The Monist*, v. 41 (1931) and by W. H. Werkmeister in his book *A Philosophy of Science* (Harper, New York, 1940), pp. 272-277.
10. Karl R. Popper, *The Logic of Scientific Discovery* (Basic Books, New York, 1959), p. 249. The characteristic passage in H. Spencer's *Prin-*

ciples of Psychology (New York, Appleton, 1897), I, p. 502, may serve as a model to our contemporary defenders of determinism: "The irregularity and apparent freedom are inevitable results of the complexity; and equally arise in the inorganic world under parallel conditions. . . . A body in space, subject to the attraction of a single body, moves in a direction that can be accurately predicted. If subject to the attractions of two bodies, its course is but approximately calculable. If subject to the attractions of three bodies, its course can be calculated with still less precision. And if on all sides of it are multitudinous bodies of various sizes at various distances, as in the middle of one of the great star clusters, its motion appears uninfluenced by any of them: it will move in one indefinable way that looks self-determined: it will seem to be *free*."

11. Heisenberg, *op. cit.*, pp. 20 f.
12. G. Bachelard, *La Formation de l'esprit scientifique* (Paris, 1947). The subtitle is characteristic: "Contribution à une Psychanalyse de la connaissance objective."
13. Louis de Broglie, *Continu et discontinu en physique moderne* (Paris, 1941), p. 67.
14. E. Schrödinger, "Über die Unanwendbarkeit der Geometrie im Kleinen," *Naturwissenschaften*, Vol. 22 (1934), p. 519.
15. A. Einstein, "Remarks Concerning the Essays Brought Together in This Cooperative Volume" in *Albert Einstein: Philosopher-Scientist*, in particular Einstein's answer to Born, Pauli, Heitler, Bohr, and Margenau, pp. 666-670; L. de Broglie, "La physique quantique restera-t-elle indéterministe?," *Bulletin de la Société française de Philosophie*, séance du 25 avril 1953; also *Nouvelles perspectives en microphysique* (Paris, 1956), pp. 115-165; David Bohm, *Causality and Chance in Modern Physics* (London, Routledge and Kegan Paul, 1957), especially Chaps. III, IV; Jean Pierre Vigier, *Structure des micro-objets dans l'interprétation causale de la théorie des quanta* (Paris, 1956). Einstein's criticism of quantum theory and especially his identification of indeterminism with positivism and even solipsism would require a very careful and detailed analysis. A considerable part of his criticism may be accepted without agreeing with his determinism; for, contrary to his belief, contingentism is *not* equivalent to positivism or Berkeleyan idealism.
16. A. N. Whitehead, *Science and the Modern World*, pp. 172-173.
17. A. E. Eddington, *The Nature of the Physical World*, p. 225.
18. Philip Frank, *Philosophy of Science: The Link Between Science and Philosophy* (Englewood Cliffs, N.J., Prentice-Hall, 1957), p. 215.
19. P. Frank, *ibid.*, p. 230.
20. Chapter VI, above, Note 3.
21. E. T. Whittaker, *A History of the Theories of Aether and Electricity*, Vol. I, p. 21; I. Newton, *Optics*, qu. 8; B. Cohen, *Franklin and Newton*, p. 165.
22. Cf. Chapter IX, above, Note 4.
23. C. F. von Weizsäcker, *The History of Nature*, tr. by F. D. Wieck

(University of Chicago, 1949), p. 57; F. A. Lindemann, *op. cit.*, p .107.
24. Cf. Note 29 below.
25. W. Finkelburg, *Atomic Physics* (New York, McGraw-Hill, 1950), p. 236.
26. *Albert Einstein: Philosopher-Scientist*, pp. 172-73; 205.
27. P. Jordan, "Die Erfahrungsgrundlagen der Quantentheorie," *Naturwissenschaften*, Vol. XVII (1929), p. 504.
28. D. Bohm, *op. cit.*, pp. 79-80. A reserved but on the whole neutral attitude toward Bohm's view is adopted by N. R. Hanson, in *Patterns of Discovery* (Cambridge University Press, 1958), pp. 172-175.
29. R. D. Evans, *The Atomic Nucleus* (New York, McGraw-Hill, 1955), p. 61.
30. E. Schrödinger, *What is Life? and Other Scientific Essays* (Garden City, Doubleday, 1958), p. 175.
31. F. A. Lindemann, *op. cit.*, p. 88.
32. R. D. Evans, *op. cit.*, Chap. VIII, p. 276 (about the nonexistence of nuclear electrons).
33. H. Poincaré, *La Science et l'hypothèse* (Paris, 1909), p. 30: "De la célèbre formule, le continu est l'unité dans la multiplicité, la multiplicité seule subsiste, l'unité a disparu." Cf. H. Weyl, "Das Kontinuum," in *Kritische Untersuchungen über die Grundlagen der Analysis* (Leipzig, 1918): "im 'Kontinuum' der reelen Zahlen in der Tat die einzelne Elemente so isoliert stehen, wie etwa die ganze Zahlen." About the discrepancy between the intuitively given continuum and the mathematical continuum: H. Bergson, *Creative Evolution*, p. 170; E. Cassirer, *Determinism and Indeterminism in Modern Physics*, tr. by O. Th. Benfey (Yale University Press, 1956), p. 170.
34. L. de Broglie, "La physique quantique restera-t-elle indéterministe?," *Bulletin de la Société française de Philosophie*, séance du 25 avril 1953; the same author, *Nouvelles perspectives en microphysique* (Paris, 1956), p. 140.
35. Cf. Chapter VII, pp. 108-116.
36. Cf. Chapter XI, above, Note 31.
37. Cf. *Bulletin de la Société française de Philosophie*, séance du 6 avril 1922, p. 112.
38. Quoted by Louis de Broglie, *Nouvelles perspectives en microphysique*, pp. 187-88.
39. Cf. Chapter XIII, above, Note 16.
40. H. Weyl, *Was ist Materie?* p. 84; cf. also his *Philosophie der Mathematik und Naturwissenschaft* (München and Berlin, 1927), pp. 132-34.
41. L. de Broglie, *op. cit.*, p. 236.
42. L. de Broglie, "Souvenirs personnels sur les débuts de la mécanique ondulatoire," *Revue de métaphysique et de morale*, 48e année (1941), pp. 1-23; reprinted in *Physique et microphysique* (Paris, 1947), especially pp. 181-190.
43. L. de Broglie, *Matière et lumière* (Paris, 1937), pp. 234-35.
44. L. de Broglie, *Nouvelles perspectives en microphysique*, pp. 199-200.

45. L. de Broglie, *op. cit.*, pp. 220-226. D. Bohm is only consistent when he hopes that on the deeper subquantic level the alleged "atoms of energy" will be found still divisible. This is another illustration of the close connection between classical determinism and the dogma of spatiotemporal continuity. (*Op. cit.*, p. 81.)

46. Chapter X, especially pp. 146-149.

47. C. S. Peirce, "The Doctrine of Necessity Examined," *The Monist*, Vol. 2 (1892-93); reprinted in *Collected Papers of C. S. Peirce*, ed. by C. Hartshorne and P. Weiss, Vol. VI, p. 35.

48. L. de Broglie, "Déterminisme et causalité dans la physique con-temporaine," *Revue de métaphysique et de morale*, année 38 (1929), p. 442: "Attribuer aux corpuscules une énergie bien determinée est la seule manière de pouvoir appliquer le principe de la conservation de l'énergie."

49. L. Goldstein, *Les théorèmes de conservation dans la théorie des chocs electroniques* (Paris, Actualités Scientifiques et Industrielles, No. 70, 1932); W. Finckelburg, *op. cit.*, pp. 279-80. Even more instructive is the case of Ernst Cassirer who while stressing the fact that the concept of energy loses its meaning on the microphysical level, still claims that the law of conservation of energy remains valid there. Cf. *Determinism and Indeterminism*, pp. 117, 191.

50. F. A. Lindemann, *op. cit.*, p. 109.

51. H. Taine, *De l'Intelligence* (Paris, 1870), I, préface. (Page 11 of the 16th edition.)

52. F. Nietzsche, *Gesammelte Werke* (München, 1926), Vol. XIX, p. 373.

53. Cf. Chapter IX, above, pp. 136-138.

XVII · THE REINSTATEMENT OF BECOMING IN THE PHYSICAL WORLD

THE EMERGENCE OF NOVELTY AND THE POTENTIALITY OF THE FUTURE

WE HAVE just completed the outline of the most important changes by which the main classical concepts have been affected. We indicated that these changes are far more radical than is generally believed and that our failure to realize it is due to unconscious or semiconscious persistence of our traditional patterns of thought. We tried as consistently as possible to eliminate the remnants of the Newton-Euclidean subconscious which survives underneath our conscious acceptance of the modern physical concepts. Although the main part of this book has thus a negative character, it has been impossible to avoid completely all hints at a positive interpretation of contemporary physics. We are now going to coordinate earlier hints into a more systematic and more explicit pattern. This will be no more than an outline of interpretation whose detailed elaboration is beyond the scope of this book.

Every philosophical interpretation of contemporary physics may appear too speculative and controversial. Our interpretation will be rejected by all those who hope that physics will return, if not to the pictorial models, at least to classical determinism. It will be equally rejected by all those who regard the problem of transsubjective reality in physics as devoid of meaning. These two preliminary warnings are hardly necessary because they follow naturally from the conclusion reached in Chapter XVI: that microphysical indeterminacy is an ultimate feature of nature, irreducible to causal mechanisms; that it is independent of any observer, whether by "observer" we mean observer's mind or body or instruments operated by his body.

By naming Chapter XVI "The End of the Laplacian Illusion" we indicated that the objectivistic interpretation of the principle of indeterminacy implies the end of the belief in the static world of Laplace and his contemporaries. It means the *reinstatement of becoming in the physical world.* We reached the same conclusion by criticizing the static misinterpretation of the relativistic union of space with time. It is needless to repeat what has been said about the persistence of the Eleatic tradition in philosophy and science and about the fallacy of spatialization, both of which have played such unfortunate roles in discussions of relativity. But no matter how convincing the arguments against the spatialization of time may appear, they can never become entirely convincing as long as strict determinism is preserved. As long as the ambiguity of the future is a mere appearance due to the limitation of our knowledge, the temporal character of the world remains necessarily illusory.

Chapter XVI noted the close connection between *reality* and *necessity* in the deterministic scheme. Spinoza's *Per realitatem et perfectionem idem intelligo,** and Hegel's *Was vernünftig ist, das ist wirklich; und was wirklich ist, das ist vernünftig,*† [1] express the equivalence of reality and rational necessity in *every* form of determinism, whether of naturalistic or idealistic type: not only everything real is necessary, but also everything necessary is real. This also means that everything *unreal* is *impossible* and vice versa. There is no middle ground left for possibility or potentiality, that is, for something which while *unreal* is *not impossible.* Possibility, as determinists from Democritus to the modern opponents of microphysical indeterminism have never tired of repeating, is merely a name for human ignorance. As the future in the deterministic framework possesses

---

* By reality and perfection I understand the same thing.
† What is rational is real, and what is real is rational.

the character of absolute necessity, it acquires *ipso facto* the status of reality; it becomes something *actually* existing, a sort of disguised and hidden present which remains hidden only from our limited knowledge, just as distant regions of space are hidden from our sight. "Future" is merely a label given by us to the unknown part of the *present* reality, which exists in the same degree as scenery hidden from our eyes. As this hidden portion of the present is *contemporary* with the portion accessible to us, the temporal relation between the present and the future is eliminated; the future loses its status of "futurity" because instead of succeeding the present it *coexists* with it.

Similar considerations apply to the past, which contains "subsequent" moments in the same timeless fashion as the present contains the future. The flight of time is thus suspended and the successive moments of the cosmic history shrink into one timeless all-embracing "Now" in which distinctions between the past, present, and future vanish entirely. As William James said concisely and eloquently as early as 1884 in his essay "The Dilemma of Determinism":

> What does determinism profess? It professes that those parts of the universe already laid down absolutely appoint and decree what the other parts shall be. The future has no ambiguous possibilities hidden in its womb: the part we call the present is compatible with only one totality. Any other future complement than the one fixed from eternity is impossible. The whole is in each and every part, and welds it with the rest into an absolute unity, an iron block, in which there can be no equivocation or shadow of turning.

The attitude of indeterminism toward the idea of possibility, James continues, is just the opposite:

> It [indeterminism] admits that possibilities may be in excess of actualities, and that things not yet revealed to our knowledge may really be ambiguous. Of two alternative futures which we conceive, both may now be really possible; and the one becomes impossible only

at the very moment when the other excludes it by becoming real itself. Indeterminism thus denies the world
to be one unbending unit and fact. It says there is a
certain ultimate pluralism in it; and, so saying, it cor-
roborates our ordinary unsophisticated view of things.
To that view, actualities seem to float in a wider sea of
possibilities from out of which they are chosen; and,
somewhere, indeterminism says, such possibilities exist,
and form a part of truth. Determinism, on the contrary,
says they exist *nowhere*, and that necessity on the one
hand and impossibility on the other are the sole cate-
gories of the real. Possibilities that fail to be realized
are, for determinism, pure illusions: they never were
possibilities at all. There is nothing inchoate, it says
about this universe of ours, all that was or is or shall
be actual in it having been from eternity virtually there.[2]

It is hardly possible to state the dilemma between determinism and indeterminism with greater clarity. We face exactly
the same dilemma in physics today; the present conflict between
two antagonistic interpretations of the principle of indeterminacy is merely a special instance of the philosophical dilemma
described by James. Is the probability of microphysical events
merely subjective or does it have a status independent of the
human observer? Our view of the status of time depends on the
alternative we choose; conversely, our view of time will determine which alternative we shall espouse. For the reality of time
implies the emergence of novelty and the emergence of novelty
is incompatible with the pre-existence of the future. The only
status which the future can have in the dynamical world is that
of *possibility* or *potentiality;* and possibility, if it is not a mere
word covering our ignorance (as determinists say it is), implies
the *genuine ambiguity* of events not yet realized. This is what
the modern process philosophers from James to Whitehead
are so intensely aware of. They were not the first thinkers to
realize it. Aristotle knew it when he insisted that the law of the
excluded middle is inapplicable to future situations. Possibility
is an indispensable category of the dynamic world; conversely,
the affirmation of time is the only way to make the concept of

objective possibility meaningful and intelligible. The choice between objective and merely apparent possibility is really the choice between the dynamic and the static universe; or, to use George Boas' expression, between *the acceptance of time* and its rejection.

But do we still have such a choice in contemporary physics? Is not the *concept of objective probability*—the technical term applied by physics to the concept of possibility—*imposed on us* by the facts of wave mechanics? In Chapter XVI we indicated the reasons why we think it is. Reluctance to admit it stems in most cases from loyalty to the classical tradition, both scientific and philosophical, which regarded *strict determinism* and *rationality* as synonymous terms. According to this tradition every kind of indetermination (especially when it is given the name "chance") must be irrational. But indetermination appears irrational only in the static world which by its very nature excludes any ambiguity and contingency of the future; it is not irrational in the dynamic universe in which indetermination is synonymous with the objective indefiniteness of the future or, more truistically, with the *futurity of the future*. There is nothing mysterious or irrational in the affirmation that the universe is in the true sense of the word *incomplete;* it is certainly a less preposterous view than that according to which time is merely a huge and chronic hallucination of the human mind.

This dynamic aspect of the universe was emphasized by James when he spoke about "the everlasting coming of concrete novelty into being"; by Bergson when he insisted that the temporal incompleteness of the universe implies the element of indetermination in each of its moments; by Whitehead when he spoke of "the creative advance of nature." [3] But it was the same dynamic aspect of reality which Reichenbach stressed in his essay "The Causal Structure of the World and the Distinction Between the Past and the Future" in 1925 or when in one of his last essays he claimed that in the light of quantum phenomena the flow of time is "a real becoming in which potentiality is transformed into actuality" [*un devenir en acte dans lequel la potentialité se transforme en actualité*].[4] Similarly A. A. Robb pointed out that the fundamental character of *before* and *after* relations excludes the concept of "the bloc universe"[5] which rigorous determinism implies; while, more recently, H. Bondi has said:

> . . . the flow of time has no significance in the logically fixed pattern demanded by deterministic theory, time being a mere coordinate. In a theory with indeterminacy, however, the passage of time transforms statistical expectations into real events." [6]

NOVELTY IS COMPATIBLE
WITH THE CAUSAL INFLUENCE OF THE PAST

The most frequent objection against the reality of novelty is its alleged incompatibility with any kind of orderly and coherent universe. According to this view the slightest degree of contingency in nature would bring about the "ruin of science" and "suicide of reason." The most plausible argument of nineteenth-century determinists was that the affirmation of real novelty in nature, no matter how small, is equivalent to the recognition of a miraculous *creatio ex nihilo*. It is true that the expression of Charles Renouvier, one of the lonely defenders of contingency at that time, "the absolute beginning" (*le commencement absolu*) easily suggested this misinterpretation; but Renouvier, pressed by the objections of Alfred Fouillée, restated his thought in a clearer and less misleading way in insisting that the concept of "absolute beginning" is incompatible with causality of the *causa aequat effectum* type, while it is not only consistent with but even requires the more general type of causal connection.[7]

Necessitarians, being aware that caricatures of their opponents are more vulnerable than the opponents themselves, picture even the modern temporalist form of indeterminism as a simple reedition of the absolute indeterminism of the medieval *liberum arbitrium* type illustrated by the famous story of Buridan's ass. As early as in 1884 James unmasked "the ejaculations of Mr. Spencer" and the caricature of indeterminism by John Fiske, who both claimed that the denial of necessity is equivalent to the affirmation of lawlessness in nature which makes impossible all ethic, history, politics and laws.[8] In spite of James's refutation the argument is still popular now. "Concede the existence of contingency," say determinists "and *anything* may occur." [9]

It is evident that similar arguments are directed against *absolute indeterminism*, which is not defended by anybody except perhaps by Dirac, advocating *liberum arbitrium naturae*.[10] Bergson pointed out that the real novelty of the present moment must not be conceived as *creatio ex nihilo;* on the contrary, the emergence of novelty is nothing but the *passage* from the antecedent past moment to the present one.[11] Thus, far from being incompatible with the continuity of the successive moments, novelty *presupposes* it. But this continuity is of a *dynamic* successive type or, speaking with Whitehead, it is a "becoming of continuity" instead of a rigid timeless implication of the Laplacian type.[12] In the temporal continuity of a real process of causation—which should not be confused with the spurious mathematical continuity of durationless instants—the causal or "mnemic" influence of the past is not denied; but the present, though *co-determined* by the past, nevertheless contains an element of irreducible novelty. The individuality of a present event or, better, its *presentness* would be irremediably destroyed without this double feature of novelty and its dynamic cohesion with the anterior phases.[13] It is the connection with, as well as the contrast to, the past which creates the specific presentness of "now." As far as the future is concerned, it is the *future* and not a disguised and hidden present as in the necessitarian scheme: it *will* arise, it *is not yet*. But because it will not emerge *ex nihilo*, but from a particular present state, its general *direction* is outlined and thus possesses some general predictable features —the more predictable, the larger the statistical complexes of the elementary events that are considered. Hence arises the possibility of practically accurate prediction of macroscopic events.

Apparently, when Emile Boutroux in 1874 claimed that his "elementary variations" (*les variations élémentaires*) are so small that they escape experimental detection by the inaccurate instruments of that period,[14] he hardly expected that within half a century the methods of observation would be sufficiently refined to confirm his bold anticipations. Today, science is not ruined and "reason" is not committing suicide, although the classical concept of causality is being given up or, more accurately, being replaced by a redefined concept purged of the inconsistencies and absurdities of the old one. Contemporary physics in its implications returns by devious and complicated ways to the evidence of our immediate experience—to one of a few evidences which are not deceptive: to that of a *really growing world with genuine novelties emerging not "out of nothing," but from past antecedents*. Other deceptive features of our macroscopic experience together with the fixed Eleatic habits of our thought have for a long time obscured this evidence.

In such a growing world every present event is undoubtedly caused, though not necessitated by its own past. For as long as it is not yet present, its specific character remains uncertain for one simple reason: that it is only its presentness which creates its specificity, i.e., brings an end to its uncertainty, by eliminating all other possible features incompatible with it. Thus every present event is by its own nature an *act of selection* ending the hesitation of reality between various possibilities. The terms "selection" and "hesitation" appear to be metaphorical and even anthropomorphic at first glance: in truth, they express nothing but the ambiguous character of the unrealized future as well as its subsequent concrete realization. *Le temps est cette hésitation même ou il n'est rien du tout* (time is this very hesitation or it is nothing), as Bergson concluded in his last book.[15]

Thus, *dynamic causation* is entirely compatible with the emergence of novelties in the genuinely growing world. Indeed, only in such a world is the causal dynamic continuity between successive phases meaningful. It has no place in either the absolutely undetermined or the absolutely determined world. For while the first eliminates causation by breaking entirely the dynamic continuity between the past and the present, the latter eliminates it equally effectively by transforming it into a so-lidified static cohesion of the Laplacian type.

Chapters VIII and IX pointed out the hesitation among classi-cal physicists whether to adopt the absolutist or the relational theory of time. According to Newton, time, being absolute—that is, independent of its physical content—is intrinsically *irre-versible;* even if the whole universe should return to the same state through which it had already passed, the corresponding two moments would remain irremediably successive, one being "before," the other "after." In other words, not even a complete recurrence of the previous state would eliminate the temporal interval separating the original moment from its subsequent *identical* repetition. A similar insistence on the separability of time from its concrete content led Gassendi to claim that time was flowing even before the beginning of the world (*absque ullo principio ante Mundum*) and will continue even if the whole world is destroyed (*destructo etiam Mundo*).[16] But it was the same Gassendi who, influenced by Epicurus, leaned toward the relational theory of time, insisting on the insepara-bility of time from events and calling it "accident of accidents." Time is thus "nothing by itself," existing only in thought, which attributes it to things (*non aliquid per se, sed cogitatione dum-taxat, seu mente attributurum rebus prout concipiuntur in eo*).[17]

Leibniz was less hesitant when he rejected in the name of the principle of the identity of indiscernibles any distinction be-tween time and concrete events; according to him, it is mean-ingless to assert the difference between two moments of *empty* time because in virtue of the homogeneity of empty time no observable difference exists. No succession can exist without the heterogeneity of the corresponding physical contents. Although Leibniz, so far as I know, did not say it explicitly, his theory implied that in the hypothetical case of a complete identical repetition of two states, we should have no right in virtue of the same principle of the identity of indiscernibles to speak of the succession of two moments; the "original" moment and its repetition would merge into one single event which would be the beginning and the end of the completed cycle.

In the corpuscular-mechanical scheme successive events were defined in terms of successive configurations; the return of the identical configuration was regarded as extremely improbable, *but not impossible*. But as "non-zero probability must appear with a non-zero frequency," [18] the identical moment must eventually reoccur and cosmic time must eventually return upon itself. But if time is cyclical, then the difference between the past and the future is blurred and "the direction of time" has only a local and "sectional" significance defined by the local increase of entropy for certain intervals of time which, no matter how long, will always be finite. For this reason, as Boltzmann stressed, there is no privileged direction of time for the universe as a whole. In certain regions of the universe time may be "running backwards"; this happens on the microscopic level, where the fluctuations of Brownian motion represent temporary decreases of entropy; this must eventually happen, according to the laws of probability, in every macroscopic region and may, according to Boltzmann, be happening now in some very distant regions of the universe.

Before we shall consider these claims of classical physics in the light of recent discoveries, we must realize that we are dealing here really with *two* different assertions which, though closely related and mutually compatible, nevertheless remain distinct. One affirms the eternal recurrence of events, the other the reversibility of the time direction. Although the cyclical theory of time clearly entails the elimination or at least relativization of the direction of time, the converse is not necessarily true; those who deny the absoluteness of the time direction do not always insist on the cyclical character of time. Neither Boltzmann, nor Reichenbach espoused the views of Nietzsche or Abel Rey about the identical reoccurrence of each particular event, although they did believe in the reversibility of time.

We intend to show that the theory of eternal recurrence, besides being incompatible with the affirmations of contemporary physics, tacitly assumes, at least in its usual linguistic rendering, noncyclical time; while the theory of reversible time is based on the semantic confusion generated by the illegitimate use of misleading metaphorical language.

The theory of eternal recurrence was based on three presuppositions:

1. The universe is made of distinct atomic entities which persist through time without any intrinsic change so that they may be identified in different successive moments.
2. The universe is finite or, more specifically, the number of its components is finite.
3. It is meaningful to speak of a definite "state of the universe" at each particular instant.

The first and the third suppositions are no longer valid. There are no permanent corpuscular entities identifiable through time (see Chapter XIV for the crisis of the concept of particle). Nor is it physically meaningful to speak about "a state of the world at a given instant" (see Chapter X for elimination of the concept of world-wide instant). Thus no recurrence of the "initial" instantaneous configuration of particles can ever occur because both the concepts involved—instantaneous configuration and particle—belong to the outdated conceptual apparatus of classical physics.

Nothing is gained if we replace the corpuscular model of the universe by the field model and if instead of "the recurrence of the same configuration of particles" we speak of "the recurrence of the same energetic state," characterized by the same distribution of the energetic value through space. Even then the concept of world-wide instant, meaningless in the light of the special theory of relativity, is presupposed.

More serious are intrinsic logical difficulties inherent in the theory of eternal recurrence. It is questionable whether the concept of *absolutely identical repetition* is meaningful at all. If a recurring cosmic situation *is in all respects identical* with the previous one, how can these two successive situations be differentiated? What is the basis for the claim that the latter situation is a *repetition* of the former? If our answer is that the situations are differentiated by their different positions in time only, we supply the assumption which destroys the whole theory. For the very basis of the eternal recurrence theory is *the relational theory of time* according to which it is meaningless to differentiate moments of time from concrete events occupying them. If two situations are identical in *all* respects, it is meaningless to speak of their succession; we are dealing *with one and the same moment,* which is both the beginning and the end of the completed temporal cycle. If we continue to say that identical cosmic cycles *succeed each other* or that the present situation is a *repetition* of an infinite number of identical previous situations, we slip unconsciously into the absolutist theory of time. Within the framework of the absolutist theory it is, of course, meaningful to speak about the succession of identical cycles; but then the universal time itself which contains such cycles *succeeding* each other is not cyclical any longer.

The impossibility of cyclical time follows from the affirmation of *real novelties* in the physical world. If every moment is irreducibly original by its own nature—as it is natural to assume if we accept the objectivistic interpretation of the indeterminacy principle—then the irreversibility of becoming cannot be denied. For the theory of perpetual emergence of novelties clearly excludes the possibility of two identical successive moments no matter how long a time interval may separate them. Such identity, required by the cyclical theory of time, would deprive the later moment of the quality of authentic novelty which it should possess. Each moment in virtue of its own authentic freshness is unique and unrepeatable. Thus novelty implies irreversibility.

We should avoid interpreting the term "moment" in its cosmic prerelativistic sense; for we know that there are no world-wide instants. We do not have to understand the irreversibility of world-history in the Newtonian sense as a linear one-dimensional series of instantaneous cosmic moments. On the other hand, we know that the relativistic universe is dynamically constituted by the network of causal lines *each of which is irreversible;* we also know that this irreversibility is a topological invariant because not only nowhere can an effect precede a cause, but not even an apparent reversion of the causal order can ever be observed, no matter what frame of reference we adopt. In this precise pluralistic sense the becoming of the universe—or rather of *the multiverse*—is irreversible.

In the eternal recurrence theory the direction of time "from the past to the future" entirely disappears. With respect to the moving present *all* other events are both past and future: whatever will happen has already happened and whatever has happened will happen again. The situation is not so clear-cut in the theories which assert reversibility without eternal recurrence. These theories, based on relational theories of time, claim that time, being inseparable from concrete events, its "direction" or "time arrow" can be defined only in the terms of some *observable trend* in concrete events themselves. Beginning with nineteenth-century thermodynamics, the time arrow is defined by the increase of entropy, that is, by the gradual leveling of temperatures. But as the increase of entropy is only statistical, the time arrow itself acquires a statistical character and we must expect alternations of the time direction corresponding to the upgrade and downgrade slopes of the entropy curve. Any decrease of entropy, whether on the microscopic or cosmic scale, thus represents time "flowing backwards," that is, moving "from the future to the past." Thus the time direction, in being identified with the *local* and *reversible* trend of physical events, acquires itself the *local* and *reversible* character. Such a view acquired a considerable popularity, thanks partly to its plausible presentation by A. E. Eddington in 1925. It is truly surprising how many serious thinkers still accept it without any questioning. The most serious limitation of the theory is due to the fact that it is based on the questionable use of terms which can be applied to time only in a loose and metaphorical sense. These terms are "direction of time" or "time arrow."

The metaphor "direction of time" is justified to a certain extent; it expresses in spatial and kinematic terms the basic asymmetry of time, the distinction between past and future. But as soon as this metaphor is taken literally, serious difficulties arise. We may ask, for instance, "Whence and whither does time flow?" The conventional answer, "From the past to the future," seems to satisfy most people and this doubtless explains why the terms "flow" and "stream" occur so frequently. Time thus becomes a metaphysical river whose source is in the infinitely distant past and its estuary in the infinitely distant future. Newton used the verb "flow" in his famous definition of physical time, and two centuries after him William James applied the same image to our private psychological time. More abstractly, but not in an essentially different way, time is described as a motion of a point along a straight line; the moving point stands for the present instant, the path already covered corresponds to the past, the points not yet occupied correspond to the future events. But as every motion in space is relative and can be transformed into a rest by an appropriate change of the frame of reference, it is permissible to regard the present moment as *stationary* and future events as *moving toward the past* with equal and opposite velocity, to wit, opposite with respect to the velocity of the present moment in the first picture. Instead of the present advancing toward the future, future events retreat toward the motionless present, pass through it, and then sink into the deeper and deeper past. Willam James stated it in a more picturesque way when he wrote that

> . . . the specious present, the intuited duration, stands permanent, like the rainbow on the waterfall, with its own quality unchanged by the events that stream through it.[19]

Which of these descriptions is correct? Does time flow forwards, from the past to the future, or backwards, from the future to the past? The only possible answer is that the two descriptions are equally inadequate. Both are metaphorical attempts to translate into spatial and kinematic terms the elusive nature of time. As soon as we try to illustrate the nature of time by comparing it to motion, *the principle of kinematic relativity of motion* will sooner or later sneak into our illustrations and diagrams; hence, two apparently contradictory answers concerning the alleged direction of time.

No doubt the two answers reflect also different attitudes which our consciousness of time may adopt. When we adopt a passive and expectant attitude, then future events seem to come to us, and after passing through our present, they seem to sink more and more into the past. (It is not accidental that the passively expectant and retrospective attitudes are psychologically affiliated.) On the other hand, when we adopt an active attitude, then we have the feeling of moving toward the future which we *reach* and *conquer*. It is futile to argue about the "true" direction of time for the simple reason that time does not have any direction in the literal kinematic sense.

On the other hand, both apparently antagonistic descriptions are clumsy translations into geometrical and kinematic terms of the *irreversibility of becoming*, which follows logically from the emergence of novelties. We have seen how this idea cannot be separated from the affirmation of the potentiality of the future in contrast to the already completed reality of the past. Once we realize that the nature of temporal process consists in the perpetual transformation of the potential future into the actuality of the present, as Hans Reichenbach correctly stressed in the article quoted above, then the thesis of reversibility of time will strike us as an utter absurdity which cannot be even stated in a self-consistent language. A reversal of the time-direction means—if we forget all misleading spatial metaphors— that the opposite process, the process of un-becoming or re-potentialization of the past takes place; in other words, that what *has* already happened is being transformed into something which has *not yet* happened. Even St. Thomas Aquinas, who certainly was reluctant to impose any limit on the divine omnipotence, had to admit that even for God this was impossible to achieve: *Praeterita autem non fuisse contradictionem implicat* (however, for the past not to have been involves a contradiction).[20] He follows in this respect Aristotle, whom he quotes: "Of this one thing God is deprived—namely, to make undone the things that have been done." [21] This is what Whitehead more recently called "the immortality of the past" and P. W. Bridgman "the irrevocability of the past." [22]

If, however, we forget that the word "direction" is borrowed from geometry and kinematics and therefore can be applied to time only in a metaphorical sense, we may thoughtlessly draw all consequence from the alleged analogy between "movement of time" and movement of bodies. Thus we may think that as the direction of motion in space may change, the time direction may change too; as a material point may reverse its motion and pass through the positions previously occupied, "the moving present" can return to the past; or as motions in space may be circular, the course of time may be circular too. Both the theory of reversible time and the theory of eternal recurrence rest on such false kinematic analogies.

For these reasons all attempts at defining time in terms of some process which is reversible in principle, even if not in fact, are doomed to failure. In this respect Bridgman's incisive words are entirely convincing:

> But in no case is there any question of time flowing backward, and in fact the concept of backward flow of time seems absolutely meaningless. . . . If it were found that the entropy of the universe were decreasing, would one say that time was flowing backward, or would one say that it was a law of nature that entropy decreases with time? [23]

Jean Perrin considered the probability of a brick being lifted, by the effect of Brownian motion only, to the level of the second floor and found that the time necessary for such an event would far surpass the geological periods of the earth. But no matter how extremely improbable such an event is, it is *not impossible* as long as the kinetic model of entropy is retained. We cannot rule out the possibility that all molecular impacts impinging on a brick from below will have parallel upwards directions.[24] Similarly, Bertrand Russell observed that with a sufficient time at our disposal we would eventually see a pail of water placed on fire to freeze.[25] But even in such a fantastic world of bricks rising up in the air and water freezing by contact with fire, time would still continue to flow without changing its "direction"; for the exceptional intervals of entropy decrease would still be intervals of *time*, that is, they would *follow* the intervals of the previous normal entropy increase and they would *precede* other intervals in which the entropy-curve again would have the upward slope. On the microscopic scale such alleged reversals of time occur in the phenomena of fluctuations of Brownian motion, and yet it would be absurd to claim that some microscopic animals which are of the same order of magnitude as molecular oscillations are experiencing a "backward running time."

Reichenbach, who—in strange contrast to his defense of becoming—adhered to the idea of reversible time, was nevertheless vaguely aware of this difficulty when he conceded that the allegedly "counterdirected" segments of time are still contained in "supertime." This would clearly imply that they *succeed* each other, and with the admission of the asymmetrical before-after relation the irreversibility or "unidirectionality" of time is reinstated. This, however, Reichenbach was reluctant to concede, and he believed he had circumvented the difficulty by claiming that supertime has only ordinal properties of temporal betweenness without possessing any direction.[26] This fallacious distinction between temporal betweenness and temporal direction is again based on the superficial and the deceptive analogy of the "course of time" with a geometrical line. The irreversibility of becoming is of a *qualitative* nature, and any attempt to translate it into spatial imagery and geometrical symbolism generates only sophisms and misunderstandings.

Does this mean that in refusing to interpret time in terms of entropy increase we reject *any* relational theory of time and that we thus recommend a disguised return to the Newtonian idea of empty irreversible time independent of events? By no means. On the contrary, in the course of this book the inseparability of time from concrete events has been repeatedly stressed. It would be otiose to dwell again on the relativistic fusion of time-space with its concrete and changing physical content. We reject only that special form of the relational theory which regards time in the Epicurean sense as "accident of accidents," that is, as depending on changing and *recurring* configurations of particles. Only in a relational theory of such a type does the reversibility of time follow from its definition.

For this reason time cannot be defined by entropy increase as long as the latter itself is interpreted in classical kinetic terms in Boltzmann's fashion. But as this interpretation is now doubtful in view of the established inadequacy of the corpuscular-kinetic scheme of nature, it becomes increasingly clear that the deeper meaning of the second law of thermodynamics is yet to be found. There is an increasing tendency among contemporary physicists to give up futile attempts at deriving macroscopic irreversibility from the allegedly basic reversible microprocesses.[27] What will follow is only a very incomplete sketch of this trend.

When in 1905 Pierre Duhem insisted on the basic irreversibility of physical becoming and on the artificial and even absurd character of the concept of reversible process,[28] he was guided mainly by his Aristotelian preconceptions and by a distrust of mechanical explanations which at that time was only partly justified. A few years later, Henri Bergson, admittedly influenced by Duhem, called the second law of thermodynamics "the most metaphysical law of physics because it points out without interposed symbols, without artificial devices of measurements, the direction in which the world is going." [29] This happy guess was not accidental. It was inspired by Bergson's philosophical conviction about the intrinsic irreversibility of cosmic duration, and this conviction in turn led him to doubt the adequacy of the kinetic interpretation of entropy. When the relativity theory and the theory of quanta discredited corpuscular-kinetic models, the basis of the kinetic interpretation of the second law of thermodynamics was in danger; for the general disintegration of classical mechanism made the very concept of a reversible process highly questionable.

In 1925 Arthur S. Eddington was one of the first physicists to reverse the traditional classical procedure and express the view that the macroscopic irreversibility, instead of being a mere phenomenon—or rather epiphenomenon—derivable from basic reversible processes, is the primary feature of the physical reality of which the positive entropy gradient is a mere human symbol. He expressed his view or rather his *feeling* that

> . . . there is something as yet ungrasped behind the notion of entropy—some mystic interpretation, if you like—which is not apparent in the definition by which we introduce it into physics. In short, we strive to see that entropy-gradient may *really* be the moving on of time (instead of *vice versa*).[30]

In spite of the groping vagueness of this passage its last sentence indicates that the positive entropy gradient is *one of the manifestations* of the irreversibility of time instead of being identical with it. (In this respect the popular presentation of Eddington's theory as the identification of the time arrow with the increase of entropy is not correct, at least not as far as the quoted passage is concerned.)

In 1931 "this as yet ungrasped" process of which the positive entropy gradient is a partial aspect, was identified by Lemaître with *the expansion of the universe*. His bold and ambitious theory linked together three apparently unrelated facts: the recession of galaxies, the gradual dissipation of energy, and the existence of cosmic rays. It is interesting that, according to Lemaître himself, the formulation of both laws of thermodynamics in the terms of quantum theory was one of the inspiring motives of his cosmogony:

> Thermodynamic principles from the point of view of quantum theory may be stated as follows: (1) Energy of constant total amount is distributed in quanta. (2) The number of distinct quanta is constantly increasing.

If we go back in the course of time we must find fewer
and fewer quanta, until we find all the energy of the
universe packed in a few or even in a unique quantum.[31]

World history thus began by a "super-radioactive explosion"
of the original single quantum, and the development of the
universe is a continuation of this process of fragmentation of
energy into the increasing number of smaller and smaller quanta.
The enormous energy of cosmic rays is merely a "fossil remnant" of the high-frequency radiation from the original phase
of cosmic history.

Lemaître's cosmogonic theory has some features to which we
have already called attention in discussing the relativistic physics:

1. The relativistic fusion of mass with energy gives Lemaître
the right to call the original superphoton also "the primeval
atom" and to regard present radioactive disintegrations as small-
scale replicas of the process of fragmentation of energy by
which the universe began a few billions of years ago.

2. The relativistic fusion of space-time with its physical content has one particular consequence within the framework of
this cosmogony: the explosion of the primeval atom and the
expansion of space are *aspects of one and the same process*. The
explosion of the original quantum of energy did not take place
in the pre-existing container of Euclidean space, but space itself
came into being *with* this process. Lemaître's space is, of course,
not the space of Euclid and Newton, but that of Cayley-Klein;
though it is an elliptical space, its radius of curvature is constantly increasing, causing galaxies to recede. In this respect it
differs from the "static" cosmological model of Einstein in
which the variation of space-constant is admitted only on the
local scale. (In Newtonian cosmologies this constant is everywhere and at all levels of magnitudes unchangingly equal to
zero.)

3. The second consequence of the relativistic fusion of space-
time with its content concerns time. In Lemaître's cosmology
the dynamization of space by its union with time is even more
obvious than in the general theory of relativity, and we have

already had the opportunity to stress it briefly. The prophetic idea of the French mathematician Calinon at the end of the last century about the possibility of a *physical space* with a varying space constant was thus vindicated, in spite of Russell's warning that this would lead to "the grossest absurdities." [32]

There was even one implication of the theory which cannot be found in the previous "static" cosmological models and which profoundly affected one classical feature which had until then survived all evolutionary changes: *the infinity of classical time* or its *beginningless eternity*. This early Greek idea, revived in the sixteenth century by Giordano Bruno, dominated classical thought without exception; all philosophers and scientists, irrespective of their philosophical preferences, accepted it without discussion. Whether they believed in the eternity of the physical universe or not, they agreed on this point. The only difference between the deistically minded Gassendi and Newton on one side and the pantheistically minded Spinoza or atheistically intransigent La Mettrie and Laplace on the other side, was that for the former there was the eternity of *empty* duration *before* the beginning of the world while for the latter the eternity of the past has been always filled by the material content. Even Kant's famous antinomy dealt with the dilemma whether the world began *in* time or not.

Lemaître's theory, in the true relativistic spirit, dismisses the idea of empty time as devoid of physical meaning; to ask what was *before* the beginning of time is as meaningless as to ask what is behind the spherical space. In the theory of the expanding universe, contrary to the classical claims made in the name of the homogeneity of time, *there are* the unique epochs in cosmic history; the universe is not a cyclical machine running through homogeneous repeatable phrases, but the process whose successive phases are heterogeneous. Especially such a unique moment is the beginning of the universe, "zero time," which, unlike all other subsequent moments, is without ancestors. *Non in tempore sed cum tempore finxit Deus mundum* (God made the world not *in* time but *with* time),[33] wrote St. Augustine, and if we disregard his theological language, we can hardly deny that his thought anticipated both the finiteness of the cosmic past and the coextensiveness of time with concrete physical process.

Very few thinkers of the classical period adopted St. Augustine's "finitist" attitude toward the cosmic past. Renouvier and his school in France, F. C. S. Schiller in England, De Witt Parker in the United States, and a few others dared to challenge the official dogma of infinitism which has been accepted almost exclusively.[34]

In denying empty time and in insisting on the coextensiveness of time (more accurately, time-space) with the physical universe, Lemaître's theory is unquestionably a *relational theory* of both time and space. But, unlike Boltzmann's theory, it not only is compatible with the irreversibility of time—it even requires it. In the unidirectional expansion of the universe, the irreversibility of becoming finds its most striking expression. We have seen that the irreversibility of time as well as time itself— the expressions are inseparable—remained ghostly and diaphanous entities within the classical kinetic-corpuscular framework; it was very difficult to express them in the terms of *recurring* configurations of *immutable* particles. This is why it was impossible to define the irreversibility of time by means of the entropy gradient kinetically interpreted. The situation is different in the theory of the expanding universe, which is asymmetrical in respect to the past and the future. It is true that we can postulate *successive cycles of expansion and contractions* by which the classical infinity as well as reversibility of time can apparently be saved.

But what makes such attempts suspect is that they are too obviously inspired by the classical thought patterns. The urge to draw "the course of time" backwards, beyond the "zero time" is too strong to be resisted unless we remember the inadequacy of all static geometrical and especially *Euclidean* analogies when we deal with the problem of time. To ask what was "before time" is as meaningless as to ask what is *behind* the spherical space. Within the Euclidean framework the question of Archytas and Lucretius, "What is *behind* the alleged edge of the world?", was meaningful because the second and especially the third postulate of Euclid implied the infinitude of space; but the same question is devoid of meaning if we accept the geometry of Riemann. Similarly, the question "What was *before* the alleged beginning of the world?" is unavoidable as long as we picture time by a Euclidean straight line which can be extended in either direction. But we know that not only Euclidean, but *all* geometrical analogies are intrinsically inadequate for expressing the nature of time; even static non-Euclidean analogies may lead us to the absurd idea of "curved" or even "closed" time, while the analogy of time with a Euclidean straight line leads to the self-contradictory idea of the actually infinite past. Only when succession and change are incorporated into the very foundations of geometry is there a better chance of expressing the dynamic nature of becoming, including its irreversibility.

Even less than the infinity can the classical reversibility of time be restored by the theory of alternating expansions and contractions of space. It is true that if we *define* the time direction by the expansion of space, its *contraction* will define the *opposite* direction of time. But then we face the same difficulty that we found in Reichenbach's theory of *counterdirected* segments of time *succeeding* each other. The very word "succeeding" introduces a sort of supertime which must be regarded as irreversible, "unidirectional," if our language is to remain self-consistent in the most elementary sense. For *either* we claim that the periods of expansion and contraction *succeed* each other, and then the asymmetrical relation of *before-after* creeps in and with it the irreversibility; or we say with Reichenbach that supertime has only the *ordinal* properties in a geometrical sense; in other words, that it is *devoid* of succession, like the mountainous plateau by which Reichenbach symbolized the entropy curve. In this last case we arrive at the absurd conclusion that the counterdirected segments of time are really *simultaneous*, or, applied to Lemaître's cosmogony, that the universe is simultaneously expanding and contracting!

We affirmed the irreversibility of time as a consequence of

the emergence of novelty at each moment. While Lemaître does not insist on the logical link between these two features of temporality, he rightly stresses that his theory is not deterministic. This may appear surprising, because the general theory of relativity was deterministic in virtue of its macroscopic character. But here precisely lies the difference between the classical relativistic cosmology and the cosmology of Lemaître; the latter by its very nature bridges the gap between the macroscopic and microscopic level. For such a gap has *not* existed in the past: the universe originated from the primeval superphoton which was subject to the principle of indeterminacy.

> Clearly the initial quantum could not conceal in itself the whole course of evolution; but, according to the principle of indeterminacy, that is not necessary. Our world is now understood to be a world *where something really happens;* the whole story of the world need not have been written down in the first quantum like a song on the disc of a phonograph. The whole matter of the world must have been present at the beginning, but the story it has to tell may be written step by step. [Italics added.] [35]

It is true that Lemaître's cosmogony is not the only one. There are rival "steady-state theories" of Hoyle, Bondi, and Gold which preserve two features of classical physics—infinity of space and time—only by sacrificing the constancy of matter. What is important is that the dynamic aspect of the universe finds its expression in the rival theories as well—in the idea of continuous creation of matter. But, as Whitrow observed, besides some other difficulties, the controversial concept of the actually infinite past remains a weak point of the theory. Its justification by the clearly traditional idea of the homogeneity of nature ("Perfect Cosmological Principle) makes it hardly more convincing, especially when we remember the surreptitious influence of the Euclidian imagery on the formation of the concept of the beginningless past.[36]

In any case, when dealing with cosmological and cosmogonical questions we should never forget that we are treading on very controversial ground. In this respect Bridgman's remarks in his essay "On the Nature and Limitations of Cosmical Inquiries" are as pertinent now as they were a quarter of a century ago when they were written.[37] For this reason, our discussion of cosmological problems has been very cursory and has a character of appendix rather than of a more systematic treatment. One fact is certain: the classical conceptual framework has been transformed to such an extent that the classical cosmogony of the periodical or quasi-periodical universe was deprived of its foundation. Although the definite shape of the future cosmogony is still obscure, there is growing evidence that the irreversible and creative character of becoming will find in it the same important place as in relativity theory and wave mechanics. We have seen that relativity theory established the *successive* character of causality, that is, nonsimultaneity of cause and effect, by eliminating all instantaneous actions; that it reasserted the asymmetry between the past and the future by establishing the irreversibility of world lines. We have also seen that wave mechanics restored the potentiality of the future by recognizing the objective probability of events. It is difficult to believe that these features will not be reflected in future cosmological and cosmogonical theories.

NOTES FOR CHAPTER XVII

1. B. Spinoza, *Ethica*, Book II, def. 6 (see also prop. 39). G. W. F. Hegel, *Grundlinien der Philosophie des Rechtes, Sämtliche Werke* (Stuttgart, 1928) VII, p. 33.
2. W. James, "The Dilemma of Determinism" in *The Will to Believe and Other Essays in Popular Philosophy* (London, Longmans Green, 1917), pp. 150-51.
3. W. James, *Some Problems of Philosophy* (London, Longmans Green, 1940), p. 149; H. Bergson, *Creative Evolution, passim;* A. N. Whitehead, *The Concept of Nature*, p. 178.
4. H. Reichenbach, "La signification philosophique du dualisme ondes-corpuscules" in *Louis de Broglie: physicien et penseur* (Paris, 1953), p. 133.
5. A. A. Robb, *Geometry of Time and Space* (Cambridge University Press, 1936), p. 22.

6. H. Bondi, "Relativity and Indeterminacy," *Nature*, Vol. 169 (1952), p. 660. The incompatibility of the Laplacian determinism with the relativistic causal order was recently stressed by H. Torneböhm, *A Logical Analysis of the Theory of Relativity* (Stockholm, 1952), p. 45. Similarly, A. N. Whitehead linked the causal independence of contemporary events with the indetermination in the universe. *Adventures of Ideas* (Macmillan, New York, 1947), p. 255.

7. Charles Renouvier, "Les arguments psychologiques pour et contre le libre arbitre," *Critique philosophique*, Vol. XII (1884, II), pp. 49 f.

8. W. James, "The Dilemma of Determinism," p. 157; *The Principles of Psychology*, Vol. II, p. 577.

9. E. Cassirer's criticism of "unlimited indeterminism" (*schrankenlos Indeterminismus*) belongs to the same category as the objections of Spencer and Fiske. This is also the view of W. H. Werkmeister, who identifies indeterminacy with "the principle of chaos" according to which "anything might happen" (*A Philosophy of Nature*, p. 276) and of Max Planck. (*Determinismus oder Indeterminismus?*, Leipzig, 1948). For the opposite view see the excellent essay of Charles Hartshorne "Order in a Creative Universe" in *Beyond Humanism* (Willett, Clark, Chicago, 1937), pp. 125-149.

10. P. A. M. Dirac, *The Principles of Quantum Mechanics* (Oxford, Clarendon Press, 1930), p. 4; *Electrons and Photons*, pp. 263-65.

11. H. Bergson, *Essai*, p. 126; *Matière et mémoire*, p. 205. Similarly, Mario Bunge rejects in the name of "the genetic principle" the emergence out of nothing without, however, denying novelty and without accepting the mechanistic principle "causa aequat effectum." Cf. his *Causality. The Place of the Causal Principle in Modern Science* (Harvard Univ. Press, Cambridge, 1959), pp. 24-25; 203-206.

12. Whitehead, "Time," in *Proceedings of the Sixth International Congress of Philosophy* (London, Longmans Green, 1927), p. 64.

13. Bergson, *Creative Evolution*, p. 4.

14. E. Boutroux, *De la contingence des lois de la nature*, 8th ed. (Paris, 1915), Chap. IV.

15. Bergson, *La Pensée et le mouvant*, p. 117.

16. Pierre Gassendi, *Opera omnia* (Lugduni, 1658), I, Syntagma philosophicum, p. 220.

17. Gassendi, *Philosophi Epicuri Syntagma*, I, c. 16.

18. H. Reichenbach, *The Direction of Time*, p. 111.

19. W. James, *The Principles of Psychology*, Vol. I, p. 630.

20. Aquinas, *Summa Theologica*, Q. 25, art. 4.

21. Aristotle, *Ethica Nicomachea*, book VI, ch. 2.

22. A. N. Whitehead, *Process and Reality* (New York, Macmillan, 1930), *passim*; *Adventures of Ideas* (New York, Macmillan, 1933), pp. 247-48; P. W. Bridgman, *The Logic of Modern Physics*, p. 79.

23. P. W. Bridgman, *Reflections of a Physicist* (New York, Philosophical Library, 1955), p. 251.

24. Jean Perrin, *Les Atomes*, p. 125.

25. Quoted by Bridgman, *Reflections of a Physicist*, p. 255.

26. H. Reichenbach, *The Direction of Time*, p. 129.
27. L. L. Whyte, "One-Way Processes in Physics and Biology," *British Journal of the Philosophy of Science*, Vol. VI (1955), p. 110: "We should give up the long struggle with the question: 'How does irreversibility arise if the basic laws are reversible?' and ask instead: 'If the laws are of a one-way character, under what . . . conditions can reversible expressions provide a useful approximation?'"
28. P. Duhem, *L'Evolution de la mécanique*, pp. 237-38.
29. H. Bergson, *Creative Evolution*, p. 265.
30. A. Eddington, *The Nature of the Physical World*, p. 95.
31. G. Lemaître, "The Beginning of the World from the Point of View of Quantum Theory," *Nature*, Vol. 127 (1931), p. 706; reprinted in *The Primeval Atom: An Essay on Cosmology* (New York, Van Nostrand, 1950), pp. 17 f.
32. Cf. Chapter III, above, Note 23. Calinon's views were expounded in his article "Les espaces géometriques" in *Revue philosophique*, Vol. 27 (1889), pp. 588-595.
33. St. Augustine, *De Civitate Dei*, XI, 5.
34. Charles Renouvier, *Les Principes de la nature*, 2d ed. (Paris, 1892), pp. 82-83; F. C. S. Schiller, *Riddles of the Sphinx: A Study in the Philosophy of Humanism* (London, Swann Sonnenschein, 1910), pp. 45-46; De Witt Parker, *Experience and Substance* (University of Michigan Press, 1941), pp. 177-180. The criticism of the concept of actual infinity was recently revived by Max Black (cf. "Achilles and the Tortoise," *Analysis*, XI, 1950-51, pp. 91-101; also *Problems of Analysis*, Cornell University Press, Ithaca, 1954, pp. 95-154) and John O. Wisdom ("Achilles on a Physical Racecourse," *Analysis*, XII, 1951-52, pp. 67 f.), but neither of them applied it to the concept of infinite past. This, however, was done by G. J. Whitrow when, in criticizing the steady-state theory of the universe, he defended Kant's proof of the first thesis against the superficial criticism of Russell. (Cf. his article "The Age of the Universe" in *The British Journal for the Philosophy of Science*, V (1955), pp. 215-225; cf. also his book *The Structure and Evolution of the Universe* (Harper, New York, 1959), pp. 195-96.
35. Lemaître, *The Primeval Atom*, pp. 18-19.
36. Some philosophical objections against Hoyle's theory were stated by Herbert Dingle in his article "Cosmology and Science," *Scientific American*, Vol. 193 (Sept. 1956), pp. 224 f., especially p. 236. Hoyle's article "The Steady-State Universe" appeared in the same issue (pp. 157-166) together with the article of G. Gamow "The Evolutionary Universe" (pp. 136-156). Cf. Fred Hoyle, *The Nature of the Universe* (Harper, New York, 1950); H. Bondi, W. B. Bonnor, R. A. Lyttleton, G. J. Whitrow, *Rival Theories of Cosmology* (Oxford University Press, 1960). As for Whitrow's critical comment, cf. note 34.
37. *Scientific Monthly*, Vol. 37 (1933), p. 385; reprinted in P. Bridgman, *Reflections of a Physicist*, pp. 278-308. Cf. also the discussion by G. J.

360 Philosophical Impact of Contemporary Physics

Whitrow and H. Bondi "Is Physical Cosmology a Science?" in *The British Journal for the Philosophy of Science*, Vol. IV (1953-54), pp. 271-283; also the symposium "The Age of the Universe" in the same journal, Vol. V, pp. 181-274 in which M. Scriven, J. T. Davies, E. J. Opik, G. J. Whitrow, R. Schlegel, and B. Abramenko took part. In the same issue Milton Munitz's article "Creation and 'New' Cosmology" appeared (pp. 32-46) which was later incorporated in his book *Space, Time and Creation* (Free Press, Glencoe, 1956).

XVIII · IN SEARCH OF NEW WAYS
OF UNDERSTANDING

AFTER such radical transformation of the basic classical concepts of space, time, matter, and motion, very little is left of the traditional corpuscular-kinetic scheme of nature. It is natural that rigorous determinism of the Laplacian type would be seriously questioned now that the scheme on which it was based is disintegrating. The close connection between the corpuscular-kinetic model of nature and strict determinism can be seen in the very form in which the latter has been stated: Given the state of the universe at a given instant, i.e., given a certain instantaneous configuration of all particles composing the world and their moment, then all future (as well as all past) configurations, of which cosmic history consists, are completely and unambiguously determined.

Not a single component of this Laplacian model of nature remained unaffected by the contemporary storm in physics. There is no such thing as a "state of the world at a given instant"; the theory of relativity showed the impossibility of instantaneous cuts across the four-dimensional world history. Moreover, in the light of the principle of indeterminacy, not even on the microphysical level are such cuts possible. There is no such thing as an "instantaneous configuration"; every configuration implies a juxtaposition of simultaneously coexisting

361

elements, and no juxtaposition, no simultaneity in the objective sense is possible in time-space. The theories of quanta and wave mechanics indicate that there are no continuous trajectories whose continuity in space and time would guarantee the identity of the particles at different positions and instants. Besides, since 1932 physicists have been acquainted with the absence of permanency (which is only another name for the absence of identity in time) of elementary "particles." Furthermore, not even at one instant can we speak about a definite particle; for particle is defined by the association of definite momentum and definite location which, according to the principle of indeterminacy, cannot be found in nature.

It is true that the indeterminacy principle may be regarded as a mere human and technical limitation which hides from us "the hidden causal parameters." But such a hypothesis of determinism on the subquantum level is highly improbable; it would imply the divisibility of the atom of action and thus would mean a disguised return to some obsolete features of classical physics, in particular to the concept of spatiotemporal continuity. The elimination of rigorous determinism means that the physical world regains, to use Eddington's expression, "the dynamic quality" which has been implicitly eliminated in classical thought. In other words, the static universe of Laplace is being replaced now by "the open world" of Weyl.[1]

Is this reinstatement of the dynamic character of physical reality so surprising? If it appears surprising to us, it only shows to what exent our thinking is still haunted by the perennial tradition which has dominated both philosophy and physics. There is no need to restate the reasons given in Chapter IX why the reality of time was so obscured in the classical picture of the physical world and how the tendency to degrade time to the phenomenal or epiphenomenal level was common to naturalistic determinism as well as to philosophical idealism from Plato to Bradley. In reaffirming the reality of time, modern physics merely lends added weight to the objections which have been raised against the elimination of time on epistemological grounds.

We have already called attention to Helmholtz's view, significant because expressed at the time of the greatest triumphs of classical physics. According to Helmholtz, temporal character is the *only* feature which is shared by both transphenomenal physical reality and our experience.[2] In all other areas of our sensory experience, perception is only symbolical and the dissimilarity of the stimulus and its conscious registration is striking: the impact of photons is translated into visual qualities, the impact of air waves into auditory qualities, while direct molecular impacts on various parts of the human body are interpreted by our consciousness in different ways as the sensations of touch, warmth, cold, taste, and scent. While it is true that spatial character clearly belongs to visual and tactile sensations, it is more controversial to claim that it belongs to *all* sensations, as some psychologists and philosophers believe. On the other hand, temporal character pervades *all* our experience; not only our sensations but also our memory images, thoughts, emotions, and volitions are clearly in time, while the latter groups do not show even a trace of spatiality. It is difficult to believe that no objective feature in physical reality would correspond to such an all-pervasive character of our experience. In Helmholtz's words

> Events, like our perceptions of them, take place in time, so that the time-relations of the latter can furnish a true copy of those of the former. The sensation of the thunder follows the sensation of the lightning just as the sonorous convulsing of the air by the electric discharge reaches the observer's place later than that of luminiferous aether.[3]

All attempts to eliminate time from physical reality create an unsolvable metaphysical enigma: How can timeless reality be transformed or unrolled into its illusory successive manifestation? Such attempts are even more grotesque when they are made by naturalistically minded scientists with behavioristic leanings; for consciousness, which is often dismissed by them either as an epiphenomenon or even as a mere remnant of "mentalistic metaphysics," is suddenly credited with the impossible achievement of transforming the static and becomingless character of reality into a successive and changing pattern. How can consciousness ever achieve such a magic trick, especially if it is associated with neural processes, that is, with a certain portion of the physical world which is allegedly timeless? Strictly speaking, for those who deny the temporal character of physical reality it is inconsistent even to use such a dynamic term as "neural *process*." To claim that consciousness *creeps* along the world line already drawn in the direction of the "future" implies an intolerable dualism of the temporal world of consciousness and the static world of physics. By postulating such dualism, which is strikingly similar to the Kantian dualism of "phenomena" and "noumena," nothing is gained, nothing is explained; on the contrary, one additional—and entirely superfluous—problem is created. On the other hand, the difficulty disappears immediately if we concede frankly and without reservations the objective reality of becoming.

We must admit, however, that the quoted view of Helmholtz needs some important qualifications. First, it apparently implies that the *extensive* character of our sensory perception is purely phenomenal; in other words, that nothing objective corresponds to this in nature. Helmholtz suggests that the primary qualities of matter are constituted not by its geometrical and mechanical properties, but by the temporal relations of the further unspecified events. This seems to be fairly close to the conclusion reached in Chapters XI and XIV about the dynamic nature of time-space, and about the primacy of events. But what physics eliminates is only the instantaneous static space, not spatiality in general. Attempts to derive spatiotemporal relations from purely temporal relations fail, and for this reason it is more accurate to speak of the dynamization rather than the temporalization of space. More specifically, we have to remember that we must assume *more than one causal temporal series* in order to account for the concept of spatiotemporal distance and spatiotemporal neighborhood, which cannot be deduced from the bare "before-after" relation; and that this plurality of contemporaneous or co-becoming causal series is the very basis of this generalized

concept of spatiality.[4] Even the word "spatiality" is misleading.
It is easily misunderstood in the sense of "space" separable from
time. It is more accurate to say that spatiality is merely that
aspect of the indivisible dynamic reality of time-space which is
different from the bare relation of succession, while not being
equivalent to the static relation of juxtaposition. It may be called
"the transversal width of becoming" provided that we bear in
mind that "transversal" is not "perpendicular": "perpendicular"
cuts in four-dimensional becoming are impossible.

It has been pointed out that relativity theory, while eliminating the concept of simultaneity of instants, retains the concept of
"simultaneity of fluxes" or of "contemporary intervals"; and this
relation of *contemporary independence* is what we designate
by the metaphorical term "the transversal width of becoming."
We find such transversal width both on the cosmic and the
microphysical scale; we pointed out that the concept of world
lines without any transversal width is another instance of deceptive geometrization by which concrete temporal series are as-
similated to one-dimensional geometrical lines. For this reason
the term "causal tubes" is less misleading than "causal lines."
If we concede that becoming is extensive in its nature, then the
extensive character of our perception cannot be a mere phenomenon or epiphenomenon, and the extensiveness or spatiality in
the sense explained above must be listed among the primary
qualities of the physical world.

The second reservation concerns Helmholtz's claim that "the
time-relations of our perceptions can furnish a true copy of the
time-relations of events." This is true only in a very limited
sense. From the example used by Helmholtz it is clear that the
temporal relations of our perceptions disclose only the temporal
relations of physical stimuli affecting directly the surface of our
bodies or our sensory organs. The time relations of other physical events (i.e., *outside* our bodies) are *always* inferred, and
our sobering experience with the classical concept of simultaneity has shown how deceptive such inferences may be. Further, the sequences of our perceptions are "true copies" of only
those physical stimuli which succeed each other at a rate not

too different from the temporal rhythm of our consciousness. To be perceived, successive stimuli must not be separated by too small intervals; otherwise they fuse into the spurious simultaneity of the specious present. We had occasion to see how the temporal span of our sensory perception prevents us from perceiving *microchronic relations;* to the subjective temporal indivisibility of our sensory qualities correspond millions of successive microscopic events. This may be expressed by saying that the psychological present has an incomparably wider temporal span than the present of physical events.

Yet, this very statement about the difference between the time experienced by us and the time of physical events contains also the cue to their structural similarity. For it is increasingly clear that the concept of instantaneous present (the "knife-edge present" of William James) is inapplicable not only to psychological time but to the time of physics as well. Since the days of James psychologists have generally agreed that the mathematical present is a mere ideal fiction to which nothing concrete in the stream of consciousness corresponds. On the other hand, the very term "specious present" indicated its contrast to the allegedly true mathematical, i.e., durationless, present which, while it cannot be found in our experience, remains the authentic present of the physical world.

It would be superfluous to repeat what has already been said about this subject in Chapter III: how the belief in the existence of physical instants was an aspect of the belief in the infinite divisibility of time and how all available evidence in classical physics apparently supported it. Not until the recently discovered facts of quantum theory and wave mechanics emerged were fresh doubts raised about the legitimacy of the concept of durationless instant even in the realm of physical events. These doubts led to the atomistic theories of time, but it has been pointed out how unsatisfactory they were: the concept of "chronon" implied a disguised return to the concept of instant which it purported to eliminate.

Even some mathematicians are aware of the limited usefulness of the concept of spatiotemporal continuity on the microphysical level. Karl Menger's "topology without points," that is, the topology of lumps without precise boundaries, is a symptom of this growing awareness. The difficulty is that our visual subconsciousness at once surreptitiously introduces spatial symbols; and as long as the "course of time" is symbolized by a geometrical line, its infinite divisibility imposes itself on our minds. When we try to stop the process of ideally subdividing time (or space) into smaller and smaller intervals, we feel any imposed limit as arbitrary; and even when we concede the existence of "lumps," the idea of pointlike extremities by which they are separated from neighboring "lumps" immediately crops up.

But if the time of our consciousness and the time of physics are both pulsational in their nature, can we obtain a better insight into "the topology without points" in exploring the structure of psychological time? Is it possible to find an adequate scheme sufficiently general and sufficiently flexible to be applicable to physics and psychology?

This approach is not as thoroughly new as it may appear. Even at the time when the sharpest distinction was drawn between "mental" and "physical," it was believed that there is a categorial scheme sufficiently general to apply to both physics and psychology. This categorial scheme was the substance-attribute relationship. Descartes believed that both physical and mental entities are substances, differentiated only by their attributes. Since the time of Descartes this substantialist categorial scheme has dominated all rationalist thought, and even empiricism, whether in British or continental form, has never quite got rid of it. The concept of substance survived in a disguised form not only in the Transcendental Ego of Kant (in spite of Kant's criticism of the substantial soul) but in the sensualism of Hume, Condillac, and Mach as well. Empiricists merely cut the Cartesian substance into tiny pieces which, whether they were called "impressions" by Hume, "sensations" by Condillac, or simply "elements" by Mach, retained the characteristics of the Cartesian substance on a smaller scale.[5]

At that time it was not sufficiently clear that the substance-attribute relation reflected too slavishly the linguistic noun-adjective relation; it had been uncritically assumed that grammatical structure is a true replica of the structure of reality. Only under the impact of James, Ward, and the Gestalt psychology were the fictitious substantial psychical atoms dissolved into the dynamic wholeness of the stream of thought. Although in physics the concept of substance seemed to be fairly well established at the turn of the century, it eventually yielded to the growing pressure of the recently discovered facts. The substantial aether as well as substantial material particles are being replaced by events. In Jeans's words:

> Thus the events must be treated as the fundamental objective constituents, and we must no longer think of the universe as consisting of solid pieces of matter which persist in time, and move about in space. . . . Events and not particles constitute the true objective reality. . . .[6]

The same conclusion is reached by such widely different thinkers as Russell, Jeans, Whitehead, Bergson, and Bachelard. A few lines after the passage just quoted Jeans quotes Russell approvingly:

> The events that happen in our minds are part of the course of nature, and we do not know that the events which happen elsewhere are of a totally different kind.[7]

Evidently there is a growing realization not only that the category of substance should be superseded by that of process but also that process is a category applicable to both physical and mental realms. Bertrand Russell's words indicate not only that the traditional substantialism is dead both in physics and psychology but also that the Cartesian distinction between the mental and the physical must be given up, because in either realm the concept of event becomes fundamental. This does not mean that the distinction between the two realms is completely wiped out. Although both "matter" and "mind" are constituted by events, the differences between "physical" and "psychological" events remain. One most conspicuous difference

has already been mentioned: *the difference of temporal span.*
Perhaps along this line the true solution of the traditional mind-
body problem should be looked for, and Bergson's *Matter and
Memory* represents an interesting attempt in this direction.

But this problem is beyond the scope of this book; what is
important for our present purpose is that, once the substantialist
prejudice and the sharp Cartesian dualism are removed, the way
is open to a search for new modes of understanding, altogether
different from the traditional models. If we accept the conclusion of Part II that changes have superseded spatial displacements
and the events have replaced particles, would it not be possible
to acquire a better insight into some paradoxical features of the
world of contemporary physics by exploring and analyzing
those strata of experience in which change and events are experienced, if not immediately, then at least with the maximum of
immediacy and purity—that is, in our introspective awareness
of becoming?

Naturally, at first nothing sounds more suspicious than the
phrase "introspective models in physics"; the fear of being accused of the relapse into animism or hylozoism prevents many
serious thinkers from even considering this approach at all. Yet
such fear is irrational and those who are obsessed by it do not
realize to what extent they are still dominated by the traditional
and today untenable Cartesian dualism which relegates *all*
qualities exclusively into the mental realm while upholding
pangeometrism and panmathematism in the physical world. It is
certainly unfair to place Leibniz's or Whitehead's panpsychism
epistemologically on the same level as pre-Socratic hylozoism or
primitive animism.

To avoid any misunderstanding let us state quite unambiguously that there is no question of reintroducing secondary qualities into the objective world of physics. We propose the very
opposite: the confinement of the primary qualities within our
private experience. If there are qualities in the physical world,
they are certainly different from the sensory qualities as we
experience them. To deny these transcendent qualities would be
as uncritical as for a colorblind person to deny colors, for a

deaf person to deny sounds, or for human beings to deny the qualities which some animals undoubtedly experience under the impact of ultrasonic waves of ultraviolet rays. But although physical events cannot be perceived in their immediacy and their qualitative specificity, they have certain structural features in common with the events constituting our stream of consciousness, to wit, their dynamic, eventlike character. It is this dynamic character which we have to analyze, believing with Whitehead that "the texture of observed experience, as illustrating the philosophical scheme, is such that all related experience must exhibit the same texture." [8]

What follows will be a mere sketch. Systematic elaboration is beyond the scope of this book. Although temporal character pervades the whole of our experience, sensory as well as introspective—Kant expressed this in his usual abstruse terminology by calling time "the form of inner as well as of outer sense"— it is certainly present with *different degrees of conspicuousness* in its different strata. It is least conspicuous in the realm of visual and tactile sensations; this accounts for the fact that, in the corpuscular-kinetic model of nature which was built of the same sensory elements, the reality of time was so obscured. For the only form in which time could manifest itself in this scheme was that of *motion* of *constant* matter through *unchanging* space. As we have seen, it was psychologically natural then that the constancy of matter and the immutability of space should tend to overshadow the reality of motion. Even when the attention of physicists was focused on motion, they were attracted by its spatial characteristics, which, together with the conservation laws of dynamics, pushed its dynamic and successive nature into the background.

The situation is different when we turn our attention to auditory sensations. Since the times of ancient atomism these sensory qualities have been excluded from "the nature of things," to use Lucretius' term, and we certainly do not pretend to re-endow them with the status of objectivity as the neorealists tried to do. We are convinced that for a physicist today it is impossible to accept Dewey's "postulate of immediate empiricism" according to which "things are what they are experienced as." [9] But the striking dynamic character of auditory data will disclose on analysis the general character of becoming more clearly than other data, and thus will be helpful in understanding the nature of physical becoming as well.

Let us consider a piece of music—for instance, a melody or, better, a polyphonic musical phrase. It is hardly necessary to underscore its successive character. As long as its movement is going on, it remains incomplete and in its successive unfolding we grasp in the most vivid and concrete way the incompleteness of every becoming. At each particular moment a new tone is added to the previous ones; more accurately, each new moment is constituted by the addition of a new musical quality. But here we have to be on guard against the usual arithmetical connotation of the word "addition," and against the creeping spatial connotations which are associated with it. Arithmetical units remain distinct and qualitatively homogeneous no matter how they are grouped together; their grouping is purely external and does not affect their nature in any way. A "new" unit is added *ab externo* to other units without modifying them and without being modified by them. Although arithmetical addition—which is merely a regrouping of pre-existing units—takes place, like any other mental operation, in time, its result can always be represented by a spatial symbolism, that is, as a juxtaposition of simultaneously existing units. The relation of the arithmetical units to their sum total is the same as the relation of *the parts to the whole in space*.

In the musical experience of melody or polyphony the situation is considerably different. The quality of a new tone, in spite of its irreducible individuality, is tinged by the whole antecedent musical context which, in turn, is retroactively changed by the emergence of a new musical quality. The individual tones are not externally related units of which the melody is additively built; neither is their individuality absorbed or dissolved in the undifferentiated unity of the musical whole. The musical phrase is a *successive differentiated whole* which remains a whole in spite of its successive character and which remains differentiated in spite of its dynamic wholeness. Like every dynamic whole it exhibits a synthesis of unity and multiplicity, of continuity and discontinuity; but it is not the unity of an undifferentiated simultaneous whole nor is it the plurality of juxtaposed units; it is neither continuity in the mathematical sense of infinite divisibility nor is it the discontinuity of rigid atomic blocs. For this reason, paradoxical as it may sound, the traditional distinction between succession and duration must be given up.[10]

Since the time of Heraclitus, philosophers who insist on the dynamic nature of reality struggle with the extreme difficulties of expressing in adequate linguistic form this paradoxical "unity of opposites" which every temporal process realizes. No wonder that Heraclitus, like Bergson many centuries later, was called "obscure." Our language, in particular our written language, is made of discontinuous and static signs whose discontinuity and immutability is unconsciously conferred upon even the dynamic meanings which they express and which are thus distorted. This discrepancy between the lucidity of our temporal awareness and the difficulty of putting it into words was expressed in St. Augustine's famous saying:

> "What then is time? If no one asks me, I know: if I wish to explain it to one that asketh, I know not . . ."[11]

Today we know the cause of this discrepancy. As long as our attention is shifted from our auditory experience of melody to the visual marks by which it is symbolized on a sheet of paper —as long as we shift our attention from any experienced temporal whole to its static symbolism—such discrepancy is inevitable. Hence Whitehead's conclusion that in analyzing time, an ultimate appeal must be made to intuition, that is, to our direct awareness of time.[12]

What particular bearing has the foregoing analysis, sketchy though it is, on the problem of physical becoming? What light is shed on the problems of contemporary physics? Let us summarize it briefly. Every musical structure is by its own nature unfolding and incomplete; so is cosmic becoming, the time-space of modern physics. The musical structures, in virtue of their essentially temporal nature, cannot be subdivided *ad infinitum* without being destroyed; they are, as Ehrenfels pointed out long ago,[13] *zeitliche Gestalten* whose duration is their existential minimum, which cannot be shortened without being destroyed. As Whitehead says, "a note of music is nothing at an instant, but also requires its whole period to manifest itself." [14] For this reason musical wholes—like physical processes—are not infinitely divisible; in either case durationless instants are mere ideal limits, arbitrary cuts in the dynamic continuity of becoming.

It is unfortunate that the term "continuity" in the mathematical sense in fact means infinite divisibility, that is, discontinuity infinitely repeated—the very opposite of continuity in the dynamical sense.[15] But if the concept of mathematical continuity is inapplicable to the concrete continuity of psychological as well as of physical processes, it would be equally incorrect to pass to another extreme and to speak of "the atomic structure of duration." As pointed out in Chapter XIII, the main shortcoming of the chronon theory is that it replaces the succession of durationless instants by that of atomic blocs on whose boundaries the allegedly eliminated instants reappear. As this theory basically does not depart from the geometrical symbolization of time, it merely replaces the mutual externality of point-instants by the mutual externality of contiguous segment-intervals.

But in concrete temporal experience the emergence of novelty is possible, so to speak, only on the contrasting background of its immediate past; in a similar way a new musical quality of the (provisionally) last tone acquires its individuality in contrast to, as well as in connection with, its antecedent musical context. There are no instantlike boundaries separating two successive moments of the experienced duration; only when in our imagination we stretch a fictitious geometrical line underneath the qualitative continuum of duration are we tempted to posit such boundaries, without realizing that they belong not to the temporal process itself, but only to its symbolical substitute.

Two successive "specious presents" are not separated by

imaginary durationless instants, but *by their qualitative differences*. The term "separation" is misleading; it suggests separation in a spatial sense. We need to realize that the qualitative differences of successive moments of duration are untranslatable into spatial imagery. To differ qualitatively and to be distinct in space are two different notions. Unless we do realize this, the pulsational continuity of duration will remain to us forever obscure.

The term "pulsational" is preferable to "atomic"; "atomic" suggests too strongly the image of a solid block with sharply defined surfaces. But the choice of metaphor is not critical, provided that we keep in mind the imageless meaning of a duration whose heterogeneous continuity is as foreign to the mathematical continuity of durationless instants as to the contiguity of sharply delimited segments.

The dynamical pattern just analyzed is not confined to auditory experience; the perception of a musical phrase discloses it only most conspicuously. The same pattern is present in every type of our experience, whether sensory or introspective; as Bergson showed, even the visual perception of a motionless object *when attentively analyzed* exhibits basically the same pulsational continuity.[16] This is hardly surprising. *All* our experience is temporal, as even the most resolute despisers of time concede. Indeed it was precisely the obtrusive "phenomenal reality" of time which led Plato and all who followed in his footsteps to invent the allegedly true realm of timelessness and immutability.

Perhaps a more attentive analysis of concrete temporal wholes will yield a clue to the solution of the vexed antinomy of "corpuscles versus waves" which contemporary physics faces and which the term "complementarity" merely hides without removing. In the concrete experience of pulsational process, individuality and continuity do not appear antithetic and mutually exclusive; they become so only when we try to visualize them. Similarly, the terms "waves" and "corpuscles" remain incompatible as long as they retain their classical connotations, i.e., as long as we insist on constructing pictorial models. But will they still appear incompatible if the imageless dynamic "model," patterned on concrete temporal experience, replaces the classical visual connotations? We have listed important reasons why microscopic "particles" can be regarded neither as isolated bits of material preserving their identity indefinitely nor as motions of an elastic quasi-material medium. Although we can still speak of their *individuality*, it is the individuality of *events* rather than that of *things;* the alleged "permanence of a particle through time" (which seems to be always, contrary to the claims of classical atomism, of *limited* duration) is in reality nothing but a string of events. The individual world lines of "particles" are constituted by the succession of chronotopic pulsations. But precisely this succession of events is responsible for the "vibratory" or "undulatory" character of particles— the imageless frequency "associated" with every mass according to De Broglie's relation. This is what Whitehead expressed in *Science and the Modern World*:

> Thus in the organic theory, a pattern need not endure in undifferentiated sameness through time. The pattern may be essentially one of aesthetic contrasts requiring a lapse of time for its unfolding. A tune is an example of such a pattern. Thus the endurance of the pattern now means the reiteration of its succession of contrasts. This is obviously the most general notion of endurance on the organic theory, and "reiteration" is perhaps the word which expresses it with most directness. *But when we translate this notion into the abstractions of physics, it at once becomes the technical notion of "vibration."* This vibration is not the vibratory locomotion: it is the vibration of organic deformation. [Italics added.] [17]

In this passage there are some esoteric terms which need to be clarified. First, we would prefer the term "qualitative contrast" or simply "qualitative difference of successive moments" to "aesthetic contrast." As far as the term "organic deformation" is concerned, it is explained by Whitehead only a few pages before the passage quoted as "vibratory change of pattern," contrasted with "vibratory locomotion." But these slight terminological differences apart, there is an agreement between the passage quoted and our conclusion that "changes supersede displacements" and "events replace particles." In the theory of pulsational becoming the antithesis between "particle" and "wave" disappears.

It is not without interest that the same conclusion is reached by contemporary French thinkers like Roger Blanché and René Le Senne. In the words of the latter, *le temps doit être l'onde et grains à la fois* (time must be at once wave and particles).[18] The contradiction between "particle" and "wave" pictures reappears only if both terms become pictorial, that is, when their classical visual connotations sneak back to our mind. This unfortunately is a normal case. It will remain so as long as the "psychoanalysis of knowledge," recommended by Gaston Bachelard, is not practiced more systematically.

The above solution of the antinomy "wave versus corpuscle" is stated in a language too concise and general to be entirely convincing; its concrete elaboration would require not only another chapter, but another book. No such elaboration is possible as long as no new interpretation of the *extensive* character of becoming, that is, of what we called the "new meaning of spatiality" is given. This will be our last step; before considering it, let us add one more sentence: the compatibility of the emergence of novelty with the causal influence of the past is clearly exhibited in the perception of musical phrases and, by an attentive analysis, can be detected in the perception of *any* temporal whole. Introspectively, the (provisionally) last tone of a melody is an emergent present, while its musical antecedent context, which is joined to it by the dynamic link of immediate memory, represents the causal or "mnemic" impact of the past. Neither the absolute determinism of the "all is given" type nor the absolute indeterminism of "creation out of nothing" adequately characterizes the everlasting emergence of novelty in any temporal process, whether physical or psychological. For this reason the terms "relative determinism" or "dynamic determinism" are more nearly adequate, provided the word "determinism" is freed of the Laplacian and predestinationist overtones which hover reminiscently around it and which the simple addition of a qualifying adjective merely pushes into the background, without eliminating them.

So far we have tried to illustrate the dynamic nature of reality by auditory models. Do the same models shed any light on the new meaning of spatiality which replaced the discredited concept of static Newtonian space? Indeed they do; but while the phenomenological analysis of melody was sufficient earlier, it is not so here. Nothing in a bare succession of tones corresponds to anything even remotely analogous to the relations in space. The situation, however, is different when we turn our attention to the dynamic structure of polyphony. The dynamic pattern in this case is more complex. In a contrapuntal composition two or several melodically independent movements, whether harmonious or dissonant, are going on. The component melodic movements, besides each being unfolded successively, are also in a certain sense *beside* or *alongside* each other, and this relation "beside" is analogous to the relation "beside" in space, as the French psychologist Théodule Ribot observed at the beginning of this century.[19]

This analogy has its limitations. The spatial relation of juxtaposition implies a complete mutual *externality* of the *static* elements, whereas in polyphonic movement the component melodies not only proceed together toward the future but also overlap "transversally," so to speak, without losing melodic individuality and autonomy. But while the dynamic togetherness of the component melodies is different from the static relation of juxtaposition, it is on the other hand akin to what we called the *co-existence* or rather *co-becoming* or *co-fluidity* of world tubes in relativistic time-space.

The plurality of co-becoming causal tubes cannot be derived from the bare relation of succession (cf. pp. 215 f.). Relativistic physics does not exclude the *transversal width* or *extension* of becoming, even though this width can never be conceived as an instantaneous three-dimensional cross section. Thus the polyphonic pattern is a concrete exemplification of what Whitehead called by the term, significantly borrowed also from the language of music, "unison of becoming," and Bergson "the simultaneity of fluxes." [20] This simultaneity of fluxes, as Bergson correctly observed, can never become the simultaneity of juxtaposed instants; such instantaneous cross sections in four-dimensional becoming are as impossible as instantaneous cuts across a polyphony or any temporal structure. Like the causal world tubes the parallel moving melodies are *contemporaneous* but never co-instantaneous, because in either case the instants are mere conceptual artefacts, ideal limits. They are conceivable by our geometrizing imagination, but nothing in the concrete flux of nature corresponds to them. Instants would exist if time were to cease flowing; but this never happens—except in the imagination of some philosophers.

Thus in the light of auditory models some recently discovered features of physical reality lose their paradoxical character. In the concrete and attentively analyzed awareness of polyphonic structure the following traits, which remain unintelligible and even absurd within the visual scheme of classical physics, become intuitively clear:

The incompleteness of becoming and its pulsational character;
The compatibility of the emergence of novelty with the causal influence of the past;
The individuality of events within the continuity of the flux;
The fictitious character of instantaneous cuts and, consequently, the impossibility of instantaneous space;
The replacement of the relation of juxtaposition or co-instantaneity of points by that of co-becoming or contemporaneity of the causal tubes.

All these features defy any consistent attempt at visualization. The first function of auditory models is *negative;* they free our mind from the exclusive and tyrannical sway of spatial imagery. But besides this negative function there is also a positive one which should not be overlooked.

The present transformation of physics is far more radical than the famous "Copernican revolution" of the sixteenth century. To say nothing of the historical inaccuracy of the adjective

"Copernican" (it gives Copernicus the credit which really belongs to Giordano Bruno, the first to depart wholeheartedly and consistently from Aristotelian cosmology),[21] the transition from the closed world to the infinite universe was not excessively difficult for human imagination: the earth merely exchanged its position with that of the sun, while the celestial spheres were swept away. The effort of imagination required for such steps was relatively small. This explains why they were anticipated by the Greeks—the heliocentric system by Aristarchus of Samos, the infinity of space by Archytas and the atomists. The resistance against the world view of Copernicus and Bruno stemmed mainly from mental inertia and emotional reluctance to give up the cosmological scheme which was regarded as the core of medieval religious doctrine. But the new Newtonian view of the universe was as pictorial as the old Aristotelian one; indeed, it was even more so. After elimination of secondary nonvisual qualities, which had been reified by Aristotle and medieval science, its visual character became even more pronounced. In the Newtonian picture of the world, only the tactile elements had a place comparable to that of the optical ones.

Today we are in the midst of a far more radical transformation of our view of nature. The most revolutionary aspect of this transformation consists in the fact that the words "picture" and "view" lose entirely their etymological meaning. As the so-called primary qualities of matter now join the secondary qualities in their exit from the objective physical world, it is clear that the future conception of matter ought to be devoid of *all* sensory qualities, including even those which are subtly and implicitly present in seemingly abstract mathematical notions. This seems to be in contradiction to what has been said about the significance of auditory models. But we do not pretend to reinstate auditory qualities into physical reality in some neorealistic fashion. The positive significance of the auditory models is in the discovery of *imageless dynamical patterns*[22] structurally similar to those which, according to growing empirical evidence, constitute the nature of physical reality.

A concrete interpretation of contemporary physics is therefore not impossible, as long as we bear in mind that the terms "concrete" and "pictorial" (or "sensory") are *not* synonymous. For the same reason the term "imageless model" of matter is *not* self-contradictory. The search for such models will sooner or later become imperative for critical realists who, while refusing to consider any disguised return to the deceptive Cartesian clarity of the classical models, are not satisfied by either phenomenalism or panmathematism, both of which are fashionable today. In this search the observed isomorphism of psychological duration and physical becoming will constitute one of the most significant clues.

NOTES FOR CHAPTER XVIII

1. A. S. Eddington, *The Nature of the Physical World*, pp. 92 f.; H. Weyl, *The Open World* (Yale University Press, 1932), especially p. 55.
2. Cf. Chapter XII, above, Note 27.
3. Translated by W. James, *The Principles of Psychology*, Vol. I, pp. 627-28.
4. Cf. Chapter XIII, above, especially pp. 214-216.
5. D. Hume, *A Treatise on Human Nature*, Book I, Part IV, Sec. V; A. E. Murphy, "Substance and Substantive," *Univ. of California Publications in Philosophy*, IX, 64; M. Čapek, "The Reappearance of the Self in the Last Philosophy of William James," *The Philosophical Review*, LXII, No. 4 (Oct. 1953), p. 534.
6. J. Jeans, *The New Background of Science*, p. 288.
7. B. Russell, *Outline of Philosophy*, p. 311.
8. A. N. Whitehead, *Process and Reality*, p. 5.
9. John Dewey, "The Postulate of Immediate Empiricism," in *The Influence of Darwin on Philosophy and Other Eassays on Contemporary Thought* (New York, Holt, 1910), pp. 226 f. This principle was upheld by Dewey in his *Experience and Nature* (1925) and defended against Reichenbach in 1939 (in *The Philosophy of John Dewey*, ed. by Paul Schilpp, pp. 534-543).
10. Cf. my article, " 'Stream of Consciousness' and 'Durée réelle,' " *Philosophy and Phenomenological Research*, Vol. X (1950), especially p. 351, Note 37.
11. St. Augustine, *Confessions*, Book XI.
12. Whitehead, *op. cit.*, p. 32.

13. C. Ehrenfels, "Über Gestaltqualitäten," *Zeitschrift für wissenschaft-liche Philosophie*, Vol. XIV (1890), pp. 249-292.
14. A. N. Whitehead, *Science and the Modern World*, p. 54.
15. Cf. Chapter XIII, above, and Chapter XVI, Note 33.
16. H. Bergson, *Creative Evolution*, p. 4. The pulsational character of duration was even more strongly stressed by W. James in his inter-pretation of Bergson in *A Pluralistic Universe*, Ch. VI, especially pp. 229-232.
17. A. N. Whitehead, *Science and the Modern World*, p. 193.
18. Cf. the excellent article of R. Blanché "Psychologie de la durée et la physique du champ," *Journal de Psychologie*, Vol. 44 (1951), pp. 411-424; R. Le Senne, *Etudes philosophiques* (janvier-mars 1948), p. 4.
19. Th. Ribot, *Logique des sentiments* (Paris, 1905), p. 151.
20. A. N. Whitehead, *Process and Reality*, pp. 189-192; H. Bergson, *Durée et simultanéité*, p. 68.
21. Cf. Chapter "The Conservatism of Copernicus" in Herbert Butter-field's *The Origins of Modern Science 1300-1800* (Macmillan, New York, 1959); Thomas S. Kuhn, *The Copernican Revolution* (Random House, New York, 1957), pp. 144-148. About the significance of Bruno, cf. H. Höffding, *A History of Modern Philosophy*, I, pp. 123-130, and A. Koyré, *From the Closed World to the Infinite Universe*, pp. 39-54. G. de Santillana, *The Age of Adventure* (Mentor, 1957), pp. 244 f.
22. By a curious coincidence the study of imageless thought began ap-proximately at the same time as modern physics came into being. Alfred Binet's article "La pensée sans images" appeared in *Revue philosophique* in 1903, that is three years after Planck's quantum theory. On the significance of imageless thought see in particular A. Burloud, *La pensée conceptuelle* (Paris, 1927) and Brand Blanshard, *The Nature of Thought* (George Allen & Unwin, London, 1939), especially Chapter VII.

XIX · SUMMARY

PART I showed how classical physics viewed space as a three-dimensional homogeneous container, independent of its physical content, physically inert, infinite in extent, infinitely divisible. Its rigid structure was described by the axioms and theorems of Euclidean geometry. These properties were not logically independent; with the exception of its three-dimensional character, all were derivable from two basic features which, without being identical, were nevertheless closely related: its homogeneity and its Euclidean character.

Not a single feature listed remains unchallenged, either directly or implicitly, by contemporary physics. In the light of the general theory of relativity the following classical properties of space must be given up: its homogeneity, its Euclidean character, its rigidity, its causal inertness and independence of physical content, possibly even its infinity (though not its limitlessness). This follows from the relativistic fusion of space with its diversified and changing content.

The only property of classical space which seemingly has not been affected by the relativity theory is its continuity. However, under the impact of the quantum theory and wave mechanics, serious doubts about the applicability of spatial continuity on the microphysical level appeared. Attempts to introduce a minimum length, the so-called hodon, are merely symptoms of the growing realization that the concept of infinitely divisible space is hardly an adequate tool for dealing with the apparently irreducible individuality of microphysical events.

What is even more serious is that the relation of juxtaposition, which was regarded as the very essence of spatiality, does not seem to have any objective physical counterpart. According to the special theory of relativity, there are no absolute juxtapositions in nature; to claim the contrary would mean to assert the existence of absolute simultaneity which relativistic physics denies. For we do not have to overlook that the *juxtaposed* elements, whether called "points" or "events," are by their very nature simultaneous, i.e., devoid of succession. Thus the elimination of absolute simultaneity entails the elimination of absolute juxtaposition, that is, of absolute Newtonian space.

The full meaning of this statement is somehow obscured by the fact that the less radical word "relativization" is substituted for that of "denial." We believe we do justice to the logic of relativity by merely joining the adjective "relative" to the nouns "space" and "simultaneity" without realizing that when old words are retained, their old connotations are often unconsciously retained too. There is no question but that such unconscious or semiconscious remnants of the Newtonian conceptual framework seriously affect the interpretation of new physical theories.

We reach the same conclusion by considering the nature of the relativistic fusion of space with time. In the classical picture of nature world history was represented by the continuous succession of instantaneous spaces, all of them perpendicular to the time axis and each representing "the world at a given instant." At each particular moment it was presumed to be possible to separate an instantaneous three-dimensional cross-section from the four-dimensional world process. At every moment space was, so to speak, a transversal momentary cut in four-dimensional world history. In relativistic space-time (whose more appropriate name would be time-space) such instantaneous spaces containing absolutely simultaneous events are mere artificial and conventional cuts to which nothing objective in nature corresponds. If we continue to operate with such cuts in relativistic time-space, they will be different in different frames of reference. Although these differences are negligible in our ordinary experience, they cannot be disregarded on the cosmic scale or when velocities approaching the velocity of light are considered.

Consequently, although the concept of local "now" retains its practical justification on the human and even planetary scale, the concept of a huge three-dimensional "now" entirely loses its physical significance. There are no world-wide instants, as Eddington emphasized; or, in Whitehead's words, there is no such thing as "nature at an instant." The elimination of this concept represents one of the most serious threats to the classical Laplacian world scheme.

If static instantaneous space is a mere artificial cut across four-dimensional becoming, it is clear that the theory of relativity incorporates space into time rather than vice versa. The fusion of the two concepts is more appropriately characterized as a *dynamization of space* than as a *spatialization of time*.

It is true that the opposite, static interpretation can be found not only in some popular and semipopular expositions, but occasionally also in more technical books written by outstanding physicists and philosophers. In this interpretation relativistic space-time is regarded as a sort of four-dimensional hyperspace of which time is merely one dimension, not basically different from other dimensions. The fact that Minkowski himself used the expression "the four-dimensional world" (*vierdimensionale Welt*) instead of "four-dimensional becoming" certainly contributed to this misinterpretation. But the tendency to represent time as an additional geometrical dimension of space was a part of the classical scientific tradition of which the alleged spatialization of time in the relativity theory is only the last instance.

Moreover, such spatialization of time is only a particular form of another perennial illusion which can be traced to the very dawn of Western thought: the belief that becoming can be reduced to being, process to substance, time to the timeless, *events* to *things*. Long would be the list of those who from Parmenides up to Bradley and McTaggart tried by various subtle devices to eliminate change and to establish the static character of "true reality." It is hardly accidental that those who favor the static interpretation of space-time, like James Jeans and Kurt Gödel, are aware of their affinity with this philosophical tradition. Even if we do not speak of the extreme epistemological difficulties to which the static view of reality leads, there are more specific reasons against its application to the facts of relativistic physics. They are as follows.

1. There is an upper limit for the velocity of all causal actions; none of them can ever surpass the critical value of the velocity of light, c. As there are no instantaneous actions, effects are never simultaneous with their causes; in other words, causal links (world lines) remain incurably successive, thus conferring the dynamic character upon the world which they constitute.

2. At each particular moment classical Euclidean space is a mere conventional and artificial cross section in four-dimensional world history: conventional, because it is different in different frames of reference; artificial, because nothing objective in nature corresponds to it. Thus, contrary to wide-spread prejudice, the relativization of simultaneity weakens the ontological status of space, but not that of time.

3. The order of events constituting the causal chains (world lines) is the same in every frame of reference. The irreversibility of world lines is a *topological invariant*. *There are absolute successions in the world, although there are no absolute juxtapositions.* Because the "world" (a misleading word!) is nothing but the texture of the causal lines, the irreversible character of the latter is conferred upon world history as a whole.

4. The only type of succession which is relativized is the spurious succession of causally unrelated events. The true meaning of this kind of relativization may be stated as

follows: *the order of effects* of causally unrelated events may be reversed by a suitable choice of the frame of reference, thus producing the *illusion* that *the order of the events themselves is reversed.*

5. The dynamization of space is even more conspicuous in the general theory of relativity, in which time-space is merged with its changing physical content. But this elimination of the distinction between the static and passive container and the changing physical content had been foreshadowed in the special theory, in which spatiotemporal structure and causal structure are two words for one and the same thing.

The concept of time does not remain unaffected by its union with the concept of space. But its transformation is far less radical than that of space. Simultaneity and succession of isotopic events remain unaffected by the choice of a system of reference; the meaning of the relativization of simultaneity of distant events has been already explained. It is important to emphasize that the *metrical* relativity of time intervals as it manifests itself in the so-called "dilatation of time" is purely referential in the special theory, being only an *apparent* distortion due to kinematic perspective ("perspective of velocity").

In the general theory the concept of time is more seriously affected. By virtue of the fusion of time-space with its changing and diversified content, time loses its three classical features: its independence from concrete events, its causal inertness, and its homogeneity. The time of the general theory, instead of being homogeneous and "flowing uniformly without regard to anything external," becomes heterogeneous and, so to speak, "polyphonic" or "polyrhythmic"; this explains why the dilatation of time in gravitational fields is *real* and not merely referential.

Yet, as pointed out in Chapter XII, this dilatation is never a *retardation;* it never entails any *dislocation* of temporal series. The detailed analysis of Langevin's thought-experiment shows that in a certain non-Newtonian and nonmetrical sense *time remains universal* because the same stretch of duration underlies various discordant time series in spite of the fact that it is reckoned differently in each series. Although the relativistic universe excludes the concept of simultaneity, it preserves the relation of *contemporary independence;* various metrically discordant series are contemporary even though their events are never *co-instantaneous.* This relation of contemporaneity offers the clue to the new meaning of spatiality. (I purposely substitute the term "spatiality" for "space," for the latter is too uncomfortably tinged with Newtonian associations.)

Of all classical properties of time—homogeneity, uniform fluidity, independence of physical content, causal inefficacy, infinity, and infinite divisibility—all but the last two are being challenged by the relativity theory. But even the last two features are threatened by the development of postrelativistic physics. The absence of the beginning of time was one of the most cherished dogmas of classical thought; it mattered little whether the infinity of the past was interpreted theologically as the infinity of the divine duration (Newton) or naturalistically as the beginningless cosmic duration (Bruno and others). Yet even this dogma is now being challenged by some cosmogonic theories, in particular by the theory of the expanding universe. In fact, unless we amend this theory by some additional assumptions, the denial of the beginningless past follows from it. (It is possible to avoid this consequence by assuming successive periods of expansion and contraction, but this would be precisely an amending assumption.)

The continuity (infinite divisibility) of time faces a situation analogous to that confronting the concept of space. The whole concept of spatiotemporal continuity, which was so wonderfully fruitful on the macroscopic and even on the molecular level, apparently loses its applicability on the electronic and quantic level. This accounts for the simultaneous appearance of the "hodon" and "chronon" hypothesis. The shortcomings of these hypotheses—in particular their *ad hoc* character, their prerelativistic separation of space from time, their surreptitious assumptions of the very concepts of points and instants which they purport to eliminate—should nevertheless not blind us to increasing evidence that the concept of infinite divisibility of space and time is, to use the words of Erwin Schrödinger, "an enormous extrapolation" of what is macroscopically accessible to us.

In view of the close union between time-space and its physical content, the traditional concepts of *matter* and *motion* were both transformed—and it is no exaggeration to say that they were transformed beyond recognition.

The limitations of the concept of matter appeared in repeated failures of the mechanical models of aether. It became increasingly clear that our traditional notion of matter as *impenetrable something* which fills space, in spite of its usefulness on the macroscopic and even molecular level, cannot be profitably applied to what used to be called "imponderable matter" of the hypothetical interplanetary and intermolecular medium. But the *coup de grâce* came from relativity theory. The special theory showed that even the simplest kinematic properties are inapplicable to the alleged aether. At the same time the fusion of mass and energy dimmed the distinction between material bodies and their surrounding space; for the total mass of any material aggregate is not a simple arithmetical sum of its corpuscular components, but depends also on the mass contained in the energetic binding between them.

In the general theory of relativity, the denial of the distinction between "the full and the empty" is far more pronounced. On this distinction the traditional concept of any material corpuscle, whether aethereal, atomic, or molecular, was based; without this distinction the concept of material body, whatever its dimensions may be, loses its definiteness. It is meaningless to speak about a "particle" when no definite boundaries which would separate it from its surrounding void exist; we do not have the right to use even the expression "matter *in* space" when matter is dissolved into a local irregularity *of* space, or more correctly, *of* time-space. Although Bergson's and Whitehead's claim about the "omnipresence" of particles is exaggerated—it does not take into account the *finite* velocity by which local irregularity is propagated—it nevertheless stresses correctly the absence of clear-cut boundaries between "corpuscles" and their environment.

The extensive and spectacular verification of the relativistic fusion of mass and energy showed the profound difference which separates the "particles" of modern physics from the traditional particles of atomism. The relativistic increase of mass with velocity showed that the microphysical "particles" are not constant; the facts of annihilation and creation of electronic couples showed that they are not even permanent, that is, enduring through time and space. Some particles have such a vanishing duration that to apply to them the term "corpuscles," so indissolubly associated with the idea of hardness and permanence, is positively misleading; they deserve much more to be called "events" or, at the most, "events-particles," as Whitehead proposed.

Not only can a microphysical particle not be observed twice, as Schrödinger stressed, *but not even once,* as the consistent application of Heisenberg's principle of indeterminacy shows. Not even once can we observe a microphysical "particle." To do so would imply the possibility of finding in nature a conjunction of definite momentum and definite position. But such possibility does not exist—not because of some temporary limitation of our experimental and observational technique, but simply because the conjunction of position and momentum *does not exist in nature,* as Eddington and, more recently, Philip Frank have emphasized. What then is left of the classical concept of particle when even its constitutive properties—momentum and position —cannot exist together?

By such radical transformations of the concept of matter the classical concept of motion is also seriously affected. Motion in the classical sense of displacement was possible only because a bit of matter, persisting through time, could detach itself from the position previously occupied in order to move to other positions. But if a "particle" is merely a certain more complex region of time-space, how can it detach itself from something which, so to speak, constitutes its very nature? What actually happens when we see a material body moving from one place to another is not a transfer of some substantial entity from one place to another, but the *disappearance* of the local curvature in one place and its appearance in an adjacent region. The situation is comparable to a little concavity traveling on the surface of an insufficiently inflated ball; its "displacement" too is the product of two concomitant changes of local curvature, that is, the vanishing of a concavity in one place and its appearance in the neighboring region. It is the continuity of the movement of our eyeball which creates here the illusion of the identity of a "thing traveling in space."

Thus what we call displacement of a body in space is in fact, as Clifford observed prophetically in 1876, an *intrinsic change* of space (today we should say of time-space), a change of its curvature. The relation of space and time to matter and motion ceases to be the relation of passive and immutable containers to changing content. What we used to call motion *in* space and *in* time now becomes *change* of time-space, change to which time-space is not indifferent and in which it participates. Thus the *category of change* is substituted for that of displacement.

If the concept of displacement and the identity of the "thing traveling in space" are inadequate even on the macroscopic level, how misleading it is to apply them on the microphysical scale! As early as 1926 P. W. Bridgman questioned the applicability of both concepts in the microcosm, and today we know how justified his skepticism was. It is continuity of motion which guarantees the identity of a moving body, and vice versa; for only if a continuous trajectory connects the successive positions of a "traveling thing" are we able to follow its identity through space and time; conversely, the identity of a body *persisting through all instants of time and in all points of its trajectory* provides for the possibility of charting its continuous motion. Both these correlated concepts cannot be consistently applied to quantum phenomena, in which the pulsational character of time-space manifests itself.

This leads us to the *second* aspect of the revolutionary change to which the concepts of matter and motion are being subjected. Not only are matter and motion absorbed into time-space, which in its turn has lost its causal passivity and homogeneity, but they are no longer mutually exclusive. In classical thought matter and motion were mutually inconvertible: the variation of the quantity of motion never affected the mass of a moving body, while no increase of momentum of any particle could ever spring from the particle itself, but only from external mechanical causes. We have seen that in relativistic mechanics the situation is different: mass varies with velocity, kinetic energy increases the total mass of "particles." Even more significantly, the whole "rest-mass" can be converted into the kinetic energy of photons (whose "rest-mass" is zero). Thus another classical distinction is abolished: that between motion and its material vehicle.

Nernst's discovery of "zero energy," which appeared so paradoxical within the framework of classical science, becomes more intelligible when we realize that the conceptual separation of *motion* and *thing moved*, which is so strongly suggested by our macroscopic experience, loses its justification on the microphysical level. It is very probable that what was originally the distinction between motion and matter on the sensory level became later the distinction between *thing* and *event*, or *substance* and *process*, on the more abstract level. The disappearance of this distinction is even more conspicuous in wave mechanics; the discovery of De Broglie's waves shows that not only are material particles constituted by vibrations, but also there is a very limited chance to interpret these oscillations as vibratory displacements of corpuscular or subaethereal entities. "Events and not particles constitute the true objective reality" is the conclusion of Sir James Jeans, and thinkers so widely different as Bertrand Russell, Henri Bergson, A. N. Whitehead, and Gaston Bachelard agree with it.

There is a correlation between the transformation of the concept of particle and that of motion; yet, both words are retained; and even if they are sometimes set in quotation marks, their continued use tends to hide their basic inadequacy. Like simultaneity and instantaneous space, particles and motions simply *do not exist,* and we should use more adequate terms to describe the individuality of microphysical events. The eventlike nature of matter is very probably another manifestation of the pulsational structure of time-space.

After such radical transformation of the basic classical concepts of space, time, matter, and motion, very little is left of the traditional corpuscular-kinetic scheme of nature. It is natural that classical determinism of the Laplacian type is threatened when the scheme on which it was based is disintegrating. The close connection between strict determinism and the corpuscular-kinetic model of nature can be seen from the very form in which the deterministic belief was stated: "given a state of the universe at a given instant" or "given an instantaneous configuration of all particles composing the world and their momenta," then all the states of the cosmic history, whether past or future, are completely and unambiguously determined.

Not a single constituent concept of this Laplacian model of the universe remains unaffected; what has been left intact by the relativity theory was challenged by the theory of quanta or wave mechanics. Relativistically speaking, there is no such thing as a "state of the world at an instant"; there is no such thing as an instantaneous configuration of particles. Moreover, the concept of immutable and permanent particle, identifiable through space and time, is as obsolete as the concept of durationless instant. This is especially obvious in the principle of indeterminacy according to which neither the correlation of definite momentum and definite position nor that of definite energy and definite time can be found in nature. It is certainly not accidental that this principle, which is a mere consequence of the atomicity of action, is equally opposed to both classical determinism and the kinetic-corpuscular model of nature.

It is true that there are two conflicting interpretations of this principle. According to the first one, which is more in accordance with classical habits of thought, the indeterminacy in question is due to the disturbing effect of observation; according to the second one it is due to the contingency existing objectively in nature.

The first interpretation leaves classical determinism basically intact. It claims that underlying the statistical indeterminacy of microphysical processes there are on the subquantum and sub-electronic level micromechanisms determining each particular event. The merits and demerits of this deterministic interpretation can be seen especially clearly when it is applied to the class of radioactive phenomena. The "disturbing effect of an observer" can hardly account for the contingency of radioactive explosions which occur spontaneously and independently of external influences. The deterministic hypothesis must therefore fall back upon "hidden mechanisms" inside the nucleus by which the nuclear components are ejected.

This approach has the advantage of the clarity of Cartesian-Kelvinian models and its plausibility is increased by the fact that the radioactivity occurs spontaneously only in very complex nuclei of heavy atoms; nothing appears more plausible than to regard the contingency of radioactive disintegrations as being only spurious and to explain it by *apparently* random fluctuations of the kinetic energy of its constituent parts. On the other hand, this very trait of clarity is the greatest handicap of the deterministic interpretation; nothing is more suspicious in microphysics than the deceptive clarity of mechanical corpuscular models. What is assumed here is the pre-existence of the ejected particles in the nucleus; this is impossible in the case of beta-electrons, not to mention the established inadequacy of the concept of particle in general. When we analyze the use of corpuscular language applied to radioactive emissions, its inadequacy becomes even more obvious.

The more sophisticated defenders of the deterministic interpretation of Heisenberg's indeterminacy principle will probably disclaim any commitment to corpuscular models. They may point rightly to the fact that their "theories of hidden parameters" are closely akin to the unitary field theories in which particles are dissolved in the continuity of the field. This field, being identified with some non-Euclidean curvature or torsion, is as far as possible from classical visual models of physical reality. This, however, does not remove the basic difficulty, because the traditional concept of spatiotemporal continuity is retained. Unitary field theories as well as theories of hidden parameters are thus faced with the difficult task of explaining the grainlike structure of matter and energy. From their point of view the existence of Planck's constant h, instead of being viewed as an ultimate irreducible fact, should be explained as a by-product of the subquantic continuous structure of the field. This seems to be at present the main stumbling block of both unitary field theories and theories of hidden parameters. If we bear in mind that the concept of spatiotemporal continuity is a bold, exorbitant extrapolation of our limited macroscopic experience, it does not seem probable that this block will ever be removed. We may, therefore, conclude that the cumulative circumstantial evidence for the objective character of microphysical indeterminacy is overwhelmingly strong.

The resistance to the idea of physical indeterminacy is mainly of philosophical origin; it is mistakenly believed that contingentism in physics means a "ruin of science" and "suicide of reason." What makes the acceptance of objective indeterminacy especially difficult is the fact that classical determinism is tied not only to the corpuscular-kinetic view of nature, but also to the quantitative view of nature. Within such views physical indeterminacy must appear necessarily irrational, because it must take the form of causeless fluctuation of certain quantities, whether matter, energy, or impulse. For this reason a causeless fluctuation of the quantity of energy no matter how minute must seem just as preposterous as Lucretius' *clinamen* or any kind of *creatio ex nihilo*.

But it must not be overlooked that the indeterminacy principle is incompatible with such absolute indeterminism as much as with the strict causality of the Newtonian-Laplacian type. For in the light of this principle the concept of sharply defined quantity loses its meaning; to speak of causeless fluctuation is as meaningless as to speak of constancy. For this reason any attempt to express physical contingency in terms of the kinetic and quantitative model of nature can produce nothing but oddities and discrepancies.

The alleged irrationality of indeterminism in physics disappears when we realize that the Laplacian model of physical reality is not the only rational model of the universe and that the established inadequacy of classical determinism implies nothing more than a reinstatement of becoming into the physical world. In the classical deterministic scheme novelty and becoming were virtually eliminated. The future was regarded as implicitly contained in the present; thus time was reduced, in Bergson's words, to a "mere human infirmity to know everything at once." On the other hand, the objective character of physical indeterminacy acquires an intelligible meaning in the dynamic view of physical reality; for only in the dynamic universe can the future retain its character of *futurity* instead of being a disguised and completed present; only in the dynamic universe does novelty cease to be irrational. It is nothing less than an essential feature of becoming; only in an incomplete universe does the term "possibility," instead of being a symptom of human ignorance, designate the objective ambiguity of the future.

It is important to realize that the contingent emergence of novelties is as incompatible with the static universe of Spinoza and Laplace as with the miraculous universe of completely unrelated events in which everything can happen. On the contrary, the constraining—though not predetermining—influence of the past is an essential feature of becoming, as much as is the irreducible novelty of each present event. The applicability of probability laws to microphysical events clearly indicates that the concept of causality should be broadened rather than given up; what is to be eliminated is only its obsolete static necessitarian form.

From the affirmation of real novelties in nature the impossibility of "cyclical time" or "eternal recurrence" follows. The recurrence of the same state would imply the identity of two successive moments separated by an interval of time; but such identity would obviously eliminate the element of novelty by which the later moment is differentiated from the former. Thus becoming is by its own nature irreversible.

Besides this logical ground, there are some fresh reasons provided by physics for the rejection of cyclical time. The doctrine of eternal recurrence in its classical version presupposed the kinetic-corpuscular model of reality which today is obsolete. But even if this doctrine is freed from its connection with classical kinetism, it still has to assume the concept of "nature at an instant," which in the light of relativity theory is no less obsolete. Even more serious are intrinsic logical difficulties of the theory. The concept of absolute repetition of a previous state of the universe can be meaningful only within the framework of absolute *irreversible* time; for only in such time can two allegedly identical states of the universe be differentiated by their "temporal positions." But this would imply the very assumption which the cyclical time theory wanted to avoid—that of noncyclical time separable from concrete events. The cyclical theory of time is thus essentially self-destructive.

But the reversibility of time was also asserted in a less radical form as *the reversibility of time direction* without assuming a complete recurrence of the same state of the world history. Current theories of the "time arrow" are based on the same relational theory of time as the theory of cyclical time: time, in Lucretius' words, "being nothing by itself," must be defined in the terms of some observable trend, and if this trend is local and reversible, time itself must be local and reversible as well. The definition of time direction in terms of entropy increase naturally led to this conclusion; for the statistical and kinetic-corpuscular interpretation of the second law of thermodynamics implied the reversibility of the time direction on the molecular scale (the fluctuations observable in the Brownian motion) and in the long run even on the macroscopic scale.

The most serious limitation of the theory is the fact that it is based on a questionable use of the term "direction," which can be applied to time only in a loose and metaphorical sense. If we forget that the word "direction" is borrowed from geometry and kinematics and therefore cannot be literally applied to time, we may thoughtlessly draw all the consequences of the deceptive analogy between "movement of time" and movement in space; thus we may think that as the direction of motion in space can change, so "time direction" can change too; or as motions in space may be circular, the course of time may be circular too. The theories of reversible time and of eternal recurrence are based on such false kinematic analogies.

If we free our imagination from the obsession of spatialization, we see that the reversibility of becoming cannot even be stated in a self-consistent language. Only the deceptive analogy of time with spatial motion hides from us the intrinsic absurdity of "futurization of the past" which the postulated reversibility of time direction implies. For this reason even in the fantastic universe in which an entropy clock would run backwards, time still would flow onwards. There would still be the asymmetry between past and future, i.e., between what has happened irrevocably and what is in a potential, "not yet" state.

If we reject any attempt to define "time direction" in terms of a reversible trend, it does not mean that we reject any relational theory of time. Time *is* inseparable from concrete events; but these events, as we know today, cannot be reduced to the displacement of immutable particles whose configurations can—in principle at least—reoccur.

In view of the obsoleteness of the corpuscular-kinetic model of the universe, there is an increased tendency in contemporary physics, and especially in contemporary cosmology, to give up futile attempts to derive macroscopic irreversibility from allegedly basic reversible microprocesses. From Pierre Duhem to Eddington, this trend was becoming more and more pronounced until it found its most striking expression in the theory of the expanding universe of Lemaître. In such theory the incorporation of space into becoming is realized even more radically than in the classical general theory of relativity; at the same time, the theory of an expanding universe is a relational theory of time, because time itself is merged with its irreversible physical content. This theory also eliminates the controversial traditional concept of the actually infinite cosmic past.

Lemaître's cosmogony is not the only possible one; but whatever the definite shape of the future cosmogony may be, it can hardly be doubted that no return to the reversible models of classical cosmogony will take place for the simple reason that the concept of reversibility, besides being intrinsically absurd, has been deprived of its corpuscular-kinetic basis by both relativity theory and wave mechanics.

The revolutionary change in physics which took place in the first half of the twentieth century may be concisely characterized as the end of the Laplacian model of reality, not only because the classical Laplacian determinism is now being questioned, but also because *all* the components of Laplace's conceptual scheme have been profoundly modified. This is what we called *the disintegration of the corpuscular-kinetic scheme;* and as this scheme was *implicitly* timeless, the end of the Laplacian illusion means a reintroduction of becoming into the physical world.

Some important philosophical implications of the reassertion of the reality of becoming have already been pointed out and their agreement with freshly discovered facts of physics stressed. The fact that the classical kinetic scheme has proved to be inadequate for understanding contemporary physics means the end of all hopes of interpreting the constituent elements—or rather events—of physical reality in sensory (visual-tactual) terms. Human imagination is clearly incompetent to provide the material from which a satisfactory model of matter can be built.

In this respect the contemporary revolution in physics is more far-reaching than the so-called Copernican revolution in the sixteenth century; the heliocentric universe was in principle as imaginable as the universe of Ptolemy. But today it is obvious that the objective substrate of physical phenomena cannot be described in imaginative terms; all sensory qualities are basically on the same phenomenal level, which is a result of interaction of our conscious organism and the transphenomenal physical processes. The transphenomenal level itself seems to be thus forever inaccessible both to our perception and to our imagination; it can be neither perceived nor imagined. Abstract mathematical constructs seem to be today the only way, not to reach, but to *represent* the structure of the transphenomenal plane.

Thus the possibility of any concrete models of the transphenomenal level seems to be forever excluded. This, however, would be a hasty conclusion even though it is at present widely accepted. The plausibility of this conclusion rests on the ambiguity of the word "concrete." As long as by the word we mean "visual" or "pictorial," the conclusion is entirely justified. But "concrete" and "pictorial" are not synonymous words. Not only are there sensory qualities other than the visual ones, but there are also the nonsensory qualities of imageless thought of which psychology became aware only in recent years.

In the temporal structure of the perception of melody, features can be discovered which appear irrational in any visual-mechanical model of physical reality: the primacy of events, the absence of infinite divisibility, the compatibility of novelty and mnemic causation, the compatibility of continuity and individuality, the fusion of becoming with its concrete content. Needless to say, such use of auditory models is purely propaedeutic; it only helps to free our mind from the exclusive sway of visual imagination, whose influence may be detected even in some apparently abstract mathematical habits. No epistemologically educated person would dream of reinstating auditory or any secondary qualities into the physical world. The positive significance of the auditory experience is in the fact that from it a certain imageless dynamic pattern may be abstracted which will probably offer a key to the understanding of the nature of the type of "extensive becoming" that seems to constitute the nature of physical reality.

INDEX

Abraham, M., 105

Abramenko, B., 360

Action, atomic character, *see* Planck's constant, Quantum theory

——, at a distance, attempts to eliminate, 83-9; upheld by dynamists, 94-5

Aether, in classical physics, *see* Action at a distance, Fluid theories of matter, Plenum

——, in modern physics, 146, 151, 157, 251-2, 282-4, 304

Ambarzumian, V., 230, 242

Ampère, A. M., 98, 118

Anderson, C. D., 261

Archytas of Tarentum, 17-18, 354

Aristarchus of Samos, 379

Aristotle, cosmology, 17-19, 29, 203; doctrine of elements, 80-81, 108, 110; view of time, 51-2; view of motion, 72-4, 78, 177, 272; against atomism, 57, 113, 274; against reality of void, 120; on contingency of future, 336; on indestructibility of past, 347, 358; and modern physics, 272-3

Arrhenius, Svante, 127-8, 134

Atomism, ancient, *see* Democritus, Epicurus, Lucretius

——, in classical physics, 55-65; *see also* Corpuscular kinetic view of nature, Dalton, Daltonian atom, void

——, in contemporary physics, *see* Electron theory, Particles

——, in psychology, 6, 367-8

Auditory models, significance and limitations, 371-80; 399

Auditory qualities, elimination in classical physics, 4, 136; dynamic structure, 371-8

Augustine, St., on time, 51, 353-4, 359, 380

Axiom of free mobility (Russell), 15-26, 18, 27, 229-230

Bacon, Francis, 123, 308

Bachelard, G., 294, 299, 329-30, 376; on matter as constituted by events, 285-6, 288, 368, 391

Baer, K. E. von, 42-3, 45

Bailey, C., 10, 31, 66, 78, 90, 133, 140

Bär, R. 119

Barrow, I., on time, 36-8, 40, 51, 131, 263

Bauer, E., 329

Beck, G., 230, 240, 242

Becoming, status in contemporary physics, 333-8, 378, 395; irreversibility, 341-60, 395, *see also* "Direction" of time, Eternal recurrence; extensive character, 220-22, 255, 377, 399; *see also* Contingency, Future, Novelty, Time, Time-space

Becquerel, Jean, 194, 203, 213

Being, concept of, and concept of matter, 12-15, 54-5, 123; a superior to becoming, 136-8, 165, 384-5; immutability, 59, 137; *see also* Eleatic habits of thought, Substance

Bentley, R., 108, 118

Bergson, H., on Non-Being, 13-15; on classical space, 16, 51, 154, 157; on impenetrability, 56; influenced by Stallo, 115, 120; by Duhem, 350; on the reversibility of classical time, 126-133; on classical concept of causality, 140; against the static interpretation of Minkowski's world, 160-61; on fallacy of spatialization, 163, 173,

400